Selected Papers
on Virology

PRENTICE-HALL BIOLOGICAL SCIENCE SERIES

William D. McElroy and Carl P. Swanson, *Editors*

BIOCHEMICAL SYSTEMATICS,* by Ralph E. Alston and B. L. Turner
CLASSIC PAPERS IN GENETICS, by James A. Peters
EXPERIMENTAL BIOLOGY, by Richard W. Van Norman
FOUNDATIONS OF EXPERIMENTAL EMBRYOLOGY, by Benjamin H. Willier and Jane
    M. Oppenheimer
MECHANISMS OF BODY FUNCTIONS, by Dexter M. Easton
MILESTONES IN MICROBIOLOGY, by Thomas D. Brock
PAPERS ON HUMAN GENETICS, by Samuel H. Boyer, IV
POISONOUS PLANTS OF THE UNITED STATES AND CANADA, by John M. Kingsbury
PRINCIPLES OF BIOLOGY, by Neal D. Buffaloe
SELECTED BOTANICAL PAPERS, by Irving W. Knobloch
SELECTED PAPERS ON VIROLOGY, by Nicholas Hahon
A SYNTHESIS OF EVOLUTIONARY THEORY, by Herbert H. Ross

Concepts of Modern Biology Series

BEHAVIORAL ASPECTS OF ECOLOGY,* by Peter H. Klopfer
MOLECULAR BIOLOGY: GENES AND THE CHEMICAL CONTROL OF LIVING CELLS,
    by J. M. Barry

Foundations of Modern Biology Series

ADAPTATION, by Bruce Wallace and A. M. Srb
ANIMAL BEHAVIOR, by Vincent Dethier and Eliot Stellar
ANIMAL DIVERSITY, by Earl D. Hanson
ANIMAL PHYSIOLOGY, by Knut Schmidt-Nielsen
THE CELL, by Carl P. Swanson
CELL PHYSIOLOGY AND BIOCHEMISTRY, by William D. McElroy
CHEMICAL BACKGROUND FOR THE BIOLOGICAL SCIENCES, by Emil H. White
GROWTH AND DEVELOPMENT, by Maurice Sussman
HEREDITY, by David M. Bonner and Stanley E. Mills
THE LIFE OF THE GREEN PLANT, by Arthur W. Galston
MAN IN NATURE, by Marston Bates
THE PLANT KINGDOM, by Harold C. Bold

   * These titles are also in the Prentice-Hall International Series in Biological
Science. Prentice-Hall, Inc.; Prentice-Hall International, United Kingdom and
Eire; Prentice-Hall of Canada, Ltd., Canada.

Selected Papers on Virology

edited by

Nicholas Hahon

Aerobiology Division
U.S. Army Biological Laboratories

Prentice-Hall, Inc.
Englewood Cliffs, N.J.

PRENTICE-HALL INTERNATIONAL, INC., *London*
PRENTICE-HALL OF AUSTRALIA, PTY., LTD., *Sydney*
PRENTICE-HALL OF CANADA, LTD., *Toronto*
PRENTICE-HALL OF INDIA (PRIVATE) LIMITED, *New Delhi*
PRENTICE-HALL OF JAPAN, INC., *Tokyo*
PRENTICE-HALL DE MEXICO, S.A., *Mexico City*

Library of Congress Catalog Card Number: 64-18573

PRINTED IN THE UNITED STATES OF AMERICA
80150—C

To

Katheryn Elizabeth

and

Nicolette Kay

"In nature's infinite book of secrecy
A little I can read"

SHAKESPEARE
Antony and Cleopatra
Act II, Scene 2

Preface

The purpose of this volume is to present a collection of papers on virology that contributed prominently to the elucidation of the nature of viruses and the manifold facets of their behavior. Papers were selected which are inclusive of the period from the inception of experimental virology to recent times and are arranged chronologically in the text. Many of the discoveries recounted by the papers influenced, in varying degrees, the direction of virus research and the subsequent development of virology as a science. In consequence, a historical theme pervades the volume. The collection, however, is not a history of virology.

As a convenience to the reader unfamiliar with the technical aspects of virus research, an annotation precedes the text of each paper which provides background information and stresses the significance of each report. To keep the volume within a reasonable size, it was necessary to limit the number of papers in the collection. The selection of papers from the enormous number that were published within the past decade, was difficult due to the momentous advances in virology. Enough outstanding material appeared during this period to justify a volume in itself. Regretfully, many excellent reports were omitted due to the limitation of space.

I hope that the majority of papers in the collection will be a source of erudition and motivation for individuals who, by chance, design, or through a variety of circumstances, have become interested in or recently integrated into virus research. For students, the volume may enrich their appreciation and comprehension of virus research by providing examples of outstanding historical and current reports. For workers active in the field, the volume provides an opportunity to peruse many historical reports on virology of which they have been cognizant but may have lacked the time to locate individually.

I am grateful to the authors of the papers, the editors, and the copyright owners of the different journals for granting me permission to reprint the original articles and translations. Specific acknowledgments appear with each paper where applicable. To the authors who supplied reprints of their papers, my sincere appreciation.

NICHOLAS HAHON

Frederick, Maryland

Table of Contents

Introduction

Virology is a dynamic biological science. Within the span of approximately a little more than a half century, our knowledge of the infectious entities termed "viruses" has progressed from the mysterious concept of a "contagium vivum fluidum" to the recognition that they are composed primarily of nucleic acids and proteins and are the smallest biological units known to possess the inherent characteristics of life. In this short time, an impressive amount of knowledge, systematized and formulated to establish verifiable general laws, has been accumulated with the result that virology is now an independent discipline. The universality of viruses, shown to be associated with the diseases of plants, animals, insects, and bacteria, has attracted the interest and stimulated the imagination of individuals representing many branches of science. Because virology proffers a common ground for fundamental investigations of biological processes, its wide appeal for the scientific community has been a propitious circumstance. The knowledge and methodology of the many specialized fields that comprise the physical, chemical, and biological sciences have been applied and integrated into virus research and, undoubtedly, this has been a contributing factor to its accelerated and dramatic growth in recent times.

In common with most sciences, virology, from its inception and in its subsequent development into a full-fledged science, did not proceed along a straightforward course. It was beset by a generous share of ideological discord, technical obstacles, and the dominating influence of certain factions. Virology was precipitated by necessity (consequences of virus disease on human life, livestock, and plant produce) and given impetus by fortuitous discoveries and perspicacious experimenters, sometimes hampered by existing bacteriological concepts and methodology, and, for many decades, demarcated into divisions (plant, animal, insect, and bacterial) in accord with the major host systems that were attacked by the infectious agents. For a considerable period, each major division developed independently; each had its own special technology, terminology, and conceptions of virus disease. The remarkable technological feats, highlighted by the crystallization of viruses which provided material in a high state of purity for biochemical studies and the discovery that viruses are nucleoproteins which contain either deoxyribonucleic or ribonucleic acids as their genetic determinants, emphasized certain fundamental properties common to all viruses. The interchange of ideas and complementation of techniques that ensued gradually, infused a unified approach to virus research. The basic problems that were common to one group of viruses were germane then to the comprehension of all viruses. This outlook has been increasingly apparent in recent years.

Although virology is still concerned with the understanding, control, and alleviation of virus diseases, as it was throughout its history, it is equally concerned with exploring the fundamental processes of life. The profound revelations that have been disclosed within the past decade on the mechanisms of virus replication at the molecular level have contributed immensely to this latter viewpoint. Nucleic acids of viruses have been shown to carry the code or information to guide the biological processes and functions of the host cell for the complete replication of the infectious particle. Furthermore, in the process, the viral genetic material may redirect existing metabolic functions of the cell resulting in the alteration of cell morphology and behavior, and in the formation of new enzymes and biochemical products. Even more revealing is the knowledge that fragments of viral nucleic acid may be carried within the cell genome for generations without detection until the fragments are provoked into activity by some stimulus and then produce an overt sign to disclose their presence. The manifestations of viral infections may be regarded then as the consequence of viral nucleic acid present in the cell's hereditary apparatus.

In effect, viruses have assumed a novel and fundamental role in biological and biochemical research. They offer a form of genetic material amenable to quantitative titration and genetic analyses and, as such, are excellent models for examining the biochemical anatomy and functions of cells and for probing the mechanisms of heredity. Viral nucleic acids provide a means for studying and characterizing the reactions intrinsic to the biosynthesis of proteins and nucleic acids. The provocative demonstrations within the past two years of the synthesis of viral capsid proteins of plant, bacterial, and animal viruses in cellfree systems containing *E. coli* ribosomes, amino acids, and the specific viral RNA may be a foretoken of the eventual *in vitro* formation of complete virus particles. In broader perspectives, evidence may be accrued eventually to formulate reasonable hypotheses on the origin of viruses. Because of their intimate association with the biological processes of life, viruses may offer clues on the biochemical beginning and evolution of life on earth.

In the light of all these penetrating discoveries and their deep implications, one is confronted with excogitating a definition for the remarkable entities termed "viruses." The older and descriptive definitions based on size, pathogenicity, and obligate parasitism seem inadequate. Viruses have been envisioned now as transmitters or vehicles of information-bearing genetic material or, stated in more general terms, as "bits of infectious heredity in search of a chromosome." The recent definition of viruses expressed by S. E. Luria seems an appropriate reflection of our present knowledge "to consider viruses as genetically specific cell constituents containing coded DNA (deoxyribonucleic acid) or RNA (ribonucleic acid) which can, as one of their genetic functions, determine their own incorporation into specific vehicles for transmission to other cells."

In the preceding paragraphs, a cursory account has been given of the evolution of our present understanding of the nature of viruses, the current trends prevailing in virus research, and the vital role destined for viruses in biological research. Various facets of these areas are considered in greater detail by this collection of papers on virology.

Selected Papers
on Virology

AN
INQUIRY
into
THE CAUSES AND EFFECTS
of
THE VARIOLAE VACCINAE,
A DISEASE
discovered in some of the western counties of England,
particularly
GLOUCESTERSHIRE,
and known by the name of
THE COW POX.

―――――――――――

BY EDWARD JENNER, M.D. F.R.S. & c.

―――――――――――

――― quid nobis certius ipsis
sensibus esse potest, quo vera ac falsa notemus.
Lucretius.

―――――――――――

London:
Printed, for the author,
by Sampson Low, No. 7, Berwick Street, Soho:
and sold by law, Ave-Maria Lane; and Murray and Highley,
Fleet Street

―――――

1798.

To
C. H. Parry, M. D.
at Bath.

My dear friend,

      In the present age of scientific investigation it is remarkable that a disease of so peculiar a nature as the Cow Pox, which has appeared in this and some of the neighbouring counties for such a series of years, should so long have escaped particular attention. Finding the prevailing notions on the subject, both among men of our profession and others, extremely vague and indeterminate, and conceiving that facts might appear at once both curious and useful, I have instituted as strict an inquiry into the causes and effects of this singular malady as local circumstances would admit.

      The following pages are the result, which, from motives of the most affectionate regard, are dedicated to you, by

Your sincere Friend,
Edward Jenner.

Berkeley, Gloucestershire,
June 21st, 1798.

1798

An Inquiry into the Causes and Effects of the Variolae Vaccinae, a Disease Discovered in Some of the Western Countries of England, Particularly Gloucestershire and Known by the Name of the Cow Pox

by Edward Jenner, M.D. F.R.S. & c.

The direction of initial research on viruses may be attributable to demands for the alleviation and control of epidemic diseases which affected the condition of agricultural produce and the health of the populace. The imaginative studies of Edward Jenner, marking the inception of experimental virology almost a century and a half ago, was a consequence of these circumstances. They resulted in a method of vaccination with cowpox virus as a preventative against the ravages of smallpox. He gave scientific foundation to the folklore experience that previous exposure to cowpox afforded resistance to smallpox. Jenner's detailed experiments and observations are vividly recorded in his historical publication. The application of the tested and verified method proposed by this country physician, more famous as a naturalist, was instrumental in the worldwide decline and control of smallpox. He is credited with establishing the principle of active immunization as a prophylactic measure against viral infections. The use of an agent that, following inoculation, induces mild discomfort and in the process establishes protection against the virulent form of the disease is still today the most effective method ever devised for protecting man and animals against infectious diseases. The discovery of this basic tenet of immunization is most remarkable with the realization that the nature of the immunizing agent and the causal entity were unknown at that

5

time. Only later, with refinements of virological techniques and greater knowledge, were the agents identified as viruses— almost 100 years later. The greatness of this scientific achievement, performed in a period of superstition and primitive scientific reasoning, is a credit to the man. Unaltered in principle, his method of vaccination is still in practice today and remains a milestone in preventive medicine.

The deviation of Man from the state in which he was originally placed by Nature seems to have proved to him a prolific source of Diseases. From the love of splendour, from the indulgences of luxury, and from his fondness for amusement, he has familiarised himself with a great number of animals, which may not originally have been intended for his associates.

The Wolf, disarmed of ferocity, is now pillowed in the lady's lap.[1] The Cat, the little Tyger of our island, whose natural home is the forest, is equally domesticated and caressed. The Cow, the Hog, the Sheep, and the Horse, are all, for a variety of purposes, brought under his care and dominion.

There is a disease to which the Horse, from his state of domestication, is frequently subject. The Farriers have termed it *the Grease*. It is an inflammation and swelling in the heel, from which issues matter possessing properties of a very peculiar kind, which seems capable of generating a disease in the Human Body (after it has undergone the modification which I shall presently speak of), which bears so strong a resemblance to the Small Pox, that I think it highly probable it may be the source of that disease.

In this Dairy County a great number of Cows are kept, and the office of milking is performed indiscriminately by Men and Maid Servants. One of the former having been appointed to apply dressings to the heels of a Horse affected with *the Grease,* and not paying due attention to cleanliness, incautiously bears his part in milking the Cows, with some particles of the infectious matter adhering to his fingers. When this is the case, it commonly happens that a disease is communicated to the Cows, and from the Cows to the Dairy-maids, which spreads through the farm until most of the cattle and domestics feel its unpleasant consequences. This disease has obtained the name of the Cow Pox. It appears on the nipples of the Cows in the form of irregular pustules. At their first appearance they are commonly of a palish blue, or rather of a colour somewhat approaching

---

[1] The late Mr. John Hunter proved, by experiments, that the Dog is the Wolf in a degenerate state.

to livid, and are surrounded by an erysipelatous inflammation. These pustules, unless a timely remedy be applied, frequently degenerate into phagedenic ulcers, which prove extremely troublesome.[2] The animals become indisposed, and the secretion of milk is much lessened. Inflamed spots now begin to appear on different parts of the hands of the domestics employed in milking, and sometimes on the wrists, which quickly run on to suppuration, first assuming the appearance of the small vesications produced by a burn. Most commonly they appear about the joints of the fingers, and at their extremities; but whatever parts are affected, if the situation will admit, these superficial suppurations put on a circular form, with their edges more elevated than their centre, and of a colour distantly approaching to blue. Absorption takes place, and tumours appear in each axilla. The system becomes affected—the pulse is quickened; and shiverings succeeded by heat with general lassitude and pains about the loins and limbs, with vomiting, come on. The head is painful, and the patient is now and then even affected with delirium. These symptoms, varying in their degrees of violence, generally continue from one day to three or four, leaving ulcerated sores about the hands, which, from the sensibility of the parts, are very troublesome, and commonly heal slowly, frequently becoming phagedenic, like those from whence they sprung. The lips, nostrils, eyelids, and other parts of the body, are sometimes affected with sores; but these evidently arise from their being heedlessly rubbed or scratched with the patient's fingers. No eruptions on the skin have followed the decline of the feverish symptoms in any instance that has come under my inspection, one only excepted, and in this case a very few appeared on the arms: they were very minute, of a livid red colour, and soon died away without advancing to maturation; so that I cannot determine whether they had any connection with the preceding symptoms.

Thus the disease makes its progress from the Horse to the nipple of the Cow, and from the Cow to the Human Subject.

Morbid matter of various kinds, when absorbed into the system, may produce effects in some degree similar; but what renders the Cow Pox virus so extremely singular, is, [sic] that the person who has been thus affected is for ever after secure from the infection of the Small Pox; neither exposure to the variolous effluvia, nor the insertion of the matter into the skin, producing this distemper.

In support of so extraordinary a fact, I shall lay before my Reader a great number of instances.[3]

[2] They who attend sick cattle in this country find a speedy remedy for stopping the progress of this complaint in those applications which act chemically upon the morbid matter, such as the solutions of the Vitriolum Zinci, the Vitriolum Cupri, etc.

[3] It is necessary to observe, that pustulous sores frequently appear spontaneously on the nipples of Cows, and instances have occurred, though very rarely, of the hands of

CASE I

Joseph Merret, now an Under Gardner to the Earl of Berkeley, lived as a Servant with a Farmer near this place in the year 1770, and occasionally assisted in milking his master's cows. Several horses belonging to the farm began to have sore heels, which Merret frequently attended. The cows soon became affected with the Cow Pox, and soon after several sores appeared on his hands. Swellings and stiffness in each axilla followed, and he was so much indisposed for several days as to be incapable of pursuing his ordinary employment. Previously to the appearance of the distemper among the cows there was no fresh cow brought into the farm, nor any servant employed who was affected with the Cow Pox.

In April, 1795, a general inoculation taking place here, Merret was inoculated with his family; so that a period of twenty-five years had elapsed from his having the Cow Pox to this time. However, though the variolous matter was repeatedly inserted into his arm, I found it impracticable to infect him with it; an efflorescence only, taking on an erysipelatous look about the centre, appearing on the skin near the punctured parts. During the whole time that his family had the Small Pox, one of whom had it very full, he remained in the house with them, but received no injury from exposure to the contagion.

It is necessary to observe, that the utmost care was taken to ascertain, with the most scrupulous precision, that no one whose case is here adduced had gone through the Small Pox previous to these attempts to produce that disease.

Had these experiments been conducted in a large city, or in a populous neighbourhood, some doubts might have been entertained; but here, where population is thin, and where such an event as a person's having had the Small Pox is always faithfully recorded, no risk of inaccuracy in this particular can arise.

---

the servants employed in milking being affected with sores in consequence, and even of their feeling an indisposition from absorption. These pustules are of a much milder nature than those which arise from that contagion which constitutes the true Cow Pox. They are always free from the bluish or livid tint so conspicuous in the pustules in that disease. No erysipelas attends them, nor do they show any phagedenic disposition as in the other case, but quickly terminate in a scab without creating any apparent disorder in the Cow. This complaint appears at various seasons of the year, but most commonly in the Spring, when the Cows are first taken from their winter food and fed with grass. It is very apt to appear also when they are suckling their young. But this disease is not to be considered as similar in any respect to that of which I am treating, as it is incapable of producing any specific effects on the human Constitution. However, it is of the greatest consequence to point it out here, lest the want of discrimination should occasion an idea of security from the infection of the Small Pox, which might prove delusive.

CASE II

Sarah Portlock, of this place, was infected with the Cow Pox, when a Servant at a Farmer's in the neighbourhood, twenty-seven years ago.[4]

In the year 1792, conceiving herself, from this circumstance, secure from the infection of the Small Pox, she nursed one of her own children who had accidently caught the disease, but no indisposition ensued. During the time she remained in the infected room, variolous matter was inserted into both her arms, but without any further effect than in the preceding case.

CASE III

John Phillips, a Tradesman of this town, had the Cow Pox at so early a period as nine years of age. At the age of sixty-two I inoculated him, and was very careful in selecting matter in its most active state. It was taken from the arm of a boy just before the commencement of the eruptive fever, and instantly inserted. It very speedily produced a sting-like feel in the part. An efflorescence appeared, which on the fourth day was rather extensive, and some degree of pain and stiffness were felt about the shoulder; but on the fifth day these symptoms began to disappear, and in a day or two after went entirely off, without producing any effect on the system.

CASE IV

Mary Barge, of Woodford, in this parish, was inoculated with a variolous matter in the year 1791. An efflorescence of a palish red colour soon appeared about the parts where the matter was inserted, and spread itself rather extensively, but died away in a few days without producing any variolous symptoms.[5] She has since been repeatedly employed as a nurse to Small-pox patients, without experiencing any ill consequences. This woman had the Cow Pox when she lived in the service of a Farmer in this parish thirty-one years before.

[4] I have purposely selected several cases in which the disease had appeared at a very distant period previous to the experiments made with variolous matter, to shew that the change produced in the constitution is not affected by time.

[5] It is remarkable that variolous matter, when the system is disposed to reject it, should excite inflammation on the part to which it is applied more speedily than when it produces the Small Pox. Indeed it becomes almost a criterion by which we can determine whether the infection will be received or not. It seems as if a change, which endures through life, had been produced in the action, or disposition to action, in the vessels of the skin; and it is remarkable too, that whether this change has been effected by the Small Pox, or the Cow Pox, that the disposition to sudden cuticular inflammation is the same on the application of variolous matter.

CASE V

Mrs. H. ———, a respectable Gentlewoman of this town, had the Cow Pox when very young. She received the infection in rather an uncommon manner: it was given by means of her handling some of the same utensils[6] which were in use among the servants of the family, who had the disease from milking infected cows. Her hands had many of the Cow-pox sores upon them, and they were communicated to her nose, which became inflamed and very much swoln [sic]. Soon after this event Mrs. H. ——— was exposed to the contagion of the Small Pox, where it was scarcely possible for her to have escaped, had she been susceptible of it, as she regularly attended a relative who had the disease in so violent a degree that it proved fatal to him.

In the year 1778 the Small Pox prevailed very much at Berkeley, and Mrs. H. ——— not feeling perfectly satisfied respecting her safety (no indisposition having followed her exposure to the Small Pox) I inoculated her with active variolous matter. The same appearance followed as in the preceding cases—an efflorescence on the arm without any effect on the constitution.

CASE VI

It is a fact so well known among our Dairy Farmers, that those who have had the Small Pox either escape the Cow Pox or are disposed to have it slightly; that as soon as the complaint shews itself among the cattle, assistants are procured, if possible, who are thus rendered less susceptible of it, otherwise the business of the farm could scarcely go forward.

In the month of May, 1796, the Cow Pox broke out at Mr. Baker's, a Farmer who lives near this place. The disease was communicated by means of a cow which was purchased in an infected state at a neighbouring fair, and not one of the Farmer's cows (consisting of thirty) which were at that time milked escaped contagion. The family consisted of a man servant, two dairymaids, and a servant boy, who, with the Farmer himself, were twice a day employed in milking the cattle. The whole of this family, except Sarah Wynne, one of the dairymaids, had gone through the Small Pox. The consequence was, that the Farmer and the servant boy escaped the infection of the Cow Pox entirely, and the servant man and one of the maid servants had each of them nothing more than a sore on one of their fingers, which produced no disorder in the system. But the other dairymaid, Sarah Wynne, who never had the Small Pox, did not escape in so easy a manner. She caught the complaint from the cows, and was affected with the symptoms described in the 5th page[7] in

---

[6] When the Cow Pox has prevailed in the dairy, it has often been communicated to those who have not milked the cows, by the handle of the milk pail.

[7] The author is referring to the page of original paper.

so violent a degree, that she was confined to her bed, and rendered incapable for several days of pursuing her ordinary vocations in the farm.

March 28th, 1797, I inoculated this girl, and carefully rubbed the variolous matter into two slight incisions made upon the left arm. A little inflammation appeared in the usual manner around the parts where the matter was inserted, but so early as the fifth day it vanished entirely without producing any effect on the system.

CASE VII

Although the preceding history pretty clearly evinces that the constitution is far less susceptible of the contagion of the Cow Pox after it has felt that of the Small Pox, and although in general, as I have observed, they who have had the Small Pox, and are employed in milking cows which are infected with the Cow Pox, either escape the disorder, or have sores on the hands without feeling any general indisposition, yet the animal economy is subject to some variation in this respect, which the following relation will point out:

In the summer of the year 1796 the Cow Pox appeared at the Farm of Mr. Andrews, a considerable dairy adjoining to the town of Berkeley. It was communicated, as in the preceding instance, by an infected cow purchased at a fair in the neighbourhood. The family consisted of the Farmer, his wife, two sons, a man and a maid servant; all of whom, except the Farmer (who was fearful of the consequences), bore a part in milking the cows. The whole of them, exclusive of the man servant, had regularly gone through the Small Pox; but in this case no one who milked the cows escaped the contagion. All of them had sores upon their hands, and some degree of general indisposition, preceded by pains and tumours in the axillae: but there was no comparison in the severity of the disease as it was felt by the servant man, who had escaped the Small Pox, and by those of the family who had not, for, while he was confined to his bed, they were able, without much inconvenience, to follow their ordinary business.

February the 13th, 1797, I availed myself of an opportunity of inoculating William Rodway, the servant man above alluded to. Variolous matter was inserted into both his arms; in the right by means of superficial incisions, and into the left by slight punctures into the cutis. Both were perceptibly inflamed on the third day. After this the inflammation about the punctures soon died away, but a small appearance of erysipelas was manifest about the edges of the incisions till the eighth day, when a little uneasiness was felt for the space of half an hour in the right axilla. The inflammation then hastily disappeared without producing the most distant mark of affection of the system.

CASE VIII

Elizabeth Wynne, aged fifty-seven, lived as a servant with a neighbouring Farmer thirty-eight years ago. She was then a dairymaid, and the Cow Pox broke out among the cows. She caught the disease with the rest of the family, but, compared with them, had it in a very slight degree, one very small sore only breaking out on the little finger of her left hand, and scarcely any perceptible indisposition following it.

As the malady had shewn itself in so slight a manner, and as it had taken place at so distant a period of her life, I was happy with the opportunity of trying the effects of variolous matter upon her constitution, and on the 28th of March, 1797, I inoculated her by making two superficial incisions on the left arm, on which the matter was cautiously rubbed. A little efflorescence soon appeared, and a tingling sensation was felt about the parts where the matter was inserted until the third day, when both began to subside, and so early as the fifth day it was evident that no indisposition would follow.

CASE IX

Although the Cow Pox shields the constitution from the Small Pox, and the Small Pox proves a protection against its own future poison, yet it appears that the human body is again and again susceptible of the infectious matter of the Cow Pox, as the following history will demonstrate:

William Smith, of Pyrton in this parish, contracted this disease when he lived with a neighbouring Farmer in the year 1780. One of the horses belonging to the farm had sore heels, and it fell to his lot to attend him. By these means the infection was carried to the cows, and from the cows it was communicated to Smith. On one of his hands were several ulcerated sores, and he was affected with such symptoms as have been before described.

In the year 1791 the Cow Pox broke out at another farm where he then lived as a servant, and he became affected with it a second time; and in the year 1794 he was so unfortunate as to catch it again. The disease was equally as severe the second and third time as it was on the first.[8]

In the spring of the year 1795 he was twice inoculated, but no affection of the system could be produced from the variolous matter; and he has since associated with those who had the Small Pox in its most contagious state without feeling any effect from it.

CASE X

Simon Nichols lived as a servant with Mr. Bromedge, a gentleman who resides on his own farm in this parish, in the year 1782. He was em-

---

[8] This is not the case in general—a second attack is commonly very slight, and so, I am informed, it is among the cows.

ployed in applying dressings to the sore heels of one of his master's horses, and at the same time assisted in milking the cows. The cows became affected in consequence, but the disease did not shew itself on their nipples till several weeks after he had begun to dress the horse. He quitted Mr. Bromedge's service, and went to another farm without any sores upon him; but here his hands soon began to be affected in the common way, and he was much indisposed with the usual symptoms. Concealing the nature of the malady from Mr. Cole, his new master, and being there also employed in milking, the Cow Pox was communicated to the cows.

Some years afterwards Nichols was employed in a farm where the Small Pox broke out, when I inoculated him with several other patients, with whom he continued during the whole time of their confinement. His arm inflamed, but neither the inflammation nor his associating with the inoculated family produced the least effect upon his constitution.

CASE XI

William Stinchcomb was a fellow servant with Nichols at Mr. Bromedge's Farm at the same time the cattle had the Cow Pox, and he was unfortunately infected by them. His left hand was very severely affected with several corroding ulcers, and a tumour of considerable size appeared in the axilla of that side. His right hand had only one small sore upon it, and no tumour discovered itself in the corresponding axilla.

In the year 1792 Stinchcomb was inoculated with variolous matter, but no consequences ensued beyond a little inflammation in the arm for a few days. A large party were inoculated at the same time, some of whom had the disease in a more violent degree than is commonly seen from inoculation. He purposely associated with them, but could not receive the Small Pox.

During the sickening of some of his companions, their symptoms so strongly recalled to his mind his own state when sickening with the Cow Pox, that he very pertinently remarked their striking similarity.

CASE XII

The Paupers of the village of Tortworth, in this country, were inoculated by Mr. Henry Jenner, Surgeon, of Berkeley, in the year 1795. Among them, eight patients presented themselves who had at different periods of their lives had the Cow Pox. One of them, Hester Walkley, I attended with that disease when she lived in the service of a Farmer in the same village in the year 1782; but neither this woman, nor any other of the patients who had gone through the Cow Pox, received the variolous infection either from the arm or from mixing in the society of the other patients who were inoculated at the same time. This state of security proved a fortunate circumstance, as many of the poor women were at the same time in a state of pregnancy.

CASE XIII

One instance has occurred to me of the system being affected from the matter issuing from the heels of horses, and of its remaining afterwards unsusceptible of the variolous contagion; another, where the Small Pox appeared obscurely; and a third, in which its complete existence was positively ascertained.

First, Thomas Pearce, is the son of a Smith and Farrier near to this place. He never had the Cow Pox; but, in consequence of dressing horses with sore heels at his father's, when a lad, he had sores on his fingers which suppurated, and which occasioned a pretty severe indisposition. Six years afterwards I inserted variolous matter into his arm repeatedly, without being able to produce any thing more than slight inflammation, which appeared very soon after the matter was applied, and afterwards I exposed him to the contagion of the Small Pox with as little effect.[9]

CASE XIV

Secondly, Mr. James Cole, a Farmer in this parish, had a disease from the same source as related in the preceding case, and some years after was inoculated with variolous matter. He had a little pain in the axilla, and felt a slight indisposition for three or four hours. A few eruptions shewed themselves on the forehead, but they very soon disappeared without advancing to maturation.

CASE XV

Although in the two former instances the system seemed to be secured, nor nearly so, from variolous infection, by the absorption of matter from sores produced by the diseased heels of horses, yet the following case decisively proves that this cannot be entirely relied upon, until a disease has been generated by the morbid matter from the horse on the nipple of the cow, and passed through that medium to the human subject.

Mr. Abraham Riddiford, a Farmer at Stone in this parish, in consequence of dressing a mare that had sore heels, was affected with very painful sores in both his hands, tumours in each axilla, and severe and general indisposition. A Surgeon in the neighbourhood attended him, who, knowing the similarity between the appearance of the sores upon his hands and those produced by the Cow Pox, and being acquainted also with the effects of that disease on the human constitution, assured him that he never need to fear the infection of the Small Pox; but this assertion proved fallacious, for, on being exposed to the infection upwards of

[9] It is a remarkable fact, and well known to many, that we are frequently foiled in our endeavours to communicate the Small Pox by inoculation to blacksmiths, who in the country are farriers. They often, as in the above instance, either resist the contagion entirely, or have the disease anomalously. Shall we not be able now to account for this on a rational principle?

twenty years afterwards, he caught the disease, which took its regular course in a very mild way. There certainly was a difference perceptible, although it is not easy to describe it, in the general appearance of the pustules from that which we commonly see. Other practitioners, who visited the patient at my request, agreed with me in this point, though there was no room left for suspicion as to the reality of the disease, as I inoculated some of his family from the pustules, who had the Small Pox, with its usual appearances, in consequence.

CASE XVI

Sarah Nelmes, a dairymaid at a Farmer's near this place, was infected with the Cow Pox from her master's cows in May, 1796. She received the infection on a part of the hand which had been previously in a slight degree injured by a scratch from a thorn. A large pustulous sore and the usual symptoms accompanying the disease were produced in consequence. The pustule was so expressive of the true character of the Cow Pox, as it commonly appears upon the hand, that I have given a representation of it in the annexed plate. The two small pustules on the wrists arose also

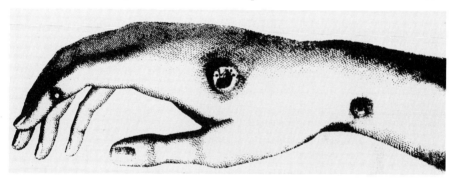

Plate 1.

from the application of the virus to some minute abrasions of the cuticle, but the livid tint, if they ever had any, was not conspicuous at the time I saw the patient. The pustule on the fore finger shews the disease in an earlier stage. It did not actually appear on the hand of this young woman, but was taken from that of another, and is annexed for the purpose of representing the malady after it has newly appeared.

CASE XVII

The more accurately to observe the progress of the infection, I selected a healthy boy, about eight years old, for the purpose of inoculation for the Cow Pox. The matter was taken from a sore on the hand of a dairy-maid,[10] who was infected by her master's cows, and it was inserted, on the

[10] From the sore on the hand of Sarah Nelmes,—See the preceding case and the plate.

14th of May, 1796, into the arm of the boy by means of two superficial incisions, barely penetrating the cutis, each about half an inch long.

On the seventh day he complained of uneasiness in the axilla, and on the ninth he became a little chilly, lost his appetite, and had a slight head-ach. During the whole of this day he was perceptibly indisposed, and spent the night with some degree of restlessness, but on the day following he was perfectly well.

The appearance of the incisions in their progress to a state of maturation were much the same as when produced in a similar manner by variolous matter. The only difference which I perceived was, in the state of the limpid fluid arising from the action of the virus, which assumed rather a darker hue, and in that of the efflorescence spreading round the incisions, which had more of an erysipelatous look than we commonly perceive when variolous matter has been made use of in the same manner; but the whole died away (leaving on the inoculated parts scabs and subsequent eschars) without giving me or my patient the least trouble.

In order to ascertain whether the boy, after feeling so slight an affection of the system from the Cow-pox virus, was secure from the contagion of the Small-pox, he was inoculated the 1st of July following with variolous matter, immediately taken from a pustule. Several slight punctures and incisions were made on both his arms, and the matter was carefully inserted, but no disease followed. The same appearances were observable on the arms as we commonly see when a patient has had variolous matter applied, after having either the Cow-pox or the Small-pox. Several months afterwards, he was again inoculated with variolous matter, but no sensible effect was produced on the constitution.

Here my researches were interrupted till the spring of the year 1798, when from the wetness of the early part of the season, many of the farmers' horses in this neighbourhood were affected with sore heels, in consequence of which the Cow-pox broke out among several of our dairies, which afforded me an opportunity of making further observations upon this curious disease.

A mare, the property of a person who keeps a dairy in a neighbouring parish, began to have sore heels the latter end of the month of February 1798, which were occasionally washed by the servant men of the farm, Thomas Virgoe, William Wherret, and William Haynes, who in consequence became affected with sores in their hands, followed by inflamed lymphatic glands in the arms and axillae, shiverings succeeded by heat, lassitude and general pains in the limbs. A single paroxysm terminated the disease; for within twenty-four hours they were free from general indisposition, nothing remaining but the sores on their hands. Haynes and Virgoe, who had gone through the Small-pox from inoculation, described their feelings as very similar to those which affected them on sickening with that malady. Wherret never had had the Small-pox. Haynes was daily employed as one of the milkers at the farm, and the disease began to shew itself among the cows about ten days after he first assisted in washing the mare's heels. Their nipples became sore in the usual way, with blueish pustules; but as remedies were early applied they did not ulcerate to any extent.

CASE XVIII

John Baker, a child of five years old, was inoculated March 16, 1798, with matter taken from a pustule on the hand of Thomas Virgoe, one of the servants who had been infected from the mare's heels. He became ill on the 6th day with symptoms similar to those excited by Cow-pox matter. On the 8th day he was free from indisposition.

Plate 2.

There was some variation in the appearance of the pustule on the arm. Although it somewhat resembled a Small-pox pustule, yet its similitude was not so conspicuous as when excited by matter from the nipple of the cow, or when the matter has passed from thence through the medium of the human subject.—(See Plate, No. 2.)

This experiment was made to ascertain the progress and subsequent effects of the disease when thus propagated. We have seen that the virus from the horse, when it proves infectious to the human subject is not to be relied upon as rendering the system secure from variolous infection, but that the matter produced by it upon the nipple of the cow is perfectly so. Whether its passing from the horse through the human constitution, as in the present instance, will produce a similar effect, remains to be decided. This would now have been effected, but the boy was rendered unfit for inoculation from having felt the effects of a contagious fever in a work-house, soon after this experiment was made.

CASE XIX

William Summers, a child of five years and a half old was inoculated the same day with Baker, with matter taken from the nipples of one of the infected cows, at the farm alluded to in page 35.[11] He became indisposed on the 6th day, vomited once, and felt the usual slight symptoms till the 8th day, when he appeared perfectly well. The progress of the pustule, formed by the infection of the virus was similar to that noticed in Case XVII., with this exception, its being free from the livid tint observed in that instance.

CASE XX

From William Summers the disease was transfered to William Pead a boy of eight years old, who was inoculated March 28th. On the 6th day he complained of pain in the axilla, and on the 7th was affected with the common symptoms of a patient sickening with the Small-pox from inoculation, which did not terminate 'till the 3d day after the seizure. So perfect was the similarity to the variolous fever that I was induced to examine the skin, conceiving there might have been some eruptions, but none appeared. The efflorescent blush around the part punctured in the boy's arm was so truly characteristic of that which appears on variolous inoculation, that I have given a representation of it. The drawing was made when the pustule was beginning to die away, and the areola retiring from the centre (See Plate, No. 3).

CASE XXI

April 5th. Several children and adults were inoculated from the arm of William Pead. The greater part of them sickened on the 6th day, and were well on the 7th, but in three of the number a secondary indisposition arose in consequence of an extensive erysipelatous inflammation which appeared on the inoculated arms. It seemed to arise from the state of the pustule, which spread out, accompanied with some degree of pain, to about half the diameter of a six-pence. One of these patients was an infant of half a year old. By the application of mercurial ointment to the

[11] Reference to original manuscript. See page 17.

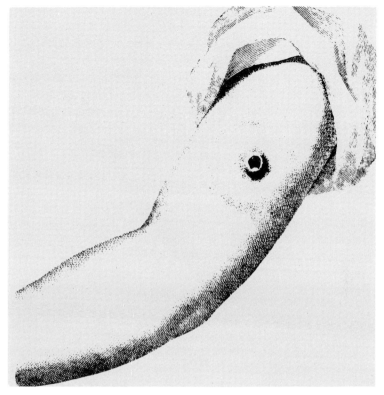

Plate 3.

inflamed parts (a treatment recommended under similar circumstances in the inoculated Small-pox) the complaint subsided without giving much trouble.

Hannah Excell an healthy girl of seven years old, and one of the patients above mentioned, received the infection from the insertion of the virus under the cuticle of the arm in three distinct points. The pustules which arose in consequence, so much resembled, on the 12th day, those appearing from the insertion of variolous matter, that an experienced Inoculator would scarcely have discovered a shade of difference at that period. Experience now tells me that almost the only variation which follows consists in the pustulous fluids remaining limpid nearly to the time of its total disappearance; and not, as in the direct Small-pox, becoming purulent. (See Plate, No. 4).

CASE XXII

From the arm of this girl matter was taken and inserted April 12th into the arms of John Marklove one year and a half old,

Robert F. Jenner, eleven months old,

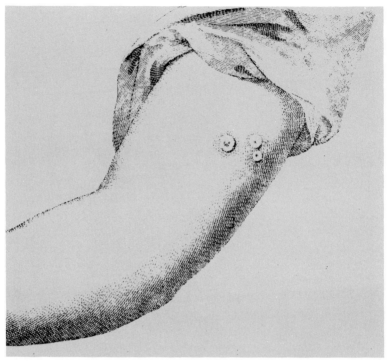

Plate 4.

Mary Pead, 5 years old, and
Mary James, 6 years old.

Among these Robert F. Jenner did not receive the infection. The arms of the other three inflamed properly and began to affect the system in the usual manner; but being under some apprehensions from the preceding Cases that a troublesome erysipelas might arise, I determined on making an experiment with the view of cutting off its source. Accordingly after the patients had felt an indisposition of about twelve hours, I applied in two of these Cases out of the three, on the vesicle formed by the virus, a little mild caustic, composed of equal parts of quick-lime and soap, and suffered it to remain on the part six hours.[12] It seemed to give the children but little uneasiness, and effectually answered my intention in preventing the appearance of erysipelas. Indeed it seemed to do more, for in half an hour after its application, the indisposition of the children ceased.[13] These precautions were perhaps unnecessary as the arm of the third child, Mary Pead, which was suffered to take its common course, scabbed quickly, without any erysipelas.

[12] Perhaps a few touches with the lapis septicus would have proved equally efficacious.
[13] What effect would a similar treatment produce in inoculation for the Small-pox?

CASE XXIII

From this child's arm matter was taken and transferred to that of J. Barge, a boy of seven years old. He sickened on the 8th day, went through the disease with the usual slight symptoms, and without any inflammation on the arm beyond the common efflorescence surrounding the pustule, an appearance so often seen in inoculated Small-pox.

After the many fruitless attempts to give the Small-pox to those who had had the Cow-pox, it did not appear necessary, nor was it convenient to me, to inoculate the whole of those who had been the subjects of these late trials; yet I thought it right to see the effects of variolous matter on some of them, particularly William Summers, the first of these patients who had been infected with matter taken from the cow. He was therefore inoculated with variolous matter from a fresh pustule; but, as in the preceding Cases, the system did not feel the effects of it in the smallest degree. I had an opportunity also of having this boy and William Pead inoculated by my Nephew, Mr. Henry Jenner, whose report to me is as follows: "I have inoculated Pead and Barge, two of the boys whom you lately infected with the Cow-pox. On the 2d day the incisions were inflamed and there was a pale inflammatory stain around them. On the 3d day these appearances were still increasing and their arms itched considerably. On the 4th day, the inflammation was evidently subsiding, and on the 6th it was scarcely perceptible. No symptom of indisposition followed.

To convince myself that the variolous matter made use of was in a perfect state, I at the same time inoculated a patient with some of it who never had gone through the Cow-pox, and it produced the Small-pox in the usual regular manner."

These experiments afforded me much satisfaction, they proved that the matter in passing from one human subject to another, through five gradations, lost none of its original properties, J. Barge being the fifth who received the infection from William Summers, the boy to whom it was communicated from the cow.

I shall now conclude this Inquiry with some general observations on the subject and on some others which are interwoven with it.

Although I presume it may be unnecessary to produce further testimony in support of my assertion "that the Cow-pox protects the human constitution from the infection of the Small-pox," yet it affords me considerable satisfaction to say, that Lord Somerville, the President of the Board of Agriculture, to whom this paper was shewn by Sir Joseph Banks, has found upon inquiry that the statements were confirmed by the concurring testimony of Mr. Dolland, a surgeon, who resides in a dairy country remote from this, in which these observations were made. With respect to the opinion adduced "that the source of the infection is a peculiar morbid matter arising in the horse," although I have not been able to prove it from actual experiments conducted immediately under my own eye, yet the evidence I have adduced appears sufficient to establish it.

They who are not in the habit of conducting experiments may not be aware of the coincidence of circumstances necessary for their being managed so as to prove perfectly decisive; nor how often men engaged in professional pursuits are liable to interruptions which disappoint them almost at the instant of their being accomplished: however, I feel no room for hesitation respecting the common origin of the disease, being well convinced that it never appears among the cows (except it can be traced to a cow introduced among the general herd which has been previously infected, or to an infected servant), unless they have been milked by some one who, at the same time, has the care of a horse affected with diseased heels.

The spring of the year 1797, which I intended particularly to have devoted to the completion of this investigation, proved, from its dryness, remarkably adverse to my wishes; for it frequently happens, while the farmers' horses are exposed to the cold rains which fall at that season that their heels become diseased, and no Cow-pox then appeared in the neighbourhood.

The active quality of the virus from the horses' heels is greatly increased after it has acted on the nipples of the cow, as it rarely happens that the horse affects his dresser with sores, and as rarely that a milk-maid escapes the infection when she milks infected cows. It is most active at the commencement of the disease, even before it has acquired a pus-like appearance; indeed I am not confident whether this property in the matter does not entirely cease as soon as it is secreted in the form of pus. I am induced to think it does cease,[14] and that it is the thin darkish-looking fluid only, oozing from the newly-formed cracks in the heels, similar to what sometimes appears from erysipelatous blisters, which gives the disease. Nor am I certain that the nipples of the cows are at all times in a state to receive the infection. The appearance of the disease in the spring and the early part of the summer, when they are disposed to be affected with spontaneous eruptions so much more frequently than at other seasons, induces me to think, that the virus from the horse must be received upon them when they are in this state, in order to produce effects: experiments, however, must determine these points. But it is clear that when the Cow-pox virus is once generated, that the cows cannot resist the contagion, in whatever state their nipples may chance to be, if they are milked with an infected hand.

---

[14] It is very easy to procure pus from old sores on the heels of horses. This I have often inserted into scratches made with a lancet, on the sound nipples of cows, and have seen no other effects from it than simple inflammation.

Whether the matter, either from the cow or the horse will affect the sound skin of the human body, I cannot positively determine; probably it will not, unless on those parts where the cuticle is extremely thin, as on the lips for example. I have known an instance of a poor girl who produced an ulceration on her lip by frequently holding her finger to her mouth to cool the raging of a Cow-pox sore by blowing upon it. The hands of the farmers' servants here, from the nature of their employments, are constantly exposed to those injuries which occasion abrasions of the cuticle, to punctures from thorns and such like accidents; so that they are always in a state to feel the consequences of exposure to infectious matter.

It is singular to observe that the Cow-pox virus, although it renders the constitution unsusceptible of the variolous, should, nevertheless, leave it unchanged with respect to its own action. I have already produced an instance[15] to point out this, and shall now corroborate it with another.

Elizabeth Wynne, who had the Cow-pox in the year 1759, was inoculated with variolous matter, without effect, in the year 1797, and again caught the Cow-pox in the year 1798. When I saw her, which was on the 8th day after she received the infection, I found her affected with general lassitude, shiverings, alternating with heat, coldness of the extremities, and a quick and irregular pulse. These symptoms were preceded by a pain in the axilla. On her hand was one large pustulous sore, which resembled that delinated in Plate No. 1.

It is curious also to observe, that the virus, which with respect to its effects is undetermined and uncertain previously to its passing from the horse through the medium of the cow, should then not only become more active, but should invariably and completely possess those specific properties which induce in the human constitution symptoms similar to those of the variolous fever, and effect in it that peculiar change which for ever renders it unsusceptible of the variolous contagion.

May it not, then, be reasonably conjectured, that the source of the Small-pox is morbid matter of a peculiar kind, generated by a disease in the horse, and that accidental circumstances may have again and again arisen, still working new changes upon it, until it has acquired the contagious and malignant form under which we now commonly see it making its devastations amongst us? And, from a consideration of the change which the infectious matter undergoes from producing a disease on the cow, may we not conceive that many contagious diseases, now prevalent among us, may owe their present appearance not to a simple, but to a compound origin? For example, it is difficult to imagine that the measles, the scarlet fever, and the ulcerous sore throat with a spotted skin, have all sprung from the same source, assuming some variety in their forms according to the nature of their new combinations? The same

[15] See Case IX.

question will apply respecting the origin of many other contagious diseases, which bear a strong analogy to each other.

There are certainly more forms than one, without considering the common variation between the confluent and distinct, in which the Small-pox appears in what is called the natural way. About seven years ago a species of Small-pox spread through many of the towns and villages of this part of Gloucestershire: it was of so mild a nature, that a fatal instance was scarcely ever heard of, and consequently so little dreaded by the lower orders of the community, that they scrupled not to hold the same intercourse with each other as if no infectious disease had been present among them. I never saw nor heard of an instance of its being confluent. The most accurate manner, perhaps, in which I can convey an idea of it is by saying that had fifty individuals been taken promiscuously and infected by exposure to this contagion, they would have had as mild and light a disease as if they had been inoculated with variolous matter in the usual way. The harmless manner in which it shewed itself could not arise from any peculiarity either in the season or the weather, for I watched its progress upwards of a year without perceiving any variation in its general appearance. I consider it then as a *variety* of the Small-pox.[16]

In some of the preceding cases I have noticed the attention that was paid to the state of the variolous matter to the experiment of inserting it into the arms of those who had gone through the Cow-pox. This I conceive to be of great importance in conducting these experiments, and were it always properly attended to by those who inoculate for the Small-pox, it might prevent much subsequent mischief and confusion. With the view of enforcing so necessary a precaution, I shall take the liberty of digressing so far as to point out some unpleasant facts, relative to mismanagement in this particular, which have fallen under my own observation.

A Medical Gentlemen (now no more), who for many years inoculated in this neighbourhood, frequently preserved the variolous matter intended for his use, on a piece of lint or cotton, which, in its fluid state was put into a vial, corked, and conveyed into a warm pocket; a situation certainly favourable for speedily producing putrefaction in it. In this state (not unfrequently after it had been taken several days from the pustules) it was inserted into the arms of his patients, and brought on inflammation of the incised parts, swelling of the axillary glands, fever, and sometimes eruptions. But what was this disease? Certainly not the Small-pox: for the matter having from putrefaction lost, or suffered a

[16] My friend Dr. Hicks, of Bristol, who during the prevalence of this distemper was resident at Gloucester, and Physician to the Hospital there, (where it was seen soon after its first appearance in this country) had opportunities of making numerous observations upon it which it is his intention to communicate to the Public.

derangement in its specific properties, was no longer capable of producing that malady, those who had been inoculated in this manner being as much subject to the contagion of the Small-pox, as if they had never been under the influence of this artificial disease; and many, unfortunately, fell victims to it, who thought themselves in perfect security. The same unfortunate circumstance of giving a disease, supposed to be the Small-pox, with inefficaceous variolous matter, having occurred under the direction of some other practitioners within my knowledge, and probably from the same incautious method of securing the variolous matter, I avail myself of this opportunity of mentioning what I conceive to be of great importance; and, as a further cautionary hint, I shall again digress so far as to add another observation on the subject of Inoculation.

Whether it be yet ascertained by experiment, that the quantity of variolous matter inserted into the skin makes any difference with respect to the subsequent mildness or violence of the disease, I know not; but I have the strongest reason for supposing that if neither the punctures or incisions be made so deep as to go *through* it, and wound the adipose membrane, that the risk of bringing on a violent disease is greatly increased. I have known an inoculator, whose practice was "to cut deep enough (to use his own expression) to see a bit of fat," and there to lodge the matter. The great number of bad Cases, independent of inflammations and abscesses on the arms, and the fatality which attended this practice was almost inconceivable; and I cannot account for it on any other principle than that of the matter being placed in this situation instead of the skin.

It was the practice of another, whom I well remember, to pinch up a small portion of the skin on the arms of his patients and to pass through it a needle, with a thread attached to it previously dipped in variolous matter. The thread was lodged in the perforated part, and consequently left in contact with the cellular membrane. This practice was attended with the same ill success as the former. Although it is very improbable that any one would now inoculate in this rude way by design, yet these observations may tend to place a double guard over the lancet, when infants, whose skins are comparatively so thin, fall under the care of the inoculator.

A very respectable friend of mine, Dr. Hardwicke, of Sodbury in this county, inoculated great numbers of patients previous to the introduction of the more modern method by Sutton, and with such success, that a fatal instance occurred as rarely as since that method has been adopted. It was the doctor's practice to make as slight an incision as possible *upon* the skin, and there to lodge a thread saturated with the variolous matter. When his patients became indisposed, agreeably to the custom then prevailing, they were directed to go to bed and were kept moderately warm. Is it not probable then, that the success of the modern practice may depend more upon the method of invariably depositing the virus in or upon the skin, than on the subsequent treatment of the disease?

I do not mean to insinuate that exposure to cool air, and suffering the patient to drink cold water when hot and thirsty, may not moderate the eruptive symptoms and lessen the number of pustules; yet, to repeat my former observation, I cannot account for the uninterrupted success, or nearly so, of one practitioner, and the wretched state of the patients under the care of another, where, in both instances, the general treatment did not differ essentially, without conceiving it to arise from the different modes of inserting the matter for the purpose of producing the disease. As it is not the identical matter inserted which is absorbed into the constitution, but that which is, by some peculiar process in the animal economy, generated by it, is it not probable that different parts of the human body may prepare or modify the virus differently? Although the skin, for example, adipose membrane, or mucous membranes are all capable of producing the variolous virus by the stimulus given the particles originally deposited upon them, yet I am induced to conceive that each of these parts is capable of producing some variation in the qualities of the matter previous to its affecting the constitution. What else can constitute the difference between the Small-pox when communicated casually or in what has been termed the natural way, or when brought on artificially through the medium of the skin? After all, are the variolous particles, possessing their true specific and contagious principles, ever taken up and conveyed by the lymphatics unchanged into the blood vessels? I imagine not. Were this the case, should we not find the blood sufficiently loaded with them in some stages of the Small-pox to communicate the disease by inserting it under the cuticle, or by spreading it on the surface of an ulcer? Yet experiments have determined the impracticability of its being given in this way; although it has been proved that variolous matter when much diluted with water, and applied to the skin in the usual manner, will produce the disease. But it would be digressing beyond a proper boundry, to go minutely into this subject here.

At what period the Cow-pox was first noticed here is not upon record. Our oldest farmers were not acquainted with it in their earliest days, when it appeared among their farms without any deviation from the phaenomena which it now exhibits. Its connection with the Small-pox seems to have been unknown to them. Probably the general introduction of inoculation first occasioned the discovery.

Its rise in this country may not have been of very remote date, as the practice of milking cows might formerly have been in the hands of women only; which I believe is the case now in some other dairy countries, and, consequently that the cows might not in former times have been exposed to the contagious matter brought by the men servants from the heels of horses.[17] Indeed a knowledge of the source of the infection is new in the minds of most of the farmers in this neighbourhood, but it has at length produced good consequences; and it seems probable from the precautions they are now disposed to adopt, that the appearance of the Cow-pox here may either be entirely extinguished or become extremely rare.

Should it be asked whether this investigation is a matter of mere curiosity, or whether it tends to any beneficial purpose? I should answer, that notwithstanding the happy effects of Inoculation, with all the improvements which the practice has received since its first introduction into this country, it not very unfrequently produces deformity of the skin, and sometimes, under the best management, proves fatal.

These circumstances must naturally create in every instance some degree of painful solicitude for its consequences. But as I have never known fatal effects arise from the Cow-pox, even when impressed in the most unfavourable manner, producing extensive inflammations and suppurations on the hands; and as it clearly appears that this disease leaves the constitution in a state of perfect security from the infection of the Small-pox, may we not infer that a mode of Inoculation may be introduced preferable to that at present adopted, especially among those families, which, from previous circumstances we may judge to be predisposed to have the disease unfavourably? It is an excess in the number of pustules which we chiefly dread in the Small-pox; but, in the Cow-pox, no pustules appear, nor does it seem possible for the contagious matter to produce the disease from effluvia, or by any other means than contact, and that probably not simply between the virus and the cuticle; so that a single individual in a family might at any time receive it without the risk of infecting the rest, or of spreading a distemper that fills a country with terror. Several instances have come under my observation which justify the assertion that the disease cannot be propagated by effluvia. The first boy whom I inoculated with the matter of Cow-pox, slept in a bed, while the experiment was going forward, with two children who never had gone through either that disease or the Small-pox, without infecting either of them.

A young woman who had the Cow-pox to a great extent, several sores which maturated having appeared on the hands and wrists, slept in the same bed with a fellow-dairy maid who never had been infected with either the Cow-pox or the Small-pox, but no indisposition followed.

Another instance has occurred of a young woman on whose hands

[17] I have been informed from respectable authority that in Ireland, although dairies abound in many parts of the Island, the disease is entirely unknown. The reason seems obvious. The business of the dairy is conducted by women only. Were the meanest vassal among the men, employed there as a milker at a dairy, he would feel his situation unpleasant beyond all endurance.

were several large suppurations from the Cow-pox, who was at the same time a daily nurse to an infant, but the complaint was not communicated to the child.

In some other points of view, the inoculation of this disease appears preferable to the variolous inoculation.

In constitutions predisposed to scrophula, how frequently we see the inoculated Small-pox, rouse into activity that distressful malady. This circumstance does not seem to depend on the manner in which the distemper has shewn itself, for it has as frequently happened among those who have had it mildly, as when it has appeared in the contrary way.

There are many, who from some peculiarity in the habit resist the common effects of variolous matter inserted into the skin, and who are in consequence haunted through life with the distressing idea of being insecure from subsequent infection. A ready mode of dissipating anxiety originating from such a cause must now appear obvious. And, as we have seen that the constitution may at any time be made to feel the febrile attack of Cow-pox, might it not, in many chronic diseases be introduced into the system, with the probability of affording relief, upon well-known physiological principles?

Although I say the system may at any time be made to feel the febrile attack of Cow-pox, yet I have a single instance before me where the virus acted locally only, but it is not in the least probable that the same person would resist the action both of the Cow-pox virus and the variolous.

Elizabeth Sarsenet lived as a dairy maid at Newpark farm, in this parish. All the cows and the servants employed in milking had the Cow-pox; but this woman, though she had several sores upon her fingers, felt no tumors in the axillae, nor any general indisposition. On being afterwards casually exposed to variolous infection, she had the Small-pox in a mild way.—Hannah Pick, another of the dairy maids who was a fellow-servant with Elizabeth Sarsenet when the distemper broke out at the farm was, at the same time infected; but this young woman had not only sores upon her hands, but felt herself also much indisposed for a day or two. After this, I made several attempts to give her the Small-pox by inoculation, but they all proved fruitless. From the former Case then we see that the animal economy is subject to the same laws in one disease as the other.

The following Case which has very lately occurred renders it highly probable that not only the heels of the horse, but other parts of the body of that animal, are capable of generating the virus which produces the Cow-pox.

An extensive inflammation of the erysipelatous kind, appeared without any apparent cause upon the upper part of the thigh of a sucking colt, the property of Mr. Millet, a farmer at Rockhampton, a village near Berkeley. The inflammation continued several weeks, and at length terminated in the formation of three or four small abscesses. The inflamed parts were fomented, and dressings were applied by some of the same persons who were employed in milking the cows. The number of cows milked was twenty-four, and the whole of them had the Cow-pox. The milkers, consisting of the farmer's wife, a man and a maid servant, were infected by the cows. The man servant had previously gone through the Small-pox, and felt but little of the Cow-pox. The servant maid had some years before been infected with the Cow-pox, and she also felt it now in a slight degree: But the farmer's wife who never had gone through either of these diseases, felt its effects very severely.

That the disease produced upon the cows by the colt and from thence conveyed to those who milked them was the *true* and not the *spurious* Cow-pox, there can be scarcely any room for suspicion; yet it would have been more completely satisfactory, had the effects of variolous matter been ascertained on the farmer's wife, but there was a peculiarity in her situation which prevented my making the experiment.

Thus far have I proceeded in an inquiry, founded, as it must appear, on the basis of experiment; in which, however, conjecture has been occasionally admitted in order to present to persons well situated for such discussions, objects for a more minute investigation. In the mean time I shall myself continue to prosecute this inquiry, encouraged by the hope of its becoming essentially beneficial to mankind.

1884

A New Communication on Rabies

by M. Pasteur, with the collaboration of MM. Chamberland and Roux[1]

Pasteur's methodical investigation of the dread disease rabies, culminating in an immunization procedure designed to prevent the disease, is an exemplary demonstration of his perspicuity and the use of the scientific method. This achievement is often cited as his greatest triumph. The theme of his research on rabies was the attenuation of the causal agent and its use, subsequently, as a preventative against the disease—the virus became the vaccine.

Although Pasteur was familiar with Jenner's work, he labored under the handicap of not possessing the equivalent of a natural immunizing agent, that is, cowpox virus. In the short span of approximately three years, however, he and his associates succeeded in developing a method for attenuating the virus. Considering the paucity of knowledge on viruses and on the disease with which he was working, Pasteur accomplished an extraordinary feat. In the process, he demonstrated that the agent of rabies was "ultra-microscopic," and that it could be cultivated by implantation in receptive tissues of laboratory animals.[2] The consequence of this latter discovery was that it furnished a means of growing the "invisible" virus as readily as cultivable bacteria. It constituted a practical contribution to the future progress of animal virology.

The paper presented here was one of a series on his investigations of rabies. Its importance lies in the demonstration that a substantial decrease in the virulence of rabies virus for dogs resulted when the virus was passed intracranially in rabbits. Other alterations were a shortening of the incubation period of the disease in rabbits from 15-30 days to 6-8 days and

[1] Reprinted from Compt. Rend. Acad. Sci. **98**: 457-463 (1884).
[2] Pasteur *et al.* C. R. Acad. Sci. **92**: (1881) 1259; **95**: 1187 (1882).

*the replacement of viciousness and excitability by a paralytic
form of the disease. The attenuation of the virus persisted and
was designated as "fixed" (Pasteur's term for stable). This procedure served as a basis or prototype of future work on virus
attenuation and, in a broader sense, exemplified an important
inherent characteristic of viruses—the phenomenon of variation. Later to prove feasible, and mentioned in the paper, is
the germ of the idea for preventing the disease by utilizing
the lengthy incubation period of rabies in man for immunization with the attenuated virus.*[3]

The Academy had received with
kindness our previous communications on rabies, although incomplete.
The Academy understood that in such research each step toward the
investigation of this disease deserves to be stimulated.

The new facts, that I have the honor to present in my name and in
behalf of my co-workers in which I should add Thuillier who before
leaving for Egypt has contributed largely in these experiments, have been
obtained by the use of two valuable methods of inoculation of rabid
virus on the brain surface by trephenation, or by injection of this virus
into the blood stream. Trephenation is regarded as a difficult and unsuccessful operation. It is not true. Several hundred operations have been
carried out in dogs, rabbits, guinea pigs, chickens, monkeys, sheep, etc.,
with a few occasional accidents. As for the skillful to carry out such
traumatizing, it can be accomplished by anybody.

A young technician was taught by Dr. Roux to practice this operation.
He is the one who does all the trephenations in our various laboratory
animals, without significant accidents. The operation is relatively short
so that the last monkey was anesthetized and operated in 20 minutes.
Less than 15 minutes later he ate a fig. In order to summarize this lecture, I will try to summarize our results as conclusions:

1. In my communication of 11 December 1882, I claimed that the
inoculation of rabid virus in the blood system often gives rise to the
paralytic forms of rabies with lack of fury and rabid barking. It is postulated that under these circumstances the rabid virus should fix and would
multiply first in the spinal cord. In sacrificing the dogs when the first
paralytic symptoms are manifested and in undertaking a comparative
study with the spinal cord virulence, especially at the level of lumbar
enlargement, and the spinal bulb virulence, we have been able to recognize that the spinal cord would be rabid while the spinal bulb was not.

[3] Pasteur, C. R. Acad. Sci. **101**: 765 (1885).

2. We have shown previously that the rabid virus was located in the brain and spinal cord. More recently we have been looking for this virus in the peripheral nerves and in the salivary glands. We have been able to produce rabies from the fragments of pneumogastric nerve taken either at its origin, at the cranium level, or at its distal portions. The sciatic nerves, the submaxillary glands, the parotids and the sublingual glands also contained viruses. The entire nervous system from the center to the periphery is susceptible to the culture of rabid virus. One can explain and understand the nervous over-excitement encountered so often in rabid cases, and often ended up in man by this strange symptom, aerophobia.

The virulence of the saliva and the salivary glands has been tested from dogs given rabies by intracranial or intravenous inoculations or from dogs with so-called spontaneous rabies.

3. We have observed previously that the rabid virus can be stored with preservation of its virulence, in brain or in spinal cord for several weeks, when post-mortem putrefaction can be avoided by a low temperature between 0° and 12° above zero.

We knew also that the pure virus enclosed in the sealed tubes with enameler's lamp can be preserved for 3 weeks to 1 month even in a summer temperature.

4. We have been checking again the presence of rabid virus in spinal fluid which revealed to be inconstant, even though the fluid could transmit rabies especially when it was clear, and did not transmit the disease when opalescent.

5. We tried many times to culture the rabid virus either from the spinal fluid or from other substances. We tried even from the spinal cord extracted from the perfectly healthy sacrificed animals. So far we did not succeed. "There might not be any rabid microbe, was told me last May by our colleague M. Bouley? I answered, all I can say in order to assure you, is that if you give me a rabid brain and a healthy one, I will be able, after the microscopic examination of material from the medulla oblongata, to tell which one is with rabies.

Both show a large number of molecular granulations; more numerous and much smaller in the rabid spinal bulb than in the normal one, so that one is forced to believe of the existence of minute microbes, which do not have the form of a bacillus nor that of a narrowed or compressed micrococcus. They appear as multiple points or dots.

So far only one method permitted us to isolate these granulations from all the other elements of the nervous matter. It consisted of intravenous injection in a rabid animal at the beginning of asphyxiation some pure virus taken from the spinal bulb of an animal dead from rabies. In a few hours, either by fixation of the normal nervous elements in the capillaries, or by digestion in the blood, nothing else is left except these fine granulations under consideration. In addition, in those very special circumstances these granulations could be easily stained by aniline dye derivatives.[4]

As for the blood taken from a rabid subject, in one instance we could produce rabies in a dog from the blood of a rabbit dead of rabies; we will come back to this important subject.

Meantime we were highly concerned about another question:

It is known that often a dog bitten, if he produces rabies, shows the fury with the tendency to bite and with this special barking known as "rabid barking." Under the present experimental conditions, when we inoculated the rabid virus intravenously or subcutaneously, we obtained the paralytic form of rabies without the usual fury nor the customary barking. The trephenation, on the contrary, produces most of the time the furious form of rabies. We have recognized that it was possible to obtain furious rabies by intravenous or hypodermic inoculation providing that we use very small amounts of virus. "Less often one uses the virus by hypodermic or intravenous inoculations, more easily one obtains the furious form of rabies."

We have recognized, on the other hand, that the inoculation of the small amounts of virus can prolong significantly the length of incubation time, and diluted to a certain limit, the virus inoculation is without effect. The interest of these conclusions pushes me to give here the details of two experiments.

On 6 May 1883, we inoculated in the vein of the right leg of 3 dogs a ground, rabid spinal bulb diluted in the sterile broth: 1/2 cubic centimeter was inoculated in the first dog, 1/100 of this dose to the second, and 1/200 to the third.

As early as day 10, the first dog had lost his usual appetite, at the 18th day he became entirely paralytic and died two days later, without manifesting the characteristic barking, nor wishing to bite. The second dog was still able to eat at day 37 post-inoculation. At the 38th day he appeared suspicious, at day 39 he had the rabid voice, and the next day he was found dead. The third dog was not affected by rabies.

In another experiment, we have inoculated intravenously in a leg of a dog 1 cc of rabid material diluted in the sterile broth, in a second 1/20th of this dose was used, and in a third dog 1/50th of it.

The incubation periods were 7 days, 20 days, and 25 days respectively. In addition, the first two dogs developed paralytic rabies while the third one presented a furious rabies with barking and biting.

We have verified the fact that when small amounts of rabid material were employed no rabies is produced, but the animal becomes susceptible to any new inoculations.

---

[4] We do not have as yet definite proof whether these granulations are the rabid microbes. We endeavor to gather these proofs.

In other words, the inoculation of small doses did not produce immunity.

6. In my previous lecture on rabies I have shown that we have found in dog cases the disappearance of the first rabid symptoms and reappearance of the disease a long time after the challenge. We have since then recognized the existence of the same fact in rabbits. Here is an example: a rabbit presented paralytic rabies 13 days after trephenation. The following day he was completely cured. The paralysis reappeared 43 days later and the animal died with rabies at day 46.

7. These facts are, however, very rare in rabbits as well as in dogs, but we have observed numerous such cases manifested in chickens. In this species death can or cannot occur after the reappearance of the disease as we have shown an example in dog in our previous communication.

I would like to point out, in the way, that the chicken when rabid, never produced any striking symptoms. These symptoms are essentially manifested by sleepiness, lack of appetite, paralysis of the limbs, and often an advanced anemia, which is recognized by the discoloration of the comb.

8. Recently we have been largely concerned about certain recent reports concerning a so-called attenuation of rabid virus by action of the cold or a pretending passage of the rabies from the mother to the fetus.

Although our experiments in these two points have been more numerous and more intensive than those who evoked this to push their ideas ahead, we have obtained negative results.

9. The surety of rabies inoculation by intravenous injection of virus is so evident and explanatory that the hypothesis of the passage of this virus from the peripheral nerves to the central nervous system cannot be considered as a unique route of dissemination, and in many cases the virus absorption is carried out by the blood system.

On the whole, this kind of observation is debatable. In order to inoculate the rabid virus in a vein, one has to create a trauma by cutting the skin and denuding the vein. Can one admit that the introduction of virus into the blood stream comes back immediately at the open wound where it finds the nerves and lymphatic vessels wide open. The following experiment discards completely this objection: many times we have inoculated the rabid virus in a vein of the ear, then immediately after with a thermocauter we have cut the ear below the point of inoculation. In all cases the rabies has broken out. In fact the thermocauter does not produce a properly so-called wound; the entire cutting surface being burned.

I am anxious to arrive at that portion of this lecture which deserves the most important credit and more attention.

The Academy has not forgotten that the discovery of the attenuated viruses with their applications, related to the prophylaxis of many diseases, shed plenty of light to this important fact of a possible experimental product having various stages of virulence of a given virus.

The rabies is above all a virulent disease. The effects and the nature of its virus are surrounded by so many mysteries that it is natural to investigate if the rabid virus could show various virulences. It has been shown experimentally that the answer to this question must be affirmative. In lieu of other methods which are still under study, we have recognized that the passage of a rabid virus in various species of animals can modify (more or less significantly) the virulence of this virus. Rabbits, guinea pigs, chickens and monkeys catch the rabies. When by successive passages the virus has reached a level of fixity appropriate to each strain, the virulence of these viruses is far from the same. In fact it differs significantly from the virulence of natural canine rabies, which has in turn a fixed virulence, obtained by numerous dog to dog passages by biting since an immemorial time. In my mind there is no spontaneous rabies.

Presently we have a virus which gives the rabies to the rabbit in 7 or 8 days, so constantly that one can predict with a few hours of difference almost the exact length of incubation which can be measured by a change in temperature or by appearance of the first external rabid symptoms. We also possess a rabid virus which gives the rabies to guinea pigs in 5 or 6 days with no less certainty in the length of incubation than the previous one.

Before reaching this fixity that I am talking about, proper for each animal species, the virulence of the rabid virus varies continuously. Our judgement is that for a given species the virulence is inversely proportional to the number of days of incubation; of course under the same experimental conditions including the amounts of virus to be inoculated and in using the same "mode of inoculation." In general, in young animals, the length of incubation is slightly shorter than in adults.

Since one ignores absolutely the stage which can reach the dog rabid virus communicated to man after a successive passage from man to man, we have been forced to try monkey to monkey rabies.

I will communicate later on the results of this highly interesting study which is not as yet complete.

I have announced that there are several dogs in my laboratory who are refractory to rabies regardless of the routes of inoculation. I can add today that they are also refractory to all types of rapid virus. However, at the time of my last lecture in the Academy concerning the rabies, I was wondering, by lack of precise observations, if these dogs were refractory to rabies by natural condition or this refractory situation was related to the previous operational circumstances that these dogs were subjected.

Today we can answer to these questions more precisely, although still surrounded by some reservation.

I believe I can confirm with certainty that our dogs were not refractory to rabies by natural constitution. In fact we have found a practical way to obtain as many refractory dogs as one desires to have. However, considering a possible long period of incubation the rabies infection which makes one doubt about the controls, I ask the Academy if the Academy would like to give me credit for this assertion. In addition, I am confined to report to the Academy for the time being that the refractory stage is obtained by systemic inoculations of various types of rabid virus. We actually possess twenty-three dogs which can be subjected without danger to virulent inoculations.

Rendering the dogs refractory to rabies would be not only a solution of the question of prophylaxis of this disease in dog but also in man, because man does not produce rabies without being bitten whether or not the virus is produced directly or indirectly by dog.

Could human medicine benefit of this long period of incubation of the rabies to establish in this intermediary time, before the manifestation of the first rabid symptoms, a refractory stage in the bitten subjects? But, before realizing this expectation a long way remains to go.

1886

Concerning the Mosaic Disease of Tobacco[1]

by Adolf Mayer

The earliest record of a virus disease of plants was "breaking" or mosaic in tulips described by Carolus Clusius in 1576. Numerous descriptive papers on plant disorders, for which a viral etiology was established later, were published in the eighteenth and nineteenth centuries but were distinguished, unfortunately, by a paucity of experimental data. The nature of plant virus diseases was elucidated, eventually, with evidence of their infectiousness.

Adolf Mayer in 1886 published an account of his investigations of the disease of the tobacco plant which he began in 1880. This report is regarded as the beginning of modern experimental work on plant virus diseases. The tobacco disease, a few years earlier, had reached damaging proportions in Holland. In his description of the disease, Mayer used the term "mosaikkrankheit" to designate the mottling pattern common on the leaves of infected plants. The term gave rise to "mosaic" which has been retained to this day. In attempting to discover the cause of the malady of tobacco plants, he studied methodically such factors as soil, fertility, seed transmission, nematodes, and air-temperature and concluded that they were not involved in the etiology. By employing capillary tubes filled with sap from infected plants and sticking them in healthy plants which, subsequently, became diseased, Mayer established the first experimental transmission of a plant virus disease. He demonstrated also that the disease was transmitted by budding and not by the soil or seeds. Although he failed to

[1] Mayer, Adolf. Ueber die Mosaikkrankheit des Tabaks. Die Landwirtschaftlichen Versuchs-Stationen. **32**: (451)-467 (1886). (With Plate III). Translation by Dr. James Johnson; abridged and reprinted from Phytopathological Classics (7) (1942), by permission of American Phytopathological Society.

isolate a bacterium after many exhaustive trials, Mayer mis-
takenly concluded, nonetheless, that a bacterium was the causal
agent.

I n those regions of Netherlands where the cultivation of tobacco flourishes, that is in the provinces of Gelderland and Utrecht, there has been prevailing for many years a disease of this cultivated plant, to which it seems to be very important to draw the attention of the agricultural sciences; because the harm done by this disease is often very great and I myself know cases where it has caused the cultivation of tobacco to be given up entirely in a certain place. In spite of this, this disease has hardly been the subject of a thorough investigation as yet, for the simple reason that until recently the scientific treatment of technical agricultural questions had not yet taken a firm root in Holland.

The manifestations of this disease may be approximately described as follows. About 3-5 weeks after the young plant has been transplanted into the field, has taken root well, and has begun to grow vigorously, commonly around the middle of June, a map or mosaic-like coloring of light and dark green appears on the leaf surfaces, while otherwise the whole leaf still seems to be healthy. Soon afterwards one can, with the aid of a lens, and a little later also with the naked eye, discern that the leaf shows a more pronounced growth in thickness in the darker colored spots.

It soon appears that these thicker places of the leaf are growing more vigorously than the paler parts, which results in manifold and irregular distortions of the leaf surface. Finally, if the disease develops in the regular manner, some of the lighter and thinner parts of the leaf die prematurely, not entirely different from, only much more extensively than, the similar spotting which often appears in the fully ripe leaves without detriment to the value of the product. In the later stages of the disease, the darker parts of the leaf may take on the transparent and varnish-colored tint, generally peculiar only to leaves that have been injected, and in which the at first sharply delimited borders between light and dark gradually grow indistinct. (Cf. Plate III, figs. 1, 2, 3.) Finally, it is characteristic and a sure way of diagnosing older leaves that have already been disfigured by the disease, that, when a leaf has become diseased, all the younger leaves of the same plant also show the symptoms in corresponding earlier stages, so that the diagnosis to determine whether the *disease* is present must necessarily always be made in the youngest leaves.

As far as concerns the distribution of the diseased plants in an affected field, one cannot set up a rule for this.

It is not unusual to find several diseased plants next to each other. Quite as often, one often finds healthy and diseased plants alternating in most arbitrary succession. It may be accepted for certain, that an obviously diseased plant is never a source of infection for its surroundings.

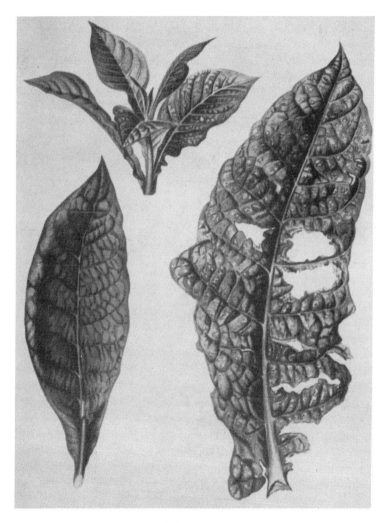

Plate III.

The disadvantages of the disease are obvious and may be listed under the following aspects:

1. Retardation of the growth and a consequent decrease in the yield.
2. Curling of the leaves, which renders them useless for the manufacture of cigars.

3. Brittleness of the leaves with the same result.

4. Insufficient ripening and, therefore, poor burn, also harmful to the aroma, as far as one can speak of such in European tobacco.

The disease that up to now is known only in Holland [Netherlands] —in spite of diligent search, I have found only once[2] in Southern Germany, near Karlsruhe, a similar phenomenon on a very small scale—has, up to now, received only regional names.

In the region of Rhenen and Amerongen it is called "bunt" (bont) referring to the first stage of spotting in the region of Wageningen and in the region mentioned above it is called "rust" (roest) referring to the later stage of the yellow colored spots that have died. "Smut" (vuil) is a name that is popular with the grower.

None of these expressions seems to me very desirable for general usage, least of all "rust," because this is used to designate a very characteristic fungus disease of all kinds of plants. In order to prevent a confusion that might easily take place, I should like to suggest for the time being as an international name "mosaic disease of tobacco." The term has not been used and gives a fair picture at least of the first apparent stage of the disease.[3]

What is the cause of this disease, and how may it be cured or avoided? These are two fundamental questions whose answers made a more thorough investigation necessary; therefore, the Experimental Station at Wageningen has devoted a continued study through several years to the subject,—with what measure of success, we shall see later in this article.

The earlier views of the growers about the causes of the mosaic disease had been widely divergent. A collection of them seems to us but a true chaos making one dizzy and at best useful to reaffirm the old experience, that man cannot exist without theories, and that the most practical of practitioners also usually has his specific favorite theories.[4]

[2] The curling, or so-called "going crazy," of the Palatinate tobacco is an entirely different disease with much less far-reaching effects.

[3] It is true, some growers claim to recognize two independent diseases in the two forms, or better, stages of the disease, but only because the first stage may not be apparent through superficial observation. The same geographical distribution and the succession in time of the two forms definitely speaks against this (theory).

[4] I have made a whole collection of examples and find in my notes among other things the following: (cf. also J. H. van Swieten: Tydschr. ter bevord. v. Nyverheid 1857, p. 157). One of the tobacco planters who fertilizes well and who, up to that time, had suffered little from the disease, maintains with an enviable sureness that only poor fertilizing, insufficient plant-food, is the cause of the disease. Many farmers blame the weather. With one it is the rays of the sun which are too strong, with others it is the cold nights or frosty fogs, with a third it is the cold together with the wet ground which causes the disease. There are very experienced farmers represented in this group. The same is true of the following group, in which the opinion has been formed that the condition of the seed (origin from plans that show the same disease) is of great influence. But here, too, serious comparative experiments to support the

FINDING THE CAUSE OF THE DISEASE

I have already mentioned incidentally that we also searched for Anguillulen (nematodes) in the tobacco-diseased soil and in others. But much earlier, immediately after the disease had first been observed on living plants, their tissues were diligently searched for fungi, animal parasites, etc., not only by me but also several times by research workers of my acquaintance. This investigation was at first without successful results. Only one authority in the field of plant diseases claimed to find fungus hyphae in the diseased parts of the leaves, "which might develop into Leptoria (Septoria?) or Phoma." However, a fully developed fungus never has been found on the living plant; these unidentified threads, therefore, must have been a secondary infection on the wilted leaf.

Then I suddenly made the discovery that the juice from diseased plants obtained by grinding was a certain infectious substance for healthy plants. For instance, if one grinds up finely a leaf that is clearly diseased with the addition of a few drops of water and sucks the thick green emulsion thus obtained into fine capillary glass tubes and then sticks these into the thick leaf veins of an older plant in such a manner that they remain without penetrating to the back of the leaf, in nine cases out of ten one will be successful in making the healthy plant, of which the leaf thus treated is a part, heavily diseased.

The time between inoculation and the first unquestionable signs of the disease is regularly 10-11 days. At the end of this period the disease puts in its appearance, not in the leaf that has been inoculated, but in the very youngest leaves, particularly those not yet developed at the time

---

theory are not cited. Furthermore, the opinion that the procedure in planting is of great influence is very widespread. This goes so far, even, that the nickname Jan Bont was given to a farm-hand in Amerongen because he was known for his unlucky hand in planting and was therefore responsible for much "bunted" (spotted) tobacco. The opinions of this group as to what is the wrong treatment in planting, are also widely "colored" (divergent). Some have not formed a definite opinion about it. Others maintain that the evil lies in choosing a seedling with too strong a tap-root. Still others, that it is the plant with a long stem or also the somewhat etiolated plants that are the cause of it.

Still others maintain with great certainty that it is the planting in ground that has just been turned that is so disastrous, because in this way too much cold is brought into the subsoil. Some very intelligent farmers also put the blame on the hot beds in which the tobacco is sown. For example, they claim to have noticed that the disease has spread to a much more pronounced degree since the time that white paper, instead of gray paper, had been chosen for the transparent covering of the first place of planting. Others point to the excessive dryness of the hot beds, or to their being fertilized with pigeon-manure, etc.

And finally, there are many who hold the disease to be entirely unexplainable, a sort of magic, and several times the warning cry has reached my ear: You will never ˛ find it, never!

of inoculation; and once a leaf shows this mosaic-like coloring, it also appears unfailingly on all the younger leaves and on all the shoots that develop in the axils of the diseased leaves. The plant is diseased in all its younger parts, with perhaps the exception of the blossom, if one does not break it off,—in all its older parts it is healthy.

It is self-evident from this that the disease will be the more violent the younger the plant is when inoculated. It seems to depend to a much lesser degree on the quantity of the inoculum. One only has to be careful that the inoculum is really sucked up, which succeeds most easily with watery inocula and when the leaves of the plant to be infected are slightly wilted.

It follows that after this striking discovery the investigation of protoplasmic bodies of the extract from diseased tobacco was again taken up with special zeal. It is true that the frequently repeated microscopic scrutinization of this extract at first did not show any decisive results, for reasons which are easily comprehensible to anyone who is familiar with anything about bacteriological investigations and such. Firstly, the juice pressed out of healthy and out of diseased tobacco is rich in almost colorless particles in the protoplasm,[5] which have a shape not unlike that of the red blood corpuscles, only a little more sickle-like (half-moon-like) and often cover up other, principally smaller, things. Besides this, the extract in both cases (although apparently predominantly in diseased leaves) is rich in smaller tetrahedric particles, which slowly disappear in hydrochloric acid and probably must be interpreted as being calcium oxalate. Whatever other smaller particles one may see in the sap they are so indefinite, even when strongly magnified, that one may not with certainty designate them as anything organized.[6]

Later I tried to isolate these questionable organisms according to Koch's method and other methods; in many cases I proved the presence of bacteriological vegetation. However, none of these, used as inoculum, were infectious to healthy tobacco. Likewise I inoculated the latter with a great number of well-known bacteria and fluids containing bacteria, which were in many cases isolated according to the method given by Zopf, without resultant disease in a single case. In order to spare other experimental workers in this field fruitless labor, I mention here as such inocula:

1. *Bacterium tumescens*
2. Lactic acid bacteria
3. *Bacterium subtilis*
4. Glycerin bacteria
5. Acetic bacteria

[5] These, however, do not show the albumen reaction, nor do they react to methyl violet, but they *are* somewhat colored by iodine.

[6] Sap from healthy plants does not produce the disease, as I have proved experimentally—although to some it may seem superfluous to have tried this.

6. Pigeon manure (a manure frequently used for tobacco hot beds)
7. Sheep manure (the usual tobacco manure in Holland)
8. Chicken excrements
9. Cattle manure
10. Outhouse manure (used several times in "practice" in cases where the disease appeared)
11. Grated old cheese
12. Horse manure
13. Extract from tobacco diseased soil
14. Putrefied legumes.

However, there is another means of answering the question, with what kind of disease one is dealing in this case, than that at present generally used by mycologists. One should realize that a definite capacity to infect, as has been proved in our case, may be determined either by an unorganized or an organized ferment. It is true that the former would be rather unusual as a cause for a disease, and also that an enzyme should reproduce itself is unheard of. Yet this situation has been taken under consideration in the following.

An organized ferment also may be: a fungus or a bacterium, and these two form-groups can be distinguished with the aid of a microscope and also by a mechanical method. May I remind you, that a mixed alcoholic and lactic acid fermentation becomes purely the latter after filtration through ordinary filterpaper, because the lactic acid bacteria go through the pores of the paper by the thousand, while the *Saccharomyces* cells do not.

The following experiments were carried out in order to weigh these three possibilities.

First the inoculum, which swarmed with cell-contents, was filtered through ordinary filter paper and the filtrate used for a great number of further inoculations.

Result: Filtered extract has about the same effect (the percentage of diseased plants is somewhat smaller) as the original. If this frequently corroborated result seems to establish the fact that the solid (organized) cell-contents are not responsible for the transmission of the infection, one may add immediately, that the particles described in more detail above, are all small enough to go through the pores in the filter paper, even though in a somewhat different relationship. It is not until one has repeated the filtration through double filters that one finally succeeds in getting a clear filtrate. This also was used for many infection experiments.[7]

Result: Filtrates that are clarified (purified) in any way do not have the capacity for infection.

---

[7] Since for all these experiments whole rows of plants were used.

With this (result) already, the possibility of an infection through an enzyme-like body would be excluded; because it definitely contradicts all the known characteristics of these peculiar substances to be removed from a fluid in which they have been dissolved by means of simple filtration. This conclusion is supported by the fact that an attempted isolation, or better, concentration of an enzyme from the unfiltered extract by precipitation with weak alcohol, and redissolving in water, a method that brings one nearer the goal with all enzymes, led to no preparation capable of producing infection, in which experiments it was, however, necessary to be careful to use finally a clear solution in which no bacteria could be found.

At the same time experiments were undertaken with extracts kept heated at certain degrees of temperatures for hours.

Result: Continual heating at 60° does not alter demonstrably the capacity for infection, at 65-75° it becomes weaker. Heating the sap at 80° for several hours kills the infectious substance.

These experiments,[8] therefore, confirm the fact that the infectious substance in question is subject to the living conditions of organic ferments. But, according to the preceding experiments the object sought could be found only in the organized particles. The question is more and more narrowed down to bacteria and fungi, and, even to this, the experiments described above give a quite unmistakable answer. Fungi universally have too great a dimension to go through the filterpaper. One might perhaps think of a gonidial stage with particularly small spore-like reproductive organs, but it would then be incomprehensible, how such a passing stage in the life cycle of a fungus could again produce the same disease of which it was a product. Also, it is impossible to assume that a fungus disease in any of its stages should not have been recognized as such by us or by experienced observers who took the trouble to inspect the diseased plants microscopically.

In short, I conclude, not basing my conclusions entirely on new experimental facts, but also deducing in part from facts already known, that we are concerned with a bacterial disease. A closer knowledge of the form and mode of life of the responsible bacteria cannot, of course, be obtained in this way and must be reserved for future research.

On the whole, I feel justified from my preliminary studies, which at least have reached somewhat of a termination, in drawing the following conclusions:

1. The mosaic disease of tobacco is a bacterial disease, of which, how-

---

[8] Of further experiments, whose point of departure are not connected in any way with the presentation here chosen, I attempted: Infection of diseased plants with the sap of healthy plants and infection of other Solanaceae with the sap of diseased tobacco—both without success.

ever, the infectious forms are not isolated nor are their form and mode of life known.

2. The capacity for infection of the disease from plant to plant under the artificial conditions of extract mixture is proved with certainty. Under natural conditions no significant infection takes place from plant to plant. The seed from diseased plants can produce healthy plants.

3. The spreading of the disease substance must be looked for in the soil of the tobacco plantations and in the hot beds; because certain and particularly fields repeatedly grown to tobacco are especially likely to be diseased. A case of transmission of the disease with the soil has not been verified.

Of course, for the time being only uncertain precautionary measures can be mentioned, whose introduction by way of trial is nevertheless commendable.

Wherever the disease appears in the hot beds, one should in any case change the soil and on the tobacco plantations themselves a rotation of crops should be instituted. The diseased plants standing in the fields and the stalks remaining in the fields after the harvest should be removed in such a way that no part of them is returned to a tobacco field.

If possible, one should fertilize with materials that have no lower organisms in them, as, for instance, pulverized peat and artificial fertilizers (among which a mixture of saltpeter and potassium chloride is commendable); and, if this is not possible, one should use only one kind of natural fertilizer and, in any case, carefully record the experiences that are derived from this.

Ryksproefstation zu Wageningen, Fall of 1885.

1892

Practical Results
of Bacteriological Researches[1]

by George M. Sternberg, M.D., Lieutenant-Colonel
and Surgeon, United States Army

Sternberg's historical experiment on the formation of a specific antibody following infection with vaccinia virus and the subsequent neutralization of the virus by immune serum introduced a method that was to become the mainstay of virus serology. The use of the neutralization test provided, particularly to workers on animal viruses, a technique for assessing viral immunity and measuring the immune response, evaluating and standardizing antisera, a means of distinguishing antigenic similarities and differences among viruses, diagnosing virus infections, and a method for retrospective epidemiological surveys. The test was readily adaptable for use in diverse virus-host systems. Fundamental knowledge of viral infections and immunity were greatly advanced by the wide applicability of the neutralization test in virus research.

I n diseases which are common to man and the lower animals the source from which they may be obtained is evident; but in diseases peculiar to man we do not at present see just how they are to be obtained. Reasoning from the analogy afforded by the experimental evidence heretofore referred to, we infer that the blood and tissue juices of an individual who has recently suffered an attack of smallpox or scarlet fever contains an antitoxine which would neutralize the active poison of the disease in the circulation of another person immedi-

[1] Abridged and reprinted from Transactions of the Association of American Physicians. **7**: 68-86 (1892).

ately after infection. Whether a small quantity of blood drawn from the veins of the protected individual would suffice to arrest the progress of the diseases mentioned, or to modify their course, can only be decided by experiment; but the experiment seems to me to be a legitimate one. Possibly transfusion of a moderate amount of blood from one to the other might prove to be curative, or, if made in advance of infection, might confer immunity. Or it may be that an antitoxine can be obtained from the blood of vaccinated calves which would have a curative action in smallpox.

This possibility I have undertaken to determine by the experimental method, and now make the following preliminary communication relating to results already obtained.

The following experiments have been made with the kind assistance of Dr William E. Griffiths, who has for many years been engaged in the production of vaccine virus in the city of Brooklyn, and consequently is an expert in the vaccination of calves and in recognizing vaccinia in these animals:

Upon visiting Dr. Griffiths and making known to him my desires, I found him quite willing to assist me, and also that he had a recently vaccinated, and consequently immune, calf in his stable. This animal had been vaccinated in numerous places upon the abdomen and thighs fourteen days previously. The vaccination was entirely successful, and a large number of quills had been charged from the vesicles which formed. At the time of my visit for the purpose of collecting blood serum from this animal, dry crusts still remained attached at the points where vaccination had been practised two weeks previously. On the 28th of April I collected blood serum from a superficial vein in the hind leg of this calf. This blood was placed in an ice-chest for twenty-four hours, at the end of which time the clear serum was drawn off in "Sternberg's bulbs." Four drops of this serum were placed in each of two small, sterilized, glass tubes; in one of these we placed three quills charged with fresh vaccine lymph from a calf. At the end of an hour the quills were removed, after carefully washing off in the serum the lymph with which they had been charged. In the other tube we mixed with the four drops of blood serum an emulsion made from a fragment of a perfectly fresh vaccine crust from the arm of a child; this was crushed upon a piece of glass and rubbed up with a little of the same blood serum. The two tubes were now placed in an ice-chest for twenty-four hours, at the end of which time the contents were used to vaccinate a calf purchased for the purpose. Dr. Griffiths carefully shaved the thighs of this calf and scarified each thigh in several places, as he is accustomed to do in vaccinating for the propagation of lymph. The contents of the tube containing lymph from the quills was rubbed into the scarified places upon one thigh, and the contents of the tube containing the emulsified crust into the other. On the 8th of May, nine days after the vaccination, the calf was carefully examined, and it was ascertained that the result of the vaccination was entirely negative.

Evidently it was necessary to make a control experiment before we would be justified in ascribing this negative result to a neutralization of the virus by some special substance present in the blood serum of an immune calf. Possibly the blood of a non-immune calf might also, after an exposure of twenty-four hours, neutralize the specific virulence of vaccine lymph. The control experiment was made as follows:

On the 9th of May we collected blood from a vein in the leg of a non-immune (not vaccinated) calf; this was placed in the ice-chest for twenty-four hours, and the following day clear serum was collected in Sternberg's bulbs. Three quills charged with fresh lymph from a calf, of the same lot as those used in the previous experiment, were placed in four drops of this blood serum in each of two small glass tubes. As in the previous experiment, the lymph was washed from the quills at the end of an hour, and the tubes were placed aside in the ice-chest. At the end of twenty-four hours the serum in these two tubes was used to vaccinate the same calf which had served for the previous experiment. Several points were scarified upon the left thigh and upon the left side of the abdomen, which were carefully shaved for the purpose.

At the same time the animal was vaccinated upon the right thigh and upon the right side of the abdomen with virus mixed with blood serum from the immune calf. This serum, collected in Sternberg's bulbs on the 28th of April, had since been kept in the ice-chest. One hour before the vaccination four drops of this blood serum were mixed with one drop of liquid lymph, which had been recently collected by Dr. Griffiths in a capillary tube from a vaccinated calf. At the same time, three quills charged with bovine lymph were immersed in four drops of the same blood serum—from immune calf. As stated, the animal was vaccinated upon the right side of the abdomen and upon the right thigh with this virus, which had been exposed for one hour to the action of blood serum from an immune calf. The serum containing the liquid lymph was rubbed into the scarification on the right side of the abdomen, the serum containing lymph from the quills into the right thigh. On the 19th of May, eight days after the vaccination, the animal was carefully examined by Dr. Griffiths and myself, and the following results noted: Upon the left thigh and left side of the abdomen the vaccinations—from quills in non-immune blood serum after twenty-four hours contact—were entirely successful, the scarifications being surrounded by characteristic vesicles and covered by characteristic crusts. Upon the right thigh—vaccinations from quills immersed in blood serum from immune calf for one hour—and upon the right side of abdomen—vaccinations with liquid lymph mixed with blood serum from immune calf—the result was entirely negative.

Several of the scarifications had entirely healed; others were covered with a dry scab which was easily detached, and under which the scarification was healing without any appearance of vesicles such as surrounded the scarifications upon the left side.

The result of the experiments made is, therefore, very definite, and shows that the blood serum of an immune calf contains something which neutralizes the specific virulence of vaccine virus, either bovine or from humanized lymph—crust from the arm of a child.

It is my intention to follow up this line of investigation, to endeavor to isolate this antitoxine of vaccinia, and to test the question of its possible specific action in neutralizing the smallpox virus in infected individuals, either before or after the development of the disease.

DISCUSSION

Dr. W. H. Welch: There can be no doubt as to the scientific fact that the blood-serum of immunized animals may possess powerful therapeutic effects. As regards the practical application of this principle to the treatment of human beings, it does not seem to me that we as yet possess positive results entirely free from doubt as to the correctness of the interpretation put upon them. The most striking results which have thus far been reported regarding the application of this new method to human beings come from the Italian observers in the treatment of tetanus, and there are various reasons why these results should not as yet be unreservedly accepted as proof of the efficacy of this mode of treatment in human beings. There is, however, every reason to persevere in experimental work in the direction indicated. The experimental results of Dr. Sternberg regarding the antitoxic power of the blood-serum of vaccinated calves are most interesting, and we may look forward, doubtless, to further communications from him on the subject.

Dr. Kinnicutt: It is difficult to judge in regard to the accuracy of the reported results of the Italian cases. The last case, the sixth one, is the most convincing. It was a well-developed case of tetanus. The urine, on the evening before the injection of the antitoxine of tetanus, was injected into a series of five or six guinea-pigs and rats. In all, it is claimed, death followed in twenty-four hours, with well-marked symptoms of tetanus. On the third day after the daily injection of from twenty-five to fifty centigrammes of the antitoxine, the urine, when injected into a series of animals, was found to be innocuous. The blood, also, was injected, before and after the treatment with the tetanus antitoxine, and with similar results. It seems to me that this is the fullest, and perhaps the most convincing, of the reports which have been published. Some anti-tetanus toxine is being prepared in the Pathological Laboratory of the College of Physicians and Surgeons of New York, and, whenever the opportunity offers, its effects will be very critically studied.

Dr. Vaughan: I wish to express my high appreciation of Dr. Sternberg's paper, and especially of his own experimental work with regard to vaccine. Of course, the number of experiments is too limited, as yet, for positive conclusions to be drawn. We are now all convinced of the fact that it is comparatively easy to give animals immunity against a certain germ for a very short time. It can be done with the attenuated germ, with the chemical products of the germ, and it may be done with other substances which are not produced by the germ. Of course, it will take time to solve all these problems, and we must be very slow to conclude that all of this is going to be of special benefit in medicine.

Dr. Sewell is, I believe, the only one who has paid especial attention to the time over which this immunity has extended. In his experiments with the rattlesnake poison he found that he could make his birds immune, but that this immunity lasted only a few months.

It has always been a question with me whether this is not simply establishing a tolerance for a poison, instead of a true vaccine action. I am inclined to think that the action both of the toxines and antitoxines is of the nature of the ferments. No toxalbumin has ever been obtained in a pure state; we know nothing about its chemical structure. For instance, take the so-called toxalbumin of diphtheria. Inject a small quantity into animals, and a certain per cent. of them will die within a period of time that will vary with the amount injected. The only rational explanation that appears to my mind is that the substance acts as a ferment. It is not necessary for the substance to be a poison *per se*. It may, by its fermentative action, destroy certain things in the body which are necessary for the maintenance of certain cells, although not itself poisonous. The whole subject is interesting and suggestive, and we must wait for practical application.

One other point. We all know that surgical operations have an effect upon diseases where the operation is not in itself curative. A few years ago there was a great craze about circumcision as a curative in epilepsy. I had a friend who performed the operation a great number of times. In his first case the child, who had been having epileptic seizures two or three times a day, after the operation had them only once in ten to twenty days. In course of time, however, the seizures became as bad as ever. The operation has been abandoned.

There are many ways in which immunity can be secured, and we must distinguish between producing immunity and curing the disease. There is no evidence that the two are the same, although the Klemperers try to make it appear so in their work. I think the action of Koch's tuberculin should make us a little slow about accepting and drawing positive conclusions from experimental work. Experimental immunity and experimental cure is one thing, and cure in man is another thing.

Dr. Lyman: The results of laboratory experiments have been rather discouraging as showing the transient character of much of the immunity obtained by the inoculations alluded to. It appears to me that we are not so very near, as some enthusiasts think, to the time when we shall be able to protect our patients from diseases. Vaccination against smallpox seems to be almost the only case where permanence of immunity is secured. What Dr. Vaughan has said about ferments agrees with the conclusions I arrived at twenty years ago. I think that the majority of these toxines and antitoxines are of the ferment character.

Dr. Sternberg: We know something about living ferments, but when you call these substances ferments you have not explained much.

I did not purpose to say to this Association that it had been absolutely demonstrated that tetanus could be cured by antitoxine. I merely reported the cases. I admire conservatism and scepticism, but why Dr. Kitasato should be so very conservative about the results obtained upon man when they correspond so entirely with the results which he and others have obtained on the lower animals I do not understand. When I see carefully reported cases, like that of Schwartz, in which all the symptoms are carefully detailed and the results of treatment seem to be so very definite, I feel like giving considerable credit to it without admitting that the thing is proved. I am very free to say that I think the future of scientific medicine is in this direction, and that we have entered upon a field that is to be cultivated vigorously, and which will give you results that will knock the conservatism from under your feet before many years.

I believe that there is something in the blood of the immune calf that neutralizes the vaccine virus. This rests upon very few experiments, but these are so satisfactory and decided that I am thoroughly convinced that I shall get similar results on repeating them.

1898

Concerning a
Contagium Vivum Fluidum
as Cause of the Spot Disease
of Tobacco Leaves[1]

by M. W. Beijerinck

*The Russian botanist, Dimitrii J. V. V. Iwanowsky, provided
the initial physical procedure for establishing the etiology of
plant and animal virus diseases.[2] He demonstrated that the
agent of tobacco mosaic could pass through a porcelain filter
that would remove bacteria. Skeptical of his results because of
the newness of the technique and influenced by the bacterial
theory of plant disorders, he was unaware, as were others, of
the historical significance of his finding.*

*The studies of Marinus Willem Beijerinck approached more
nearly the current concept of the etiological nature of plant
virus diseases. The Dutch bacteriologist confirmed the findings
of Iwanowsky on the filterable nature of the tobacco mosaic
disorder but discarded the theory that the disease was bacterial in origin. Instead, he considered the active principle to
be a soluble substance which he named "contagium vivum
fluidum." Beijerinck appears to have been the first to use the
term "virus" for the causal agent of tobacco mosaic but it is
doubtful if the meaning ascribed to the entity was similar to
its present-day usage.*

*Beijerinck reported certain observations which provided
an important insight into the nature of virus multiplication.
That a small amount of virus can infect a large number of*

[1] Beijerinck, M. W. Ueber ein contagium vivum fluidum als Ursache der Fleckenkrankheit der Tabaksblätter. Verhandelingen der Koninklyke akademie van Wetten-
schappen te Amsterdam. 65: (2) 3-21 (1898). (With 2 plates.) Translation by Dr. James
Johnson; abridged and reprinted from Phytopathological Classics, (7) (1942), by permission of American Phytopathological Society.

[2] St. Petersb. Acad. Comp. Sci., Bul. 35, Ser. 4, 3: 67 (1894).

leaves and that material from these leaves can be used to infect unlimited numbers of new plants served to strengthen his belief that virus reproduced within the plant. He noted further that tissues where cell division was occurring favored the reproduction of virus. Beijerinck postulated that the virus must be incorporated into the living protoplasm of the cell to propagate, and though it may exist outside the plant, it cannot multiply. He believed that there may be a whole series of plant diseases caused by a contagium fluidum. These pioneer observations and experiments were fundamental to the early recognition and understanding of virus diseases.

In 1885 Mr. Adolf Mayer[3] showed that the mosaic or leaf-spot[4] disease of the tobacco plant is contagious. He pressed the sap from diseased plants, introduced it into capillary tubes, and pierced these into the leaves and stems of healthy plants growing out in the open. After a few weeks the latter were then attacked by the spot disease. He himself could not find any bacteria or other parasites in the diseased leaves through microscopic inspection. I was at that time Mr. Mayer's colleague at the Agricultural School at Wageningen, he showed me his experiments, and I, no more than he, could prove the presence of microbes in the diseased plants to which the disease could be ascribed. At that time, however, my bacteriological knowledge was so incomplete that I could not take my own direct observations as a conclusive proof.

Since that time I have been continually occupied with bacteriological experiments, and when I discovered the bacteria of the Papilionae nodules in 1887, I also took up the tobacco disease again. However, the result was also negative at that time. Since, however, in all my experiments at that time, the microscopic picture, on the one hand, had to be decisive, and on the other hand only cultural experiments pertaining to aerobes were carried out, the possibility still remained that anaerobes were vegetating in small numbers in the plant tissue, which defied direct observation, but were affecting the surrounding plant tissue with poisons, like the tetanus bacteria do with a poison, which is soluble, non-living, i.e., unable to reproduce itself.

It is well known that reduced pigments, which become colored when

[3] Landwirtschaftliche Versuchsstationen **32:** 450 (1886).

[4] The term Fleckenkrankheit (spot disease) as contrasted to Mosaikkrankheit (mosaic disease) and Pockenkrankheit (pock disease) as used in German by many writers, is often confusing. Flecken (spots) may apparently be either chlorotic or necrotic spots. As chlorotic spots, "fleckenkrankheit" would be synonymous with either mottling or variegation.

exposed to the air, often appear[5] inside of cells of the organs of higher plants so that the possibility of the presence of anaerobes in the tobacco plant was from the very beginning not to be excluded. It is true that the presence of such microbes inside of the green organs of aerial plants, is highly improbable; yet, the discovery of "mikroaerophilie" in anaerobes[6] demands the greatest attention when facts of such far-reaching importance as those presented here are concerned, and these give special incentive to new experiments concerning the microbes appearing in the roots below the surface of the ground.

But after I had taken great pains to find anaerobes that could be causally connected with the disease, within or proximate to the diseased leaves and roots of the affected plants, but always with negative results, and I finally knew positively that these, too, were not present, the conclusion was no longer to be denied, that the spot disease is an infectious one that is not caused by microbes.

Then, in 1897, the resources of the newly erected bacteriological laboratory of the Polytechnical Institute at Delft were put at my disposal. This included a greenhouse with heating facilities, which I started using that same year for further experiments on the spot disease. I was, therefore, able to carry out a series of incontestable infection experiments the results of which I shall now briefly describe.

My experimental plants belonged mainly to the local variety from Amerongen and partly they came from seeds from Erfurt.[7]

1. THE INFECTION IS NOT CAUSED BY MICROBES, BUT BY A CONTAGIUM VIVUM FLUIDUM

It soon became evident that the sap of diseased plants remains infectious when filtered through porcelain, through which process all aerobes are held back. However, I was not only concerned with the search for aerobes alone, but I also carried out careful experiments to determine the presence of anaerobes in the filtered juice, but with negative results, so that the sap used appeared entirely sterile.

The quantity of candle filtrate necessary for infection is extremely small. A small drop put into the right place in the plant with a Pravaz syringe can infect numerous leaves and branches. If these diseased parts are extracted, an infinite number of healthy plants may be inoculated and infected from this sap, from which we draw the conclusion that the contagium, although fluid, reproduces itself in the living plant.

Since, however, experiments using the candle filtrate are still open to

[5] I remind you for instance of the presence of *Indigo white* in the labellum of Cattleya.

[6] On the relation of the obligatory anaerobes to free oxygen. Proc. Roy. Acad. Sci. Amsterdam (May 28, 1898).

[7] Diseased plants were sent to me from various sources, for which I here wish to express my thanks.

criticism, especially when the possibility of the presence of anaerobes is not excluded, and, because of this, the corpuscular nature of the contagium has not been entirely disproved, I have carried out the following diffusion experiments, which, it seems to me, have produced entirely incontestable results from both points of view.

Drops of the extracted juice of diseased leaves, as well as ground-up diseased leaves, were put on the surface of thick (poured) agar plates, and left to diffuse with water for several days. I hoped in this way to separate the virus from the raw leaf substance, as well as from all bacteria, through diffusion, since the virus, if at all capable of diffusion, could penetrate into the agar downwards and sideways, thereby leaving as a residue all discrete parts, aerobic and anaerobic bacteria and their spores. The experiment was, therefore, decisive in determining whether the contagium was actually capable of diffusion and, accordingly, had to be considered as soluble in water, or if not capable of diffusion, therefore, as extremely minutely distributed, yet as corpuscular, that is, as *contagium fixum*. It appeared that the substance causing the infection may penetrate into the agar plate to no small depth, as may be seen from the following circumstances.

When I thought a sufficient time had elapsed for the virus to have penetrated the agar plate to a considerable depth, if diffusion takes place at all, the plate was first cleansed with water, then washed off with a sublimate solution, and finally a layer of agar about half a millimeter thick was removed by means of a sharp platinum spatula from the outer surface of the spot, where the raw material of the leaves or the extracted juice had lain. The mass lying immediately below was then removed in two successive layers and both parts used for the infection of healthy plants. The results left no room for doubt, in both cases the characteristic symptoms of infection were brought about, very intensively by the upper and more weakly by the lower layer of agar.[8] After ten days the distance covered by the virus may have been at least two millimeters, perhaps considerably more. Although a diffusion distance of only a few millimeters was involved here, it seems nevertheless proved that the virus must really be regarded as liquid or soluble and not as corpuscular. This result might be of special interest in so far as it points to the fact that a similar forward movement of specific vital bodies inside of the plant meristem must be considered possible.[9]

The candle filtrate has a somewhat weaker effect on the plant than

[8] Egg albumin and cooked potato starch also penetrate slowly into agar plates, which may be followed in the latter through the iodine reaction. Drops of soluble starch laid on gelatin plates diffuse much more easily than ordinary starch and also sideways to a relatively long distance.

[9] I came to an identical conclusion earlier concerning the cecidiogene bodies causing gall formation: these bodies, too, must be soluble in water and capable of diffusion inside of the meristematic tissue.

the extracted juice that has not yet been filtered. This may be seen from the following circumstance. Fresh extracted juice not only produced the peculiar spots of the leaves, which later become necrotic and are characteristic of the disease, but, if considerable quantities are used, it also causes an actual malformation of the leaves, which also remain small since the midrib does not reach its full size, and are less deeply lobate through disturbances in the growth of the edges and often show palmate-veining through which they become quite different from the normal tobacco leaves. Such malformations also may be produced by means of candle filtrates, if one wishes to do so, only much more material must be used for this. From this we must conclude that the virus is held back in the filter pores, at least at the beginning of the filtration process. How incorrect it would be to conclude from this that the virus is of corpuscular nature may be shown by the following experiment.

As is well known, a malt diastase consists mainly of a mixture of two enzymes, granulase and maltase, which may be separated by diffusion.[10] If, for example, a drop of malt extract is placed on a gelatin plate containing starch, the maltase soon precedes the granulase in diffusion. Maltase produces erythrodextrin and maltase from starch, while granulase produces only dextrin, aside from maltase, from starch as well as from erythrodextrin, which are not colored by iodine, so the action of iodine on the diffusion field of the diastase mixture will show the relative amount of maltase as compared with granulase through a red ring of erythrodextrin on a blue background, which ring surrounds the colorless field of granulase. If the same malt-extract is passed through a porcelain candle, a considerable widening of the maltase rings is found in carrying out the diffusion experiment with the first parts of the filtrate, from which may be concluded that the filter pores more easily retain granulase, which diffuses slowly, than maltase, which diffuses more quickly. Later, when the wall of the filter is saturated with granulase, the original width of the maltase ring returns.

Therefore, it was to be expected that a substance like the virus, which does not diffuse easily would flow through in a diluted form at the beginning of the filtration process yet without being composed of corpuscular parts because of this behavior.[11]

Although I had known for a long time that bacteria were not directly concerned with infection, I performed many inoculations on my experi-

---

[10] The third enzyme of malt extract, glucase, is to be found only in small quantity in it.

[11] I, therefore, cannot agree with the conclusion of Mr. Loeffler as regards the corpuscular nature of the virus of the foot and mouth disease (Centralblatt. für Bacteriologie. Part I. Vol. 24, p. 570, 1898). It would be interesting to know if the watery solutions of gold and platinum, produced by Mr. Bredig by means of the electrical luminous arc between metal electrodes in water, would pass the pores of the Bougie and could diffuse into gelatin or agar jelly.

mental plants with the forms that happened to occur on the diseased tobacco leaves, as well as with those that developed in the extracted sap of diseased leaves, in order to make this fact absolutely sure. I always had negative results when the experiments were carried out correctly; never did a bacterial culture, free from the virus, produce symptoms of infection. However, I shall show that, under these circumstances, it is not easy to entirely separate from the virus the bacteria isolated from the sap of diseased leaves, for these same bacteria, even after reinoculations, can contain enough virus to result in most marked chlorsis.

A proper experiment for the purpose of determining the fact that any microbe isolated from a diseased plant is not capable of causing the disease, therefore presupposes a carefully carried out colony culture, consisting of the isolated single germs that have been rinsed with much water and, under certain circumstances, even after repeated reinoculations, which are continued until the last traces of the virus, which has been absorbed or is clinging to the bacteria, have disappeared.

I believe that these remarks are not without importance. For I see in them an analogy to the experiences of the pathologists, according to which the organisms causing certain infectious diseases lose their virulence through culture outside of the organism and can increase it by repeated passage through susceptible animals. Although the analogy is not a very close one, it is certain that there is an analogy.

2. ONLY THOSE ORGANS OF THE PLANT THAT ARE GROWING AND WHOSE CELLS ARE DIVIDING ARE CAPABLE OF BEING INFECTED; HERE ONLY DOES THE VIRUS REPRODUCE ITSELF

Only those tissues and organs of the tobacco plant are attacked by the virus that are not only in a state of active growth but in which the division of cells is still in full progress; all tissue that has reached its full growth is immune from it, but may under certain circumstances transport the virus. Leaves that are growing, but are beyond the expansion stage, can no longer be infected, although they are still suitable for the transmission of the virus to the stem.

If the stem is inoculated, only the young leaf-buds and the leaves that are newly developing from these growing points are infected. If young leaves are inoculated, the same thing takes place; the virus returns to the stem from the leaf and infects either the axillary buds or rises to infect the terminal bud. If fully matured organs are used for infection, be it stems or leaves, and very little virus is used, failure is certain;—obviously the virus then remains in the matured cells without having any effect. A larger quantity of the virus may, however, move out of the matured parts into the surrounding new tissues and affect them.

In any case, it is reasonably certain that the virus in the plant is capable of reproduction and infection only when it occurs in cell tissues that are dividing, while not only the matured, but also the expanded tissues are unsuitable for this. Without being able to grow independently, it is drawn into the growth of the dividing cells and here increased to a great degree without losing in any way its own individuality in the process. In conformity with this, no ability of reproduction outside of the plant could be proved. It is true that a Bougie extract that was filtered clear and was entirely free from bacteria could be kept for over three months[12] without losing its virulence or even seeming to decrease it. But an increase of infectivity was not to be observed, not even in the first period of the experiment, even though the extract had been prepared in such a way that not only diseased parts but also healthy buds and leaves were extracted, so that if nourishment in the usual sense had been able to bring about reproduction, this should have taken place. Also, in transferring the virus to appropriate gelatin-media, the color and index of refraction of the latter apparently remains unchanged throughout.

Yet, judging the original quantity of the virus, which is reproducing independently in the plant used for infection, is after all, difficult, and, since the question naturally is of special importance, new experiments in this direction are to be expected. For the time being I must, as I say, take for granted that propagation results only when the virus is connected with the living and growing protoplasm of the host-plant.

The behavior of the virus in connection with the growing tissues reminds one of similar relationships in gall formation, for the cecidiogenen substance also can affect only growing parts. As far as the movement is concerned, the latter bodies behave differently from the virus; they must, in order to be effective, be brought into meristematic tissues and they move only through these.

The method of reproduction of the virus reminds one in certain ways of that of the amyloplasts and chromoplasts, which also grow only with the growing cell protoplasm, but can also exist and function independently.

*　　*　　*

10. OTHER INFECTIOUS PLANT DISEASES CAUSED BY A CONTAGIUM FLUIDUM AND NOT BY PARASITES

Even if the symptoms of the spot disease coincide so closely with certain forms of albinism or bunt (mosaic) that both may unhesitatingly be put under the category of infectious diseases of the chlorophyll bodies, there yet remains, according to known observations, a difference in the principle of the mode of transmission of the contagium, a difference that leads one to consider both of them as separate kinds of diseases, each with its particular virus. The form of albinism (variegation) suitable for

---

[12] How long the extract may be kept I am not prepared to say as yet; in any case, longer than three months.

transmission is namely transferred only when the living albino tissues grow together with the living-tissues of the green plant by means of grafting or budding, while simple inoculation of green plants with the tissues or the extracted juice of variegated varieties of the same kind, remains entirely without results[13] according to my several-times-repeated experiments with *Ulmus campestris, Acer negundo, Pelargonium zonale,* and *Utrica diocia.* It appears, therefore, that the contagium of variegation is transmissible but that it stands in a much closer relationship to the protoplasm of the plant than the contagium of the spot disease, in that it cannot exist, like the latter, outside of the plant and dies when the plant cells that carry or continue it themselves die. My preceding observations, however, sufficiently show that the last word has not yet been spoken on this subject. Since the question of the contagiousness of variegation is important, for the evolution theory as well as for the theory of variability, further experiments on the subject would be very desirable.

Another disease, which surely belongs here, is that known in America as "peach yellows." [14] The symptoms of this disease consist mainly in immaturity of the fruits, growth of the latent buds at unusual places into thin brooms, which are often colorless, and yellow discoloration of the leaves, which is followed in a few years by the death of the tree. According to Mr. Smith, bacteria and parasites are definitely not the cause. Nevertheless, it was easy to transmit the disease to healthy trees simply through grafting or budding with a bud of a diseased tree. This experiment showed that it is necessary for the bud to unite if the disease was to be transmitted, for the virus is not capable of infecting healthy trees without the connection of the living tissues, according to Mr. Smith. He neglects to point to the agreement of this observation with the mode of transmission of variegation in Abutilon and Jasminum.

"Peach rosette" is, according to Mr. Smith, another nonparasitic disease, closely related to "peach yellows," which is easily transmissible through budding and root grafting. The disease manifests itself in that all buds, dormant as well as active ones, grow into small rosettes that

[13] It is true that some researchers have doubts as to the transmissibility of variegation as such and have expressed the opinion that those green plants that become variegated themselves through grafting with variegated ones would have become so without any grafting whatsoever, i.e., through spontaneous bud variation. They remark that the stocks used (Abutilon, Jasminum, Pelargonium) are garden plants whose green specimens have a strong tendency towards variegation anyway. Such objections, however, are not sufficiently grounded (see Lindemuth, Vegetative Bastardenerzeugung durch Impfung, Landwirtschaftliche Jahrbücher 1878, no. 6 and Vochting, Transplantation, pp. 13, 22, 92, and 112, Tübingen (1892).

[14] Erwin F. Smith, Peach Yellows and Peach Rosette, U.S. Department of Agriculture. Farmers' Bulletin No. 17, Washington (1894). I know this short but interesting discussion only through the separate which the author kindly sent. Much to my astonishment, I was not able to find a word about it in the scientific literature available to me.

consist of single large leaves and several hundred small leaves. The color of the leaves is yellow. The fruit does not ripen but dries and falls to the ground prematurely. Here, too, we find the peculiarity I have described in the spot disease, that the virus moves laterally with difficulty but upwards with ease, so that a tree may become diseased on the side on which the rosette bud was grafted, while the opposite side remains healthy for years.[15]

Smith says that the epidemic character of yellows, as well as rosette, leads one to the conclusion that there must exist another mode of transmission than that of tissue intergrowth, but he does not believe that the virus can come from the soil; however, he notes that, particularly in rosette, a whole tree may become diseased in almost all its parts at the same time, which, as we saw earlier, is not compatible with local infection but rather points to a general infection similar to the spot disease when the tobacco plant is infected from the soil.

Since Smith did not carry out any experiments with artificially transferred sap, the possibility remains, even the probability, that these, too, could give a positive result. If this should really be the case, the virus would probably also be capable of existence outside of the plant, and infection from the soil through the roots would be possible, and yellows and rosette would then approximate much more closely the spot disease than is apparent from the descriptions given.

I consider it highly probable that many other nonparasitic diseases of unknown cause may be ascribed to a *contagium fluidum*. It seems useful to me in further research on this matter to distinguish sharply between the two forms in which, according to the available knowledge, such a *contagium* may appear, namely, firstly as an independent *contagium*, which is capable of existence outside of the plant, even if only for a time, as in the leaf-spot disease of the tobacco plant, and secondly as a *contagium* that exists only in living tissues as in the form of variegation, which is transmissible through graftage only.

EXPLANATION OF THE ILLUSTRATIONS

PLATE I

A young tobacco plant that has become diseased through artificial infection with much virus. The virus was introduced through a wound at *a*, which penetrated through the whole stem. The diseased leaves, *b, c, d,* which first developed, are malformed; those following, *e, f,* are diseased, though not malformed.

---

[15] The latter observation seems to exclude entirely the possibility that in peach rosette we are concerned with a "phytoptus" invasion, although the other symptoms of the disease seem to point to it.

Plate I.

PLATE II

Fig. 1. A young tobacco leaf, in the first stage of the disease, with a moderate amount of virus. The dark-green spots are visible next to the vein, the local changes, by the way, in the color of the chlorophyl did not produce any distinct contrasts on the photographic plate.

Fig. 2. A mildly diseased tobacco leaf in the second stage of the disease with a few brown spots that were produced through the premature necro-

Plate II.

sis of the tissues. The most important stage of the disease in which the dead, brown spots are increased by hundreds or thousands is not pictured.

Fig. 3. A vari-colored tobacco leaf of a plant that had become vari-colored through the mixed infection of the virus with *Bacillus anglomerans*.

Fig. 4 and 5. Small malformed tobacco leaves, produced by the introduction of large amounts of virus into the stem.

[These plates, in color in the original, are here presented in black and white because of the high cost for reproduction in color.]

1898

Report of the Commission for Research on the Foot-and-Mouth Disease[1]

by Friedrich Loeffler and Frosch

The filterability of viral agents, first demonstrated with a plant virus by Iwanowsky and by Beijerinck, was reported for the first time with an animal virus by Loeffler and Frosch. These latter investigators found that the virus of foot-and-mouth disease of cattle passed through a Berkefeld candle filter and that the clear filtrate was as infective as the original lymph preparation. Moreover, by a series of dilution procedures, they ascertained that the agent multiplied in the animal host. Their recognition and application of the concept, that quantitative work on viruses depended on finding the highest dilution of the material which would produce a discernible sign of disease in the host, was an essential step in establishing a quantitative basis for virological research. They speculated that infectious material from diseases such as smallpox, cowpox, measles, typhus, etc., may be shown by filtration methods to be caused by minute living organisms similar to that associated with foot-and-mouth disease.

T he undersigned commission is honored to present to your excellency the most recent results of our studies on foot-and-mouth disease.

1. STUDIES ON THE ETIOLOGY OF THE DISEASE

Thanks to the use of the telegraph to inform us of fresh outbreaks of foot-and-mouth disease, which your excellency placed at our disposal

---

[1] Reprinted from Centralbl. f. Bakt., Parasit. Infekt. Part I, **23**: 371-391 (1898). Translation reprinted from T. D. Brock, *Milestones in Microbiology* (Englewood Cliffs, N.J.: Prentice-Hall, Inc., 1961), with permission of Prentice-Hall, Inc.

through contacts with many local officials, it has been possible to obtain extensive quantities of fresh material for these studies. For this purpose, locations were selected which would permit the collection of material and its return to us on the same day, so that immediate processing of fresh material could be done. . . . Especially suitable for the etiological studies were the contents of freshly removed vesicles in the mouth and udder of sick animals, because from these places the contents of the vesicles could be obtained free from contamination at the surface. Since the feet were mostly soiled with feces it was very difficult to remove material from this area that was uncontaminated, in spite of careful disinfection of the surface layers.

Because we discovered that bacteria penetrate into the vesicles from outside after several days, we decided to always use freshly developed vesicles for these studies. Such completely fresh vesicles are relatively scarce. Even after an outbreak of the disease in a large herd, at most only one or two animals offered such vesicles to us.

The contents of the vesicle were removed after previous treatment of the vesicle with absolute alcohol. A sterilized glass capillary was plunged into the interior of the vesicle to remove the material. In this way the contents of the vesicles from 12 animals from different locations could be studied closer. The examinations were carried out with the help of bacteriological methods (hanging drop, staining, culture). As culture media, the following were used: ordinary broth, acid and alkaline broth, peptone-broth, glucose-broth, liquid and solidified serum, milk, nutrient agar, and nutrient gelatin, and with atmospheres of air, hydrogen, hydrogen sulfide, and carbon dioxide.

The results of all of these studies were completely the same. Staining and examination in hanging drop revealed no bacteria. The culture media inoculated with fluid from the vesicles remained absolutely free of any bacterial development, in most cases for weeks. In those cases where bacteria did occur, it could always be determined on the first observation that they were merely isolated colonies which had arisen from germs which had accidently entered from the air. It could be shown at the same time that these sterile fluids contained the casual factor of foot-and-mouth disease, because when this material was inoculated on the mucous membranes of the upper and lower lips of calves and heifers, they always became sick from the disease with typical symptoms in two or three days after inoculation. . . . It can be shown that we are not concerned with the action of a germ-free toxic substance produced in the vesicles from the fact that when animals are inoculated and come down with the disease, it is transferred to other animals which are housed in the same stall. From these experiments it seems certain that any species of bacteria which is able to grow on the usual culture media cannot be the etiological agent of foot-and-mouth disease. . . .

Through its efforts to find a practical method for the immunization of animals, the commission has attempted to use not only blood and lymph mixtures from immune animals, but has also attempted to introduce the blood of animals that were acutely sick with and without additions of immune blood, as well as the use of lymph which has been freed from all its cellular elements by filtration. These experiments have not as yet led to satisfactory results. However, the filtration experiments have offered extremely important results in another area. In these experiments the lymph was diluted with 39 parts of water, then inoculated with an easily culturable and identifiable bacterial species which had been cultured from lymph—*Bacillus fluorescens*—and then filtered two to three times through a sterilized Kieselguhr candle. The addition of the bacteria served to demonstrate that the filtrate was really bacterial-free, since large inoculums of this were then placed on nutrient media and examined for growth after incubation. If colonies of this bacterium did not appear on the seeded media, then it was assumed that the filtration had succeeded, and that all of the bacteria that had been previously present in the lymph were retained by the filter candle. Filtrates tested in this manner were always bacterial free. A series of calves were inoculated intravenously with measured amounts of these filtrates corresponding to 1/10 to 1/40 cc. of pure lymph, in order to ascertain if there was a dissolved substance in the lymph which would aid in the production of immunity.

The results of these injections were quite surprising. The animals inoculated with the filtrates died in the same time as had the control animals which had received corresponding amounts of unfiltered lymph. Their deaths occurred with all of the typical symptoms of the disease, such as high fever, and vesicles on the mouth and hoofs. We had the impression that the activity of the lymph was not influenced by the filtration. In order to confirm this important result, these experiments were repeated in a large number of calves and hogs. The results with the use of fresh lymph were always the same. The animals treated with the filtrate became sick just as did the controls treated with unfiltered lymph, and always in a completely typical way.

How could these surprising results be explained? For the explanation there were two possibilities: 1. The bacterial free lymph contains a soluble, extremely active toxin. 2. The casual agent of the disease, which up to now has not been found, was so small that the pores of filters which were able to hold back the smallest known bacteria were able to allow this agent to pass through. If we were dealing with a soluble poison, then it must be one with an astounding activity. With a sample of filtrate corresponding to 1/30 cc. lymph, the disease could be produced in two days in calves of around 200 kg. weight. . . .

If we assume that in the lymph of the vesicles of foot-and-mouth disease there is an active substance which is 1/500 of the lymph, in 1/30 cc. or 1/30 g. of lymph there would be 1/15,000 g. of active substance. This amount is sufficient to cause disease in a 200 kg. calf. If an equal distribution of the substance occurred through all parts of the body of the calf, then one part of toxin is distributed in 15,000 × 200,000, or 3,000,-000,000, parts of calf and is still active. Knorr has been able to produce in a tetanus culture a toxin which is toxic in 1/1,000,000 parts of rabbit, 1/150,000,000 parts for white mouse, and 1/1,000,000,000 parts for guinea pigs. The toxicity of the foot-and-mouth disease toxin would then be considerably higher than that of the highly toxic tetanus toxin. We would have in the foot-and-mouth disease toxin a poison of completely astounding activity.

However, it has been possible for us to take the lymph from the vesicles of an animal which had been infected with filtered lymph, and use only 1/50 cc. of this to induce a similar disease with typical symptoms in two days in a 30 kg. hog. The toxin has here experienced a further dilution of 1/50 × 500 × 3,000 or 1/750,000,000, so that the dilution of the original lymph is $1/2.25 \times 10^{17}$. A toxin which is this active would be truly unbelievable.

In these calculations we have made the assumption that the toxin is equally distributed throughout the whole animal. We are, however, not compelled to make such an assumption. Although in tetanus it is quite easy to demonstrate the presence of the toxin in the blood and organs of the animal, such a demonstration is not so easy in animals suffering from foot-and-mouth disease. In order to transmit the disease to healthy animals by blood of diseased ones, it is necessary to use 50-100 cc. It therefore seems quite possible that the greatest part of the toxin injected into such animals is accumulated in the vesicles which form. If we assume that an animal which has been injected with filtered lymph undergoes typical symptoms of disease after the injection of 1/30 cc. of filtered lymph, and if we further assume that all of the vesicles on the four hooves, in the mouth and on the tongue together contain about 5 cc. of fluid, which is just about right, then the original 1/30 cc. of lymph is now distributed in 5 cc. of new lymph in the vesicles, for a dilution of 1/150. But of this 5 cc. only 1/50 cc. is sufficient to induce typical disease in a 30 kg. hog in two days after intravenous injection. So that there is now a dilution of 1/150 × 1/50, or 1/7,500 which is active. If then the active toxin content of the lymph is assumed to be like that of tetanus broth, or 1/500, then there would be 1/7,500 × 1/500 = 1/3,750,000 of toxin in 30,000 g. of hog or 2,000 g. of blood. The activity of the toxin would then be such that one part in 7,500,000,000 g. of hog blood would be active. Even this calculation of the amount of toxin present in the lymph seems to indicate an exceedingly high activity. It therefore seems more appropriate to conclude that the activity of the filtrate is not due to the presence in it of a soluble substance, but due to the presence of a causal agent capable of reproducing. This agent must then be obviously so small that the pores of a filter which will hold back the smallest bacterium will still allow it to pass. The smallest bacterium presently known is the influenza bacillus of Pfeiffer. It has a length from .5 to 1.0 microns. If the supposed causal agent of foot-and-mouth disease was only 1/10 or even 1/5 as large as this, which really does not seem impossible, then this agent would not be resolved in our microscope, even with the most modern immersion system, according to the calculations of Professor Abbé in Jena. This would explain very simply why it has been impossible to see the casual agent in the lymph under the microscope, even after the most extensive search. Through careful studies we may finally be able to decide definitely over the question of the presence of the casual agent in the bacterial free lymph filtrate. In order to continue this study, the commission asks for the granting of materials and supplies. This study, aside from its purely scientific value, seems to offer eminently practical possibilities. If it is confirmed by further studies of the commission that the action of the filtrate, as it appears, is actually due to the presence of such a minute living being, this brings up the thought that the causal agents of a large number of other infectious diseases, such as smallpox, cowpox, scarlet fever, measles, typhus, cattle plague, etc. which up to now have been sought in vain, may also belong to this smallest group of organisms. If a bacterial free cowpox lymph could be produced, this would ease the agitation against vaccination for smallpox.

The bacterial free filtrates of infectious material probably offer the most suitable material for the acquisition of important new conclusions on the nature of the diseases named above.

All of these speculations indicate that it would be highly desirable to continue the studies on the action of the filtrate in a large number of animals as soon as possible.

1902

Recent Researches Concerning the Etiology, Propagation, and Prevention of Yellow Fever, by the United States Army Commission[1]

by Walter Reed, M.D.
Surgeon, U.S. Army, President of Commission

The historical studies on yellow fever by the United States Army Commission, headed by Walter Reed, are epitomized in this report. The famous experiments performed in Cuba in 1900-1901 are a superb demonstration of epidemiological deduction and investigation that culminated in a practical program of control and prevention of the disease.

That mosquitoes were involved in the occurrence of yellow fever was first expressed by Josiah Nott in 1848. Almost 40 years later, Carlos Finlay proposed the hypothesis that the disease was carried by mosquitoes. The now classical demonstration by Reed and his associates clearly proved the relationship between the insect vector and the disease. This confirmed Smith and Kilborne's earlier finding (1893) that an arthropod can act as a vector of a disease (Texas cattle fever) and focused attention on the important role of arthropods in the dissemination of infectious viral agents of both animals and plants. Subsequent investigations along these lines helped unravel some of the profound mysteries surrounding the transmission of certain infectious diseases.

The efficient control of the spread of yellow fever is a matter of such vast practical importance, both from the hygienic and commercial point of view—not only for the countries where

[1] Reprinted from J. Hyg. II (2): 101-119 (April 1, 1902).

this disease prevails as an epidemic, but also for those in which, after importation, it may assume epidemic proportions—that it has seemed appropriate to bring together in this paper a summary of the work thus far accomplished by the United States Army Commission[2] on the Island of Cuba, during the years 1900 and 1901, in order that English and Colonial readers who have not, perhaps, had access to the original contributions published in different American journals, may be able to form an intelligent opinion concerning the permanent value of this work. It will also afford opportunity for recording the more recent confirmatory observations made by others concerning the mode of transmission of yellow fever discovered by the Commission, and for calling attention to the results already obtained by the U.S. Army Medical Department in the suppression of this disease, especially in the city of Havana, through the enforcement of sanitary measures based on these later researches.

The American Commission was organized in May 1900, and began its investigations during the following month (June), being equipped with suitable laboratory facilities for practical work, both at the military garrison of Columbia Barracks, near Quemados, Cuba, and also in the city of Havana. As yellow fever was already prevailing at the tin of our arrival in Cuba suitable material for the scientific study of this se was immediately available.

THE ETIOLOGY OF YELLOW FEVER

Before giving the results of our investigations it may be well to recall the situation as regards the etiology of yellow fever at that time. Briefly it may be said that the claims of all investigators for the discovery of the specific agent of yellow fever—since modern bacteriological methods had come into use—had been disproved by the exhaustive observations of Sternberg (1), published in 1890, except that made by Sanarelli (2) for a small, motile bacillus isolated by him from the blood drawn during life in two of six cases of yellow fever, and from the blood and organs after death in seven of twelve cases of this disease (58%), studied at Montevideo and Rio de Janeiro, Brazil. The results obtained, however, by those who had promptly undertaken to investigate Sanarelli's claim for the specific character of *Bacillus icteroides,* seemed to show a lack of agreement such as has never been reported, as far as the writer can recall, in connection with the supposed specific cause of any of the other acute infections. Thus while Achinard and Woodson (3) had, during the epidemic of 1897 in New Orleans, La., isolated a bacillus, claimed by them to be identical with *B. icteroides,* from the venous blood in 4 out of 5 cases, and from

---

[2] The members of this Commission were Major Walter Reed, Surgeon, U.S. Army, and Drs. James Carroll, A. Agramonte, and the late Dr. Jesse W. Lazear, Contract Surgeons, U.S. Army.

yellow fever cadavers in 32 out of 39 cases (82%) Portier (4), working in the same city and during the same epidemic, could only obtain this bacillus 3 times in 51 autopsies, and failed to obtain it at all in cultures made from the venous blood during life in 10 cases. Again, while Wasdin and Geddings (5), in the city of Havana, were able to cultivate *B. icteroides* from blood withdrawn from the lobe of the ear, "not earlier than the third day of the disease" in 13 of 14 cases (92.8%), and to find it in 85.7% of their necropsies, Agramonte (6), studying the disease on the Island of Cuba, failed to isolate *B. icteroides* in a single instance from blood drawn from the lobe of the ear in 37 cases or from the blood drawn from a vein at the bend of the elbow in 31 cases, at various stages of the disease. The latter observer, however, reported finding this bacillus at autopsy in 11 of 35 cases (31.4%). Without going further into detail, we may say that the results obtained by Lutz (7) and da Lacerda and Ramos (8) in Brazil, and by Matienzo (9) in Mexico, were equally conflicting and unsatisfactory.

Under these circumstances it seemed to the members of the Commission of the first importance to give their entire attention to the bacteriological study of the blood of those sick with yellow fever and of the blood and organs of yellow fever cadavers, having especially in view the isolation of *B. icteroides*. We were thus able during June, July, and August to take repeated cultures from the blood during life in 18 cases of yellow fever, adopting the usual method employed in withdrawing blood from a vein at the bend of the elbow, and transferring the blood, at once, in quantities of 0.5 c.c. to each of several tubes containing 10 c.c. of nutritive bouillon which were afterwards incubated at 37°C. for a period of one week. In seven cases, four of which were designated as "mild" yellow fever and three as "well-marked" yellow fever, only one culture was made from the blood in each case, viz.: in two cases on the 1st day; in one case on the 2nd day; in three cases on the 3rd day, and in one case on the 4th day. In the remaining eleven cases, diagnosed as "severe" yellow fever, of whom four died, more frequent cultures were taken from the blood, these varying from two to six cultures on as many different days of the disease. In two of the fatal cases, cultures were made each day from the commencement of the attack and including the day on which death occurred.

The negative result of these numerous cultures taken from the blood of cases of yellow fever, as regards the presence of *B. icteroides,* was reported in a "Preliminary Note," presented at the meeting of the American Public Health Association (10), held in Indianapolis, Indiana, October 22nd-26th, 1900. To these eighteen cases we can now add six other cases, or a total of twenty-four, from which blood cultures have been made during life with negative results.

The importance of this negative finding as regards the growth of any specific bacterium will be better appreciated when it is seen, as I shall soon have occasion to point out, that yellow fever may be produced in non-immune human beings by the subcutaneous injection of a small quantity (0.5-2 c.c.) of blood withdrawn from the venous circulation of a patient suffering with this disease.

In addition to the results above recorded, the careful study of eleven autopsies was equally barren as to the presence of any particular microorganism, although the quantity of material with which our tubes were inoculated was greater than is usually made use of at autopsies.

In a word, then, the careful bacteriological study which the Commission had made in cases of yellow fever had given no indications as to the presence of the specific agent of this disease. The same may be said concerning the result of numerous microscopic examinations of fresh and stained specimens of blood which we had in the meanwhile studied with the view of finding possibly some intracellular or extracellular body. Apparently no body, bacterial or protozoan, which could be brought into view with a 1/12 Zeiss immersion objective, was present in the blood of these cases.

Although displaced from the order in which the following observations were made, it will be best to present, at this time, the results of the experiments which were later carried out by the Commission on non-immune human beings by means of the subcutaneous injection of blood, withdrawn during the active stage of the disease, as these results bear so directly upon the subject which we are now considering, viz. the etiology of yellow fever.

The only reference that I can find in the literature relative to an attempt to convey yellow fever in this way is cited by Sternberg (11), who states that at Vera Cruz, Mexico, in 1887, he saw Dr. Ruis inject into a non-immune individual a hypodermic syringeful of blood drawn from a case of yellow fever on the eighth day of the disease. The result was negative, as was also the result of two other attempts related to him by Ruis.

Our own observations, undertaken for the purpose of ascertaining whether an attack of yellow fever could be induced in a second individual by the injection of a small quantity of blood, embrace experiments made on twelve American soldiers and Spanish immigrants, all non-immune individuals.

These observations may be divided into the following classes:

1. Injection of the fresh blood taken from a vein at the bend of the elbow. 2. Injection of partially defibrinated blood. 3. Injection of partially defibrinated blood heated for ten minutes at 55°C. 4. Injection of blood-serum previously diluted with sterilized water and filtered slowly through a Berkefeld laboratory filter.

The following Table I, gives the results of these several inoculations:

TABLE I

No. of cases	Quantity and material used	Day of disease	Date of inoculation	Result	Date of attack
I	2 c.c. fresh blood	Second	Dec. 26, 1900	Negative	
II	2 c.c. fresh blood	Second	Jan. 4, 1901	Positive	Jan. 8, 1901
III	1.5 c.c. fresh blood	First	Jan. 8, 1901	Positive	Jan. 11, 1901
IV	0.5 c.c. fresh blood	Second	Jan. 22, 1901	Positive	Jan. 24, 1901
V	1 c.c. fresh blood	Second	Jan. 25, 1901	Positive	Jan. 28, 1901
VI	0.75 c.c. partially defibrinated blood	Third	Oct. 15, 1901	Positive	Oct. 20, 1901
VII	1.5 c.c. partially defibrinated blood heated for 10 minutes at 55°C.	Third	Oct. 15, 1901	Negative	
VIII	Same as No. VII	Third	Oct. 15, 1901	Negative	
IX	Same as No. VII	Third	Oct. 15, 1901	Negative	
X	1.5 c.c. of filtered blood serum	Third	Oct. 15, 1901	Positive	Oct. 19, 1901
XI	Same as No. X	Third	Oct. 15, 1901	Positive	Oct. 19, 1901
XII	⎰Same as No. X	Third	Oct. 15, 1901	⎰Negative	
	⎱2 c.c. fresh blood	Fourth	Oct. 22, 1901	⎱Positive	Oct. 23, 1901

By an examination of this table it will be seen that of the seven individuals who received subcutaneously the fresh or partially defibrinated blood in quantities of 0.5–2 c.c., six (85.7%) developed an attack of yellow fever within the usual period of incubation of the disease.

The results are of very great interest as demonstrating that the *specific agent of yellow fever is present in the blood, at least during the first, second, and third days of the attack.*

Another important point brought out by these experiments was that *the blood which conveyed the disease did not contain any bacterium which would grow on our usual laboratory media.*

In order to establish this fact, as soon as blood had been injected into the non-immune subject, additional blood was, at once, withdrawn in considerable quantity and transferred to tubes of nutritive bouillon. In one instance, where 2 c.c. of blood had been drawn into the syringe, 0.5 c.c. of this sufficed, when injected, to produce a severe attack of yellow fever, after seventy-three hours' incubation, while the remaining 1.5 c.c. transferred immediately to four tubes of bouillon gave no growth, except that from one tube we isolated on the 4th day *Staphylococcus pyogenes citreus,* found by us to be a common skin-contaminating organism in Cuba.

Table I further shows that the specific agent contained in the blood is destroyed or attenuated by heating the latter at 55°C. for 10 minutes, so that the injection of 1.5 c.c. of this heated blood was harmless (cases VII, VIII, and IX), while the injection of 0.75 c.c. of the same blood unheated sufficed to promptly induce an attack of yellow fever in a "control" individual (case VI).

Of not less interest was the fact brought out by these observations that yellow fever can be produced by the injection of a small quantity of bacteria-free serum filtrate, obtained by passing the diluted serum through a Berkefeld laboratory filter (cases X and XI), and further that the blood of a case of yellow fever, thus produced, when injected into a third non-immune subject will promptly bring about an attack of this disease (case XII); thus demonstrating that the specific agent of yellow fever can find its way through the pores of a filter which ordinarily serves to prevent the passage of all known bacteria.

I have elsewhere (12) in conjunction with one of my colleagues (Carroll) discussed the facts here presented more at length and will limit myself, therefore, to the remark that these experiments appear to indicate that yellow fever, like the foot and mouth disease of cattle, is caused by a microorganism so minute in size that it might be designated as ultra-microscopic.

THE PROPAGATION OF YELLOW FEVER

Prior to the time at which the foregoing observations were made the Commission had already turned its entire attention to the possible solution of the problem of the propagation of yellow fever, being induced thereto, not only by the fruitlessness of the investigations made thus far along bacteriological lines, but, also, by reason of certain facts which seemed to call for a better interpretation than had hitherto been accorded them.

Without entering into details, I may say that, in the first place, the Commission saw, with some surprise, what had so often been noted in the literature, that patients in all stages of yellow fever could be cared for by non-immune nurses without danger of contracting the disease. The non-contagious character of yellow fever was, therefore, hardly to be questioned.

In the second place, it had been observed that patients discharged from the wards during early convalescence could be brought into intimate association with non-immune individuals without thereby establishing fresh foci of the disease. This did not seem to indicate that any specific agent was present in the excreta of the sick.

Again, it had been noted that in certain cases of this disease no growth had been obtained on the ordinary laboratory media, either by frequent cultures from the blood during life or from the blood and organs after death.

Further, in the course of an investigation which the Commission were able to make during the last week of July, 1900, concerning the origin and spread of a small epidemic of yellow fever that had appeared in a military garrison, numbering about 900 men, at Pinar del Rio, Cuba, they had seen that by reason of the false diagnosis of "pernicious malarial fever" which had been given to these cases no disinfection of bedding or clothing had been carried out; and yet there was no indication that this neglect had contributed in the least to the spread of the disease; nor had any harm come to those non-immunes who had slept in the beds vacated by the sick, or washed the supposedly infected garments of those who had recovered or died of this disease.

Putting these various data together, it seemed probable that more progress might be made if attention should be turned to the mode of transmission of yellow fever, especially as our own observations had caused us to seriously doubt the usually accepted belief of the conveyance of this disease by means of *fomites*.

Then, too, the endemic curve of yellow fever in the city of Havana, and its well-known epidemic curve in the United States, appeared to be more intimately associated with and more affected by the rise and fall of the annual temperature curve than was to be seen in any of the acute infections, except malarial fever. The peculiar behaviour of this disease (if I may use the expression) in rapidly spreading in certain localities, when introduced, as contrasted with its failure to propagate itself in other places, where the conditions for its increase were apparently just as favourable, seemed to point in the strongest manner to the necessity for some special agent or intermediate host in the dissemination of its specific cause. If malarial fever—a disease so much affected by temperature conditions—required the agency of a special genus of mosquito for its propagation, as had in recent years been so brilliantly worked out by Ross, Grassi, Bastianelli, Bignami and others, it did not seem unreasonable to suppose that yellow fever—a disease so plainly controlled by seasonal conditions—might also depend on some such agent for its spread. Influenced by this line of reasoning, the Commission began, during the second week of August, 1900, its observations relative to the propagation of yellow fever by means of the bite of a certain species of mosquito— *Stegomyia fasciata.*

The work along this line was carried forward so rapidly that, within thirty days, eleven individuals had been bitten by infected *Stegomyia*, of whom two[3] developed well-marked attacks of yellow fever within the usual period of incubation, and under such circumstances as to positively exclude, in one case, any other possible source of infection.

Appreciating fully the importance of this discovery and in order to exclude all other possible sources of infection in our future observations, it was now determined to establish a Special Experimental Station where further observations could be made on non-immune human beings, both

[3] One of these cases was that of Dr. James Carroll, Contract Surgeon, U.S.A., a member of the Commission.

as to the propagation of yellow fever by means of the bite of the mosquito as well as by exposure to the most intimate contact with infected clothing and bedding, and this under the strictest enforcement of military quarantine. With the approval and assistance of the Military Governor of the Island of Cuba, this Experimental Station was ready for occupancy on November 20th, 1900, and was continuously occupied until March 1st, 1901.

As the results obtained at this station have already been published (13) in full elsewhere, I will here only present a brief account, first of the experiments with fomites and afterwards of those made with infected mosquitoes.

ATTEMPTS AT INFECTION BY FOMITES

I quote from a paper which the writer presented for the Commission at the meeting of the Pan-American Medical Congress,[4] held in Havana, Cuba, Feb. 4-7, 1901: "For this purpose there was erected at Camp Lazear a small frame house consisting of one room, 14 × 20 feet, and known as 'Building No. 1,' or the 'Infected Clothing and Bedding Building.' The cubic capacity of this house was 2800 feet. It was tightly sealed within with 'tongued and grooved' boards, and was well battened on the outside. It faced the south and was provided with two small windows, each 26 × 34 inches in size. These windows were both placed on the south side of the building, the purpose being to prevent, as much as possible, any thorough circulation of the air within the house. They were closed by permanent wire-screens of 0.5 mm. mesh. In addition a sliding glass sash was provided within and heavy wooden shutters without; the latter intended to prevent the entrance of sunlight into the building, as it was not deemed desirable that the disinfecting qualities of sunlight, direct or diffused, should at any time be exerted on the articles of clothing contained within this room. Entrance was effected through a small vestibule, 3 × 5 feet, also placed on the southern side of the house. This vestibule was protected without by a solid door and was divided in its middle by a wire-screen door, swung on spring hinges. The inner entrance was also closed by a second wire-screen door. In this way the passage of mosquitoes into this room was effectually excluded. During the day, and until after sunset, the house was kept securely closed, while by means of a suitable heating apparatus the temperature was raised to 92°-95°F. Precaution was taken at the same time to maintain a sufficient humidity of the atmosphere. The average temperature of this house was thus kept up at 76.2°F. for a period of sixty-three days.

"Nov. 30, 1900, the building now being ready for occupancy, three large boxes filled with sheets, pillow-cases, blankets, etc., contaminated by contact with cases of yellow fever and their discharges were received

[4] *Loc. cit.*

and placed therein. The majority of the articles had been taken from the beds of patients sick with yellow fever at Las Animas Hospital, Havana, or at Columbia Barracks. Many of them had been purposely soiled with a liberal quantity of black vomit, urine, and fecal matter. A dirty 'comfortable' and a much soiled pair of blankets, removed from the bed of a patient sick with yellow fever in the town of Quemados were contained in one of these boxes. The same day, at 6 p.m., Dr. R. P. Cooke, Acting Assistant Surgeon, U.S.A., and two privates of the Hospital Corps, all non-immune young Americans, entered this building and deliberately unpacked these boxes, which had been tightly closed and locked for a period of two weeks. They were careful at the same time to give each article a thorough handling and shaking, in order to disseminate through the air of the room the specific agent of yellow fever, if contained in these fomites. These soiled sheets, pillow-cases and blankets were used in preparing the beds in which the members of the Hospital Corps slept. Various soiled articles were hung around the room and placed about the bed occupied by Dr. Cooke.

"From this date until Dec. 19, 1900, a period of twenty days, this room was occupied each night by these three non-immunes. Each morning the various soiled articles were carefully repacked in the aforesaid boxes, and at night again unpacked and distributed about the room. During the day the residents of this house were permitted to occupy a tent pitched in the immediate vicinity, but were kept in strict quarantine.

*   *   *

"December 19th these three non-immunes were placed in quarantine for five days and then given the liberty of the camp. All had remained in perfect health, notwithstanding their stay of twenty nights amid such unwholesome surroundings.

"During the week December 20-27 the following articles were also placed in this house, viz. pajama suits, 1; undershirts, 2; night-shirts, 4; pillow-slips, 4; sheets, 6; blankets, 5; pillows, 2; mattresses, 1. These articles had been removed from the persons and beds of four patients sick with yellow fever and were very much soiled, as any change of clothing or bed-linen during their attacks had been purposely avoided, the object being to obtain articles as thoroughly contaminated as possible.

"From Dec. 21, 1900, till Jan. 10, 1901, this building was again occupied by two non-immune young Americans, under the same conditions as the preceding occupants, except that these men *slept every night in the very garments worn by yellow fever patients throughout their entire attacks,* besides making use exclusively of their much-soiled pillow-slips, sheets and blankets. At the end of twenty-one nights of such intimate contact with these *fomites,* they also went into quarantine, from which they were released five days later in perfect health.

"From January 11 till January 31, a period of twenty days, 'Building No. 1" continued to be occupied by two other non-immune Americans, who, like those who preceded them, have slept every night in the beds formerly occupied by yellow fever patients and in the night-shirts used by these patients throughout the attack without change. In addition during the last fourteen nights of their occupancy of this house they had slept each night, with their pillows covered with towels that had been thoroughly soiled with the blood drawn from both the general and capillary circulation, on the first day of the disease, in the case of a well-marked attack of yellow fever. Notwithstanding this trying ordeal these men have continued to remain in perfect health.

"The attempt which we have therefore made to infect 'Building No. 1' and its seven non-immune occupants, during a period of sixty-three nights, has proved an absolute failure."

INFECTION BY MOSQUITOES

While the experiments with fomites were being carried out in "Building No. 1," certain non-immune individuals who were lodged in tents, in a separate part of the camp, were being subjected, with their full consent, to the bites of mosquitoes which had previously fed on the blood of cases of yellow fever occurring in the city of Havana. Thus during the period from December 5th, 1900, to February 7th, 1901, we had subjected to this method of infection twelve non-immune subjects, who had previously passed their full record of quarantine in this camp. Of these 10, or 83.3%, experienced attacks of yellow fever and always within the period of incubation of this disease.

The following Table II, gives the necessary data concerning these observations.

The positive results obtained, therefore, by this mode of infection stand in striking contrast to the negative experiments made with *fomites*. Indeed, cases VIII and XI of Table II had each slept twenty-one nights in the garments of yellow fever patients while occupants of Building No. 1. As they had remained in perfect health at Camp Lazear for yet thirty days longer, they were at the expiration of this time bitten by infected mosquitoes solely for the purpose of testing their immunity and with the result that an attack of yellow fever promptly followed in each case.

It should be borne in mind, also, that of the non-immune residents at Camp Lazear, while all lived under the same hygienic conditions, only those individuals developed yellow fever who were purposely bitten by contaminated mosquitoes, or injected with the blood of those sick with this disease. Moreover, the precision with which the infection of the individual followed the bite of the mosquito left nothing to be desired in order to fulfil the requirements of a scientific experiment.

TABLE II

No. of case	Days in quarantine	Inoculation		Method of inoculation	Period of incubation in hours	Result	Order of occurrence	Date of occurrence
		Date	Hour					
I	15	Dec. 5, 1900	2 p.m.	Mosquito	$81\frac{1}{2}$	Positive	I	Dec. 8, 1900
II	9	Dec. 8, 1900	4 p.m.	Mosquito	137	Positive	III	Dec. 13, 1900
III	19	Dec. 9, 1900	10:30 a.m.	Mosquito	$83\frac{1}{2}$	Positive	II	Dec. 12, 1900
IV	21	Dec. 11, 1900	4:30 p.m.	Mosquito	$91\frac{1}{2}$	Positive	IV	Dec. 15, 1900
V	32	Dec. 21, 1900	12 noon	Mosquito	95	Positive	V	Dec. 25, 1900
VI	31	Jan. 8, 1901	10 a.m.	Mosquito	—	Negative	VI	—
VII	22	Dec. 30, 1900	11 a.m.	Mosquito	$94\frac{1}{2}$	Positive	VII	Jan. 3, 1901
VIII	69	Jan. 19, 1901	8:30 p.m.	Mosquito	$95\frac{1}{2}$	Positive	VIII	Jan. 23, 1901
IX	74	Jan. 25, 1901	10:30 a.m.	Mosquito	—	Negative	IX	—
X	6	Jan. 31, 1901	9:30 a.m.	Mosquito	$74\frac{1}{2}$	Positive	X	Feb. 3, 1901
XI	78	Feb. 6, 1901	11 a.m.	Mosquito	78	Positive	XI	Feb. 9, 1901
XII	25	Feb. 7, 1901	2 p.m.	Mosquito	70	Positive	XII	Feb. 10, 1901

Case V of Table II is of especial interest, when taken in connection with the failure to induce the disease by contact with *fomites*.

This individual, having been quarantined for thirty-two days at Camp Lazear, volunteered to enter a newly erected building in which fifteen contaminated mosquitoes had just been freed. His first visit was at noon, December 21, 1901, and the length of his stay thirty minutes. At 4:30 p.m. the same day he again entered this building and remained twenty minutes. The following day at 4:30 p.m. he, for the third time, visited this room and remained twenty minutes. During each of these visits he was bitten by mosquitoes. He did not enter the building again, nor was he exposed to any other source of infection. Nevertheless at the expiration of three days and twenty-three hours, or at 6 a.m. December 25, 1900, he was suddenly seized with an attack of yellow fever, which proved to be severe in character. That the infection was occasioned by the bites of contaminated mosquitoes was plainly shown by the immunity from the disease enjoyed by two non-immunes "controls," who, protected only by a wire-screen partition, had been present at each of the subject's visits and who, under the same conditions of security against the bites of the infected mosquitoes, continued to sleep in, and breathe the common atmosphere of this room for yet eighteen nights.

To the positive cases contained in Table II, which were produced at Camp Lazear, we are now able to add four other cases of yellow fever occasioned by the bites of infected mosquitoes, thus making a total of fourteen cases, in each of which happily recovery followed.

A very important point brought out by these observations is that an interval of about twelve days or more after contamination appears to be necessary before the infected *Stegomyia* is capable of conveying the disease to a susceptible individual. Repeated experiments made with insects which had bitten yellow fever patients two to ten days previously were always negative, although these same insects were proven capable of conveying the disease after having been kept until 17 to 24 days had elapsed. Our observations (14) further demonstrate that mosquitoes that have been kept for periods varying from 39 to 57 days after contamination are still capable of conveying disease, and further that infected *Stegomyia* may survive for a period of at least 71 days. This will explain how the contagion of yellow fever may cling to a building, although it has been vacated for a period of two or more months.

Bearing in mind that the observations made by means of blood injections (Table I) were only undertaken *after* we had succeeded in demonstrating that the disease could be conveyed by the bites of infected *Stegomyia*, it will be seen that our study of the method of propagation of yellow fever, at Camp Lazear, sufficed to prove very definitely that, while the natural mode of transmission of this disease is through the bites of infected mosquitoes, yellow fever may also be conveyed, like malarial fever, by the injection of a small quantity of blood taken from the veins of an individual suffering with this disease.

Per contra, our observations show that, notwithstanding the common belief in this mode of transmission, yellow fever cannot be induced in the non-immune individual even by the most intimate contact with contaminated articles of clothing and bedding.

Although the investigations made at Camp Lazear were only concluded one year ago, already confirmatory evidence of the strongest character has been furnished in a series of experiments carried out by Guitéras (15) at the Inoculation Station of the Sanitary Department of Havana.

I may be pardoned for quoting the paragraph with which Guitéras begins his contribution. He says: "The favourable results obtained by the United States Army Commission in their experiments with yellow fever, the continued series of mild cases resulting from these experiments without a death, suggested very naturally the continuation of their work on a larger scale; not with a view to control or confirm the conclusions of the Commission, for anyone who had followed their work with unprejudiced attention must have concluded that their solution of the problem of the etiology of yellow fever was final; but rather in the hope of propagating the disease in a controllable form, and securing amongst the recently arrived immigrants immunization, with the minimum amount of danger to themselves and the community."

Of a total of 42 individuals inoculated by Guitéras 25 were rejected by him by reason of having been bitten by insects that had been applied to cases of fever about which the diagnosis was in doubt. The following table, therefore, only includes 17 persons who were bitten by *Stegomyia* that had previously fed on unmistakable cases of yellow fever at intervals of 14 to 36 days before being applied to the non-immune subject.

A more complete confirmation of the results obtained by the American Commission could not be furnished than the date contained in the foregoing table, since they show that of 17 individuals who were bitten by infected *Stegomyia, fasciata,* eight (47%) developed the disease. Most unfortunately in three of these cases very grave symptoms ensued, such as black vomit and suppression of the urine, which eventuated in the death of the patients. I may add that in the hands of Guitéras *fomites* failed to exert any effect on non-immunes.

Whether other species of mosquitoes than *Stegomyia* are capable of conveying the parasite of yellow fever has not as yet been determined by the Commission: nor have we been able to ascertain whether the parasite passes from the mother insect to daughter insects. The experiments which we have thus far been able to make for the purpose of determining these important points, although negative, have been too few in number to warrant any definite expression of opinion.

TABLE III

No. of case	Date of inoculation	Mode of inoculation	Result	Period of incubation
1	Feb. 23, 1901	Mosquito	Positive	3 days, 10 hours
2	Aug. 4, 1901	Mosquito	Negative	
3	Aug. 4, 1901	Mosquito	Negative	
4	Aug. 7, 1901	Mosquito	Negative	
5	Aug. 8, 1901	Mosquito	Positive	4 days, 5 hours
6	Aug. 8, 1901	Mosquito	Positive	3 days, 3 hours
7	Aug. 7, 1901	Mosquito	Negative	
8	Aug. 9, 1901	Mosquito	Positive	5 days, 3 hours
9	Aug. 10, 1901	Mosquito	Negative	
10	Aug. 10, 1901	Mosquito	Negative	
11	Aug. 10, 1901	Mosquito	Negative	
12	Aug. 13, 1901	Mosquito	Positive	3 days, 19 hours
13	Aug. 13, 1901	Mosquito	Negative	
14	Aug. 14, 1901	Mosquito	Positive	3 days, 21 hours
15	Aug. 14, 1901	Mosquito	Positive	5 days, 21 hours
16	Aug. 22, 1901	Mosquito	Positive	3 days
17	Aug. 24, 1901	Mosquito	Negative	

THE PREVENTION OF YELLOW FEVER

The definite determination of the way in which yellow fever is transmitted from the sick to the well, furnishes a solution at last of that much vexed problem of how to prevent the spread of the disease. Even in the absence of more definite knowledge concerning its specific agent—knowledge greatly to be desired from the scientific standpoint—we are now able, as sanitarians, to direct our efforts along certain well-defined lines, with a feeling of security heretofore unknown.

From the point of view of prevention the situation may be briefly summed up in the following conclusion, which was presented by the American Army Commission to the Pan-American Congress of 1900,[5] viz. "The spread of yellow fever can be most effectually controlled by measures directed to the destruction of mosquitoes and the protection of the sick against the bites of these insects."

This conclusion was the logical outcome of the observations that had been made by the Commission at its Experimental Station near Quemados, Cuba.

The importance of the discovery that yellow fever is transmitted by the bite of a certain species of mosquito did not fail to attract the prompt attention of the Military Governor of the Island of Cuba, himself a physician and formerly a distinguished member of the Medical Department of the United States Army. By his direction the theory was at once subjected to a practical test in the city of Havana, in which city yellow

[5] *Loc. cit.*

fever had not failed to make its yearly appearance during the past one hundred and forty years.

Under the efficient management of the Chief Sanitary Officer, Surgeon-Major Wm. C. Gorgas, U.S. Army, the sanitary regulations were so far modified as to require that every patient having yellow fever should not only be quarantined, but that his room should be promptly protected with wire-screens, so as to prevent the possibility of mosquitoes becoming infected by sucking the blood of the patient. As a second important measure, a systematic destruction of all mosquitoes in other rooms of the patient's house, as well as in adjoining houses, was at once begun, the fumes of *pyrethrum* being relied upon to stupefy the insects, after which they were carefully swept up and burned. In other words, Surgeon-Major Gorgas relying upon the well-known slow progress of yellow fever sought to destroy all mosquitoes, infected or non-infected within a given radius of each case, while at the same time he effectually excluded all mosquitoes from access to the sick. If a secondary case occurred, the same hygienic measures were vigorously enforced along the lines above indicated.

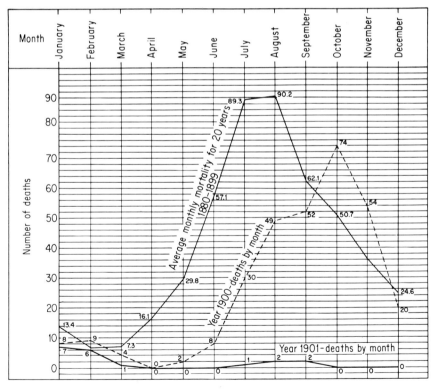

Chart I. Showing monthly mortality from Yellow Fever in the city of Havana, for the twenty years, 1880-1899, and for the years 1900-1901.

As an illustration of what has been accomplished by these newer sanitary regulations, I may state that counting from the date when they were put into force, viz. February 15, 1901—Havana was freed from yellow fever within ninety days; so that from May 7th to July 1st—a period of fifty-four days—no cases occurred. Notwithstanding the fact that on the latter date and during the months of July, August, and September, the disease was repeatedly reintroduced into Havana from an inland town, no difficulty was encountered in promptly stamping it out by the same measures of sanitation intelligently applied both in the city of Havana as well as in the town of Santiago de las Vegas, whence the disease was being brought into Havana.

As a further illustration of the remarkable sanitary victory accom-

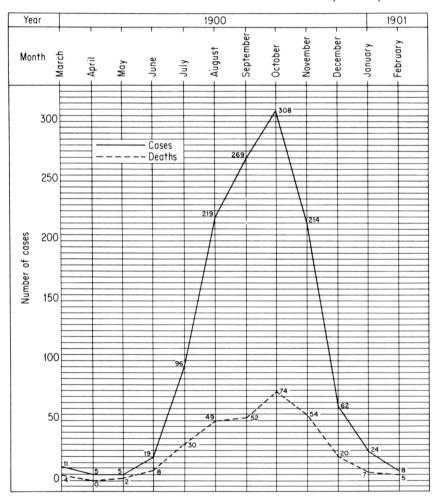

Chart II. Cases and deaths from Yellow Fever in the city of Havana, for the epidemic year, March 1, 1900, to March 1, 1901 (by month).

plished over a disease whose progress we had heretofore been powerless to arrest, I will close this paper by inviting the reader's attention, first to the accompanying Chart I, which shows the average monthly mortality from yellow fever in Havana for the twenty years, 1880-1899, inclusive, and also the mortality by month for the years 1900 and 1901. I will then ask him to examine Chart II, which shows the progress of yellow fever in Havana during the epidemic year, ending March 1, 1901, when the sanitary authorities were putting forth every effort known at that time to sanitary science in order to control the march of disease; and when he has satisfied himself that no effect whatever was produced upon the epidemic of that year, I will invite his attention to Chart III, which shows the oc-

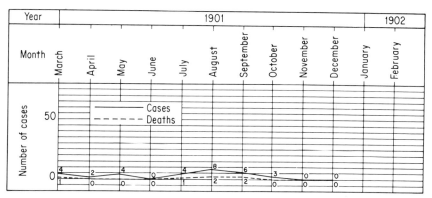

Chart III. Cases and deaths from Yellow Fever in the city of Havana, for the epidemic year, March 1, 1901, to March 1, 1902 (by month).

currence of this disease in Havana for the epidemic year March 1st, 1901, to March 1st, 1902, during which year yellow fever was fought on the theory that the specific agent of this disease is transmitted solely by means of the bites of infected mosquitoes. By carefully comparing the figures both as to deaths and cases in these two Charts, and recalling that between the years 1853 and 1900 there have been recorded in the city of Havana 35,952 deaths from yellow fever, he will then be able to more clearly appreciate the value of the work accomplished by the American Army Commission.

BIBLIOGRAPHY

1. Report on the etiology and prevention of yellow fever. (Washington, 1890.)

2. La fiebre amarilla. Conferencia dada en la Universidad de Montevideo, el 10 Junio 1897. Reprint.

3. Bacteriological study in the etiology of yellow fever. N.Y. Med. J. (Jan. 28, 1899), 109-114.

4. Summary of pathologic and bacteriologic work, at isolation, New Orleans, La. J. Am. Med. Assoc. (April 16, 1898), 884-888.

5. The etiology of yellow fever. Abstract of Report, &c. N.Y. Med. J. (August 26, 1899) , 299-302.

6. Report upon bacteriological investigations in yellow fever. The Medical News (N.Y., February 10 and 17, 1900).

7. Revista d'Igiene e Sanita Publica. **XI:** (13) 474-475 (July, 1900).

8. La bacille ictéröide et sa toxine. Archives de Médicine Expérimentale &c. **XI:** 378-398 (1899).

9. Nota para servir al estudio bacteriològico de la fiebre amarilla. Gaceta Medica de Mexico. **XXXVI:** 218-230 (1899).

10. The etiology of yellow fever. A preliminary note. The Philadelphia Med. J. (October 27, 1900).

11. Yellow fever. Buck's Reference Hand-book of the Medical Sciences. **VIII:** 48 (1889).

12. The etiology of yellow fever. A supplementary note. American Medicine. **III** (8): 301-305 (February 22, 1902).

13. The etiology of yellow fever. An additional note. J. Am. Med. Assoc. (February 16, 1901).

14. Experimental yellow fever. Transactions of the Association of American Physicians. **XVI** (1901).

15. Experimental yellow fever at the inoculation station of the Sanitary Department of Havana. American Medicine. **II** (21): 809-817 (1901).

1907

Chlamydozoa II. Jaundice
of Silkworms[1]

by Dr. S. von Prowazek

The early experimental work on insect viruses was dominated by studies on the polyhedral virus diseases because the crystalline inclusions (polyhedra) were easily visible under the light microscope which facilitated the diagnoses of affected larvae. The polyhedral disease, jaundice of the silkworm (Bombyx mori), *was probably the first virus disease of insects to be recognized. As early as 1527, the affliction was referred to in a poem by Vida. The polyhedra of this infection were first observed and associated with the disease, independently, by Cornalia and by Maestri in 1856.*

In 1907, von Prowazek whose historical paper is presented here, demonstrated that material from diseased silkworms was infectious after the polyhedra were removed by filtration through many layers of filter paper. This was a significant step toward the eventual realization that some insect diseases are caused by viruses. The subsequent studies of Acqua[2] and Paillot[3] supplied proof of the viral etiology of silkworm jaundice as well as other diseases of insects.

In subsequent publications, von Prowazek deemphasized his original interpretation of the nature of the causative agent of silkworm jaundice. He had believed that the causal entity was a protozoan and that the polyhedra were reaction products of the disease. The exact relationship between the polyhedra and the virus was the subject of extensive studies and controversy for many years. The relationship was finally clarified

[1] Abridged and reprinted by permission of the publisher from Archives für Protistenkunde **10**: 358-364 (1907).

[2] Rend. Inst. Bact. Scuola Super Agr. Portici. **3**: 243 (1918-1919).

[3] C. R. Acad. Sci. **179**: 229 (1924); C. R. Acad. Agr. **12**: 201 (1926).

and defined approximately 40 years later (see Bergold's paper).

A point of interest in Prowazek's initial report is the hypothesis he advances on the use of viruses as biological controls for insect pests. In the light of the meager knowledge available at that time on insect viruses, this was certainly a precocious idea. It was to prove, however, partially successful in later experimental trials to control with viruses such insect pests as the caterpillar of the clouded yellow butterfly in California, the European pine sawfly in Canada, and the "bagworm" in South Africa.

During my stay in Rovigno in 1903/4 I was occupied with the peculiar disease of silkworms, called "jaundice" by the breeders. I obtained the material from Mr. J. Bolle, Director of the Austro-Hungarian Agricultural Chemical Station in Görz, who had earned particular merits in connection with the investigation of this disease. For external reasons, however, the studies had to be interrupted and I have only now been able to bring them, in Hamburg, to a partial conclusion.

The jaundice attacks the silkworms in the breeding establishments especially at the time when they become ripe for spinning. The sick worms can be recognized at first by their lack of appetite; they crawl around unsteadily in the racks; their skin at first looks opaque, then becomes conspicuously shiny as a result of an inner tension; hence, these worms are also called "shiny worms (luisettes)." Later the abdomen of the worm is swollen, the skin is extremely easily injurable and there appear on it yellow spots which are confluent with one another and which actually give the disease its name, jaundice. Since the abdomen is conspicuously swollen, the disease is also called "fatty degeneration (grasserie)." From the tears in the skin which occur at every opportunity a milky yellowish liquid—the blood of the worm—trickles out. The Italian breeders call these worms vacca (cow). Finally the worms become limp, die, and flow apart into a brown sticky mass. A great many researchers had already been occupied with the jaundice of silkworms; of these I will only mention the names of E. Cornalia, Maestri, A. Cecconi, E. Verson, F. Haberlandt, Forbes, Panebianco and Bolle. A summary presentation of the research results was published in Padua, in 1896, by E. Verson and E. Quajat, entitled "Il Filugello e l'arte serica (The silkworm and the Art of Silk)."

In the blood of jaundiced spinners Maestri (Frammenti anatom. fisiolog. e patolog. del baco da seta [Anatomical, Physiological and Pathological Details of the Silkworm], Pavia, 1856) found a large number of granules which he related to the fat tissue; later E. Verson identified its crystalline nature. In 1893 Bolle (Yearbook of the Austro-Hungarian Silk Experimental Station, 1893, page 112) established that the so-called polyhedral particles consist of a protein substance.

These polyhedral particles are specific for the jaundice of silkworms.

It is possible at all times to infect worms with the abdominal-cavity fluid of a worm which contains polyhedral particles; either one strokes fresh mulberry leaves with this material by means of a brush, lets dry and feeds the leaves to the worms, or one dips an ignited needle into the above-mentioned substances and then punctures the so-called false foot of a worm. Five to seven days after the infection the worms die of jaundice. As Bolle has shown, the virus possesses a rather high tenacity: he was able to infect worms and pupae via subcutaneous injection of "one-year-old blood, dried on glass plates," always obtaining positive results. The polyhedral particles are, however, not the carriers of the virus, since one is able to eliminate them by means of repeated filtration through several thicknesses of filter paper; then for control the filtrate is centrifuged and sedimented for an extended period of time; the clear, particle-free supernatant liquid which is subjected to an accurate microscopal examination in search for any of the particles in question that may possibly be present, may then be used to produce infection with a positive result.

Silkworms which had been infected in this manner at noon on 20 June 1904 died of jaundice on 24 and 25 June, and in their abdominal cavity a large number of typical polyhedral particles was detectable.

I conceive of the polyhedral bodies as specific reaction products of the host cells to the virus. I studied their genesis on smear preparations obtained from the blood of the abdominal-cavity fluid, and above all from the fat of the sick silkworms; these (smears) were prepared by dipping them while still wet, horizontally, into a hot alcoholic sublimate solution:

Fixation: Two-thirds sublimate (concentrated hot saturated aqueous solution) + one-third 90% alcohol, 10 minutes.

Washing with distilled water; 60% iodine-alcohol; washing with 60% alcohol, then with distilled water.

Staining with dilute (commercial) Grenacher's hematoxylin, one quarter hour.

Washing with well water. Alcohol series, xylene, Canada balsam.

In the diseased cells one first notes that the nucleus has become hypertrophic; the nucleolus is very much enlarged, is stained very dark (in the blood cells) is often flapped, irregularly shaped in the fatty-body cells

and possesses a minute honeycomb structure. The chromatin of the nucleus collects into individual lumps which adhere especially to the inner
line of contour of the cell membrane (Fig. 1a). The first polyhedral particles emerge in the honeycombs of the achromatic framework; the number of these particles quickly increases. Later they enter also the protoplasm (Fig. 1). Sometimes one finds in the smear also naked, very strongly

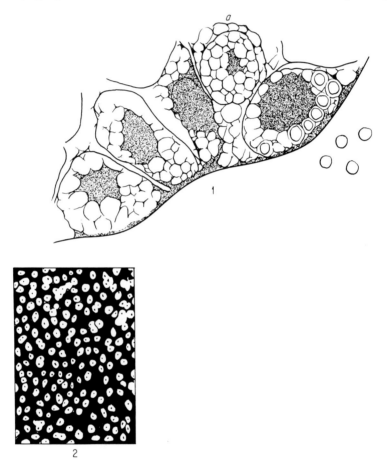

hypertrophic oval nuclei of the fatty-body cells which are completely
filled with polyhedral particles, while the chromatin adheres only to the
nucleus membrane and so stimulates a type of cyst membrane. At times
the chromatin of the nucleus adheres to the free polyhedral particle in
a hood-like manner. The polyhedral particles originate in this way at
first intranuclearly on the nuclei of all tissues of the diseased worms;
later they are detectable also in the protoplasm; when the cells fall apart
the free particles flood the abdominal-cavity fluid and blood of the diseased worms.

At the edge of these smear preparations from the abdominal-cavity fluid and blood of jaundiced silkworms, where the serum had been fixated in a somewhat thinner layer, it was possible to detect very numerous light formations in the serum clot as soon as the preparations were stained intensively several times with Giemsa's Eosine Azure, and further worked up as dry cover-glass smears (that is, dried with blotting paper and enclosed in cedar oil). (Fig. 2.) In the light, oval to round small formations, a reddish-violet or dark blue dot-like body, having the appearance of a coccus, could mostly be detected (magnification 2,250, using Auerlicht homog. immersion). These bodies at times separate into dumbbell shapes and I consider these formations as the actual causative agents of the jaundice of silkworms.

They are roundish, proliferate through a dumbbell-shaped cross division and appear to possess a gelatinous envelope (light border). I assign them the preliminary name of *Chlamydozoan bombycis*. They could be represented even better if one diluted the material strongly with distilled water, centifuged intensively, washed several times and then stained the residue with Loeffler's flagella mordant. Unfortunately I do not have any material left for these experiments, and I plan to resume these investigations at a favorable opportunity. In individual cases I noticed (these bodies) also in the protoplasm of blood cells—these would be the intracellular stages of the chlamydozoan, to be compared with analogous stages of the epithelial cells of vaccine-inoculated rabbit cornea.

As a prophylactic measure against the jaundice of silkworms Bolle recommends immediate removal and burning of the first jaundiced worms, more frequent change of the bedding of the latter and burning of the contaminated beds.

Bolle succeeded in positively infecting, by means of the virus of jaundice, also other insects such as *Antherea Jama Mai* and *A. Pernyi, Attacus Cynthria, Antherea mylitta* and larvae and beetles of *Dermestes lardarius,* only, interestingly, the polyhedral particles varied in shape from host to host. Since according to Bolle (1889) the jaundice occurs also on the feared *Psilura monacha* L., infection experiments on a large scale would be of particular importance, also from the national-economic point of view, especially since the virus, dried on glass plates, can be preserved over a year in a state capable of causing infection, and readily shipped in this manner.

I wish to express my sincere thanks to Director J. Bolle in Görz, for his manifold advice and for the furnished material.

BIBLIOGRAPHY

Bolle, J. 1894. Preliminary communication regarding the jaundice of silkworms. Atti e Memoire dell' i. r. Società agraria. Görz.

Verson and Guajat. 1896. The Silkworm and the Art of Silk. Padua.

Panebianco, R. Observations on yellow granules. Monthly Bulletin of Silkworm Culture. **II.** Ser. Jahrg. (10): 145.

Bolle, J. 1898. Cultivation of silk in Japan. A. Hartleben's Verlag.

1911

Transmission of a Malignant New Growth by Means of a Cell-Free Filtrate[1]

by Peyton Rous, M.D.

One of the first viral tumors shown to be transmitted by extracts of the tissue was rabbit myxomatosis reported at the turn of the century by G. Sanarelli.[2] Although he believed the causal agent was a virus, in the sense that it was too small to be seen under the microscope, Sanarelli did not carry out tests to demonstrate the filterability of the agent. The viral origin of animal tumors was first suggested by Borrel,[3] but it was based on evidence from a comparison of carcinomas and virus lesions of epithelial cells, i.e., pox diseases. The transmission of a form of chicken leukemia by cell-free extracts was reported by Ellermann and Bang,[4] but the possible viral nature of this neoplastic condition went unrecognized. It was Rous, in the paper reprinted here, that demonstrated conclusively the transmission of the first solid tumor. He was able to induce a neoplastic disease with cell- and bacteria-free extracts of a fowl sarcoma (later named Rous sarcoma) which could be transferred indefinitely to other animals. The filterability of the agent strongly implied that the causal entity was a virus. The concept, that some tumor formations may have a viral origin, was not readily accepted and, in fact, it encountered considerable resistance within the scientific community. Gradual acceptance of this view was forthcoming with discoveries of viral tumors in plants, insects, amphibia, and mammals.

[1] From the Laboratories of the Rockefeller Institute for Medical Research. Reprinted by permission of the author and publisher from the J. Am. Med. Assoc. **56**: 198 (1911).

[2] Centralbl. f. Bakt. **I** (23): 865 (1898).

[3] Ann. Inst. Pasteur. **17**: 81 (1903).

[4] Zentr. Babt. Parasit. **46**: 595 (1908).

In the same year, an important extension of this work was published by Rous in collaboration with Murphy.[5] They showed that sarcoma cells or filtrates induced tumors or lesions on the chorioallantoic membrane of the embryonated egg. Many years were to pass before the potential of the chick embryo in virus research was recognized, and the lesions induced by the virus of Rous sarcoma on the membranes were used as a quantitative method for assay of virus infectivity. The bold pioneer studies by Rous, although slow to be recognized and exploited, were to provide the foundation for subsequent experimental research on tumor viruses.

A tumor of the chicken, histologically a spindle-celled sarcoma, has been propagated in this laboratory since October, 1909,[6] and in the past few months has developed extreme malignancy.[7] From a bit inoculated into the breast muscle of a susceptible fowl there develops rapidly a large, firm growth; metastasis takes place to the viscera; and within four to five weeks often the host dies. The behavior of the new growth has been throughout that of a true neoplasm, for which reason the fact of its transmission by means of a cell-free filtrate assumes exceptional importance.

EXPERIMENTS

For the first experiments on the point use was made of ordinary filter-paper and the ground tumor suspended in Ringer's solution. It was supposed that the slight paper barrier, which allows the passage of a few red blood-cells and lymphocytes, would suffice to hold back the tumor and render the filtrate innocuous. Such has been the experience of other workers with mouse and dog tumors. But in the present instance characteristic growths followed the inoculation of small amounts of the watery filtrate, and followed also the inoculation of the fluid supernatant after centrifugalization of a tumor emulsion.

These results led to more critical experiments, which will be here detailed. Tumors of especially rapid growth and young, well-grown, barred Plymouth Rock fowls were used throughout.

[5] J. Am. Med. Assoc. **56**: 741 (1911).

[6] J. Exp. Med. **XII**: 696 (1910).

[7] Rous, Peyton, Metastasis and tumor immunity: observations with a transmissible avian neoplasm, J. Am. Med. Assoc: 1805 (Nov. 19, 1910).

Experiment 1.—Tumor material from the breast of Chicken 92 (tumor generation 6 A) was ground with sterile sand, suspended in a considerable bulk of Ringer's solution, and shaken for twenty minutes in a machine. The sand and tumor fragments were separated out by centrifugalization in large tubes for five minutes at 2,800 revolutions per minute. Of the supernatant fluid a little was pipetted off, and this centrifugalized anew for fifteen minutes at over 3,000 revolutions per minute. From the upper layers sufficient fluid for inoculation was now carefully withdrawn. The pure-bred fowls were injected in one breast with 0.2 c.c. of the fluid, in the other with a small bit of tumor tissue. All developed sarcoma at the site of this latter inoculation, and in seven the same growth slowly appeared at the point where the fluid had been injected.

Experiment 2.—Tumor from Chicken 90 (tumor generation 6 A) was ground, suspended, and shaken as before. But after one centrifugalization the fluid was passed through a Berkefeld filter No. 2 (coarse). Before filtration, it was pinkish-yellow, cloudy; afterwards, faintly yellow, limpid. Nine fowls were inoculated with 0.2 c.c. of the filtrate in each breast, and twenty-two more received filtrate in one breast, a bit of tumor in the other. Of the nine, one slowly developed a sarcoma in each breast, and later microscopic growths were found in its lungs. Of the twenty-two receiving both filtrate and tumor, five developed sarcoma where the filtrate had been injected; and these five showed especially large growths from the tumor bit.

The Berkefeld filter employed was later found slightly pervious to *Bacillus prodigiosus.*

Experiment 3.—The filtrate was similarly prepared except that a small Berkefeld filter (No. 5 medium), impermeable to *Bacillus prodigiosus,* was used. As before, the filtration was done at room temperature. Fowl 124 (generation 7 A) furnished the material. Twenty chickens were inoculated in each breast with the filtrate, but none have developed tumors.

Experiment 4.—In this experiment the material was never allowed to cool. About 15 gm. of tumor from Chicken 140 (generation 7 B) was ground in a warm mortar with warm sand, mixed with 200 c.c. of heated Ringer's solution, shaken for thirty minutes within a thermostat room, centrifugalized, and the fluid passed through a filter similar to that used in Experiment 3. Both before and after the experiment, this filter was found to hold back *Bacillus prodigiosus.* The filtration of the fluid was done at 38.5°C., and its injection immediately followed. In four of ten fowls inoculated with the filtrate only (0.2 to 0.5 c.c. in each breast) there has developed a sarcoma in one breast; and though the growths required several weeks for their appearance their enlargement is now fairly rapid. Pieces removed at operation have shown the characteristic tumor structure.

CHARACTERS OF THE TUMOR

As has been pointed out, the special significance of these results lies in the growth's identity as a tumor. The original sarcoma was found as a unique instance in a flock of healthy fowls; and, though susceptible normal chickens and others with the tumor have since been kept together in close quarters for long periods, no instance suggesting a natural infectivity of the growth has occurred. When inoculated, it is at first a local disease, very dependent on the good health of the host. At this time intercurrent illness of the fowl will check the nodule's growth or even cause it transiently to disappear. For long the sarcoma could be transferred only to fowls of the same pure-bred variety in which it arose, and this only in an occasional individual; but like many tumors, it has gained on repeated transplantation a heightened malignancy, and the power to grow in other varieties of the same animal. Yet in these it does not do well; and it has not been successfully transplanted to other species.

Histologically, the growth has always consisted of one type of cells, namely, spindle-cells in bundles, with a slight, supporting, connective tissue framework. The picture does not in the least suggest a granuloma; and cultures from the growth remain sterile as regards bacteria. At the edge of the invading mass there is often practically no cellular reaction, but lymphocytes in small number may be present, as is common with tumors in general. Metastasis takes place early, through the bloodstream, and the secondary nodules have the same character as the primary. Several instances of the sarcoma's direct extension into vessels have been encountered. The secondary growths are distributed especially to the lungs, heart and liver, and in the last organ are sometimes umbilicated. The host becomes emaciated, cold and drowsy, and shortly dies.

Transplantation experiments with the tumors resulting from the filtrate are at present under way. The tumor of Experiment 2, which arose in the fowl that received filtrate alone, has already been successfully transplanted.

1915

An Investigation of the Nature
of Ultra-Microscopic Viruses[1]

by F. W. Twort, L.R.C.P. Lond., M.R.C.S.

The first discovery of the existence of viruses which attack bacteria was reported by Twort. The uniqueness of the phenomenon, the degeneration of bacterial colonies by an agent which multiplied true to type and was filterable, was difficult to interpret. Twort defined it as an acute infectious disease of micrococci which, among other possibilities considered, could be caused by an ultra-microscopic virus. The report did not stir much interest and further study was curtailed during the time of World War I.

The phenomenon was rediscovered two years later by F. d'Herelle,[2] who named the causal agent "bacteriophage." In the years to follow, d'Herelle contributed much additional information to the understanding of the phenomenon and outlined a rudimentary infectious cycle for the organism. In view of the bactericidal properties of bacteriophages, much time and effort were expended without success to use them as therapeutical agents of bacterial diseases. In the 1930's the potential of these viruses as model systems for studying the nature of viruses was realized, and they assumed a new and important role in virus research.

During the past three years a considerable number of experiments have been carried out at the Brown Institution on filter-passing viruses. Many of these, previous to the out-

---

[1] This investigation was made on behalf of the Local Government Board. Reprinted by permission of the publisher from Lancet. **2**: 1241-1243 (1915).

[2] Compt. Rend. Acad. Sci. **165**: 373 (1917).

break of the war, were performed by Dr. C. C. Twort, and, unfortunately, circumstances during the present year have made it difficult to continue the work.

In the first instance attempts were made to demonstrate the presence of non-pathogenic filter-passing viruses. As is well known, in the case of ordinary bacteria for every pathogenic microorganism discovered many non-pathogenic varieties of the same type have been found in nature, and it seems highly probable that the same rules will be found to hold good in the case of ultra-microscopic viruses. It is difficult, however, to obtain proof of their existence, as pathogenicity is the only evidence we have at the present time of the presence of an ultra-microscopic virus. On the other hand, it seems probable that if non-pathogenic varieties exist in nature these should be more easily cultivated than the pathogenic varieties; accordingly, attempts to cultivate these from such materials as soil, dung, grass, hay, straw, and water from ponds were made on specially prepared media. Several hundred media were tested. It is impossible to describe all these in detail, but generally agar, egg, or serum was used as a basis, and to these varying quantities of certain chemicals or extracts of fungi, seeds, &c., were added. The material to be tested for viruses was covered with water and incubated at 30°C. or over for varying periods of time, then passed through a Berkefeld filter, and the filter inoculated on the different media. In these experiments a few ordinary bacteria, especially sporing types, were often found to pass through the filter; but in no case was it possible to obtain a growth of a true filter-passing virus.

Attempts were also made to infect such animals as rabbits and guinea pigs by inoculating two doses of the filtered material or by rubbing this into the shaved skin. In other cases inoculations were made directly from one animal to another in the hope of raising the virulence of any filter-passing virus that might be present. All the experiments, however, were negative.

Experiments were also conducted with vaccinia and with distemper of dogs, but in neither of these diseases was it found possible to isolate a bacterium that would reproduce the disease in animals. Some interesting results, however, were obtained with cultivations from glycerinated calf vaccinia. Inoculated agar tubes, after 24 hours at 37°C., often showed watery-looking areas, and in cultures that grew micrococci it was found that some of these colonies could not be subcultured, but if kept they became glassy and transparent. On examination of these glassy areas nothing but minute granules, staining reddish with Giemsa, could be seen. Further experiments showed that if a colony of the white micrococcus that had started to become transparent was plated out instead of being subcultured as a streak then the micrococci grew, and a pure streak culture from certain of these colonies could be obtained. On the other hand, if the plate cultures (made by inoculating the condensation water of a series of tubes and floating this over the surface of the medium) were left, the colonies, especially in the first dilution, soon started to turn transparent, and the micrococci were replaced by fine granules. This action, unlike an ordinary degenerative process, started from the edge of the colonies, and further experiments showed that when a pure culture of the white or the yellow micrococcus isolated from vaccinia is touched with a small portion of one of the glassy colonies, the growth at the point touched soon starts to become transparent or glassy, and this gradually spreads over the whole growth, sometimes killing out all the micrococci and replacing these by fine granules. Experiments showed that the action is more rapid and complete with vigorous-growing young cultures than with old ones, and there is very little action on dead cultures or young cultures that have been killed by heating to 60°C. Anaerobia does not favour the action. The transparent material when diluted (one in a million) with water or saline was found to pass the finest porcelain filters (Pasteur-Chamberland F. and B. and Doulton White) with ease, and one drop of the filtrate pipetted over an agar tube was sufficient to make that tube unsuitable for the growth of the micrococcus. That is, if the micrococcus was inoculated down the tube as a streak, this would start to grow, but would soon become dotted with transparent points which would rapidly extend over the whole growth. The number of points from which this starts depends upon the dilution of the transparent material, and in some cases it is so active that the growth is stopped and turned transparent almost directly it starts. This condition or disease of the micrococcus when transmitted to pure cultures of the micrococcus can be conveyed to fresh cultures for an indefinite number of generations; but the transparent material will not grow by itself on any medium. If in an infected tube small areas of micrococci are left, and this usually happens when the micrococcus has grown well before becoming infected, these areas will start to grow again and extend over the transparent portions, which shows that the action of the transparent material is stopped or hindered in an overgrown tube; but it is not dead, for if a minute portion is transferred to another young culture of the micrococcus it soon starts to dissolve up the micrococci again. Although the transparent material shows no evidence of growth when placed on a fresh agar tube without micrococci it will retain its powers of activity for over six months. It also retains its activity when made into an emulsion and heated to 52°C., but when heated to 60°C. for an hour it appears to be destroyed. It has some action, but very much less, on staphylococcus aureus and albus isolated from boils of man, and it appears to have no action on members of the coli group or on streptococci, tubercle bacilli, yeasts, &c. The transparent material was inoculated into various animals and was rubbed into the scratched skin of guinea pigs, rabbits, a calf, a monkey, and a man; but all the results were negative.

From these results it is difficult to draw definite conclusions. In the

first place, we do not know for certain the nature of an ultra-microscopic virus. It may be a minute bacterium that will only grow on living material, or it may be a tiny amoeba which, like ordinary amoeba, thrives on living microorganisms. On the other hand, it must be remembered that if the living organic world has been slowly built up in accordance with the theories of evolution, then an amoeba and a bacterium must be recognised as highly developed organisms in comparison with much more primitive forms which once existed, and probably still exist at the present day. It is quite possible that an ultra-microscopic virus belongs somewhere in this vast field of life more lowly organised than the bacterium or amoeba. It may be living protoplasm that forms no definite individuals, or an enzyme with power of growth.

In the vaccinia experiments described above it is clear that the transparent material contains an enzyme, and it is destroyed at 60°C. It also increases in quantity when placed on an agar tube containing micrococci obtained from vaccinia, and this can be carried on indefinitely from generation to generation. If it is part of the micrococcus it must be either a stage in its life-history which will not grow on ordinary media but stimulates fresh cultures of the micrococcus to pass into the same stage, or an enzyme secreted by the micrococcus which leads to its own destruction and the production of more enzyme. The fact that the transparent portion cannot be grown except on the micrococcus makes it impossible to obtain any definite evidence of these points. There is this, however, against the idea of a separate form of life: if the white micrococcus is repeatedly plated out and a pure culture obtained, this may give a good white growth for months when subcultured at intervals on fresh tubes; eventually, however, most pure strains show a transparent spot, and from this the transparent material can be obtained once again. Of course, it may be that the micrococcus was never quite free from the transparent portion, or this may have passed through the cotton-wool plug and contaminated the micrococcus, but it seems much more probable that the material was produced by the micrococcus. Incidentally, this apparent spontaneous production of a self-destroying material which when started increases in quantity might be of interest in connexion with cancers. In any case, whatever explanation is accepted, the possibility of its being an ultra-microscopic virus has not been *definitely* disproved, because we do not know for certain the nature of such a virus. If the transparent portion were a separate virus, it might be vaccinia or it might be some contaminating non-pathogenic ultra-microscopic virus, for it is conceivable that whereas a non-pathogenic variety might grow on micrococci or bacilli, a pathogenic variety might grow only on the animal it infects. As the animal experiments were negative there is no evidence that it is vaccinia, although such a virus might lose its virulence when grown outside the body. On the other hand, no evidence was obtained that it was a non-pathogenic contaminating ultra-microscopic virus. On the whole it seems probable, though by no means certain, that the active transparent material is produced by the micrococcus, and since it leads to its own destruction and can be transmitted to fresh healthy cultures, it might almost be considered as an acute infectious disease of micrococci.

In view of the results obtained with vaccinia similar experiments were carried out with other material. It will not be necessary to describe all these in detail; it will suffice to note that similar, though not such definite, results were obtained with a micrococcus and a member of the coil-typhoid group of bacilli which were obtained from the intestinal mucous membrane of a dog suffering from acute distemper, and there is some evidence that the difficulty often experienced in isolating certain known pathogenic micro-organisms may be due to the same cause. Experiments carried out with tuberculous pleural fluids and tubercle bacilli gave negative results.

More recently, that is when the investigation of infantile diarrhoea and vomiting was continued during the summer and autumn of this year (1915), similar experiments were carried out with material obtained from the intestinal tract. The general results of this investigation will be published later, and it will be sufficient here to note that after certain difficulties had been overcome it was found that in the upper third of the intestine, which contained numerous bacilli of the typhoid-coli group, some larger bacilli were also present. In some cases they grew in far larger numbers than the coli types of bacteria; but this was only so when precautions were taken to eliminate the action of a dissolving substance which infected the colonies so rapidly that they were dissolved before attaining a size visible to the eye. Here, then, is a similar condition to that found in vaccinia, and the greatest difficulty was experienced in obtaining the bacilli free from the transparent dissolving material, so rapidly was the infection increased and carried from one colony to another. Finally, cultures were obtained by growing the bacilli with certain members of the typhoid-coli group for a few generations and then plating out. From the colonies cultures were obtained on ordinary agar. Some of these cultures being slightly infected with the dissolving material rapidly became transparent and were lost, while a few grew well. The bacillus has several curious characters, and these are now being investigated. It is in no way related to the typhoid-coli group. The relation of this bacillus and the dissolving material to infantile diarrhoea has not yet been determined, but probably it will be found also in cases of dysentery and allied conditions; and I greatly regret that I have not been afforded an opportunity of investigating the dysenteric conditions in the Dardenelles to determine this and other points.

When possible, experiments should be conducted to determine the relative toxicity of cocci and bacilli when free from and when associated with the dissolving material, and vaccines prepared with the transparent material should be tested.

I regret that financial considerations have prevented my carrying these researches to a definite conclusion, but I have indicated the lines along which others more fortunately situated can proceed.

1926

Streak or Winter Blight
of Tomato in Quebec[1]

by T. C. Vanterpool [2]

*A formidable number of reports appeared in the scientific lit-
erature on plant virus diseases in the first half of the twentieth
century in which virus diseases were described or demonstrated
in 90 families, about 500 genera, and more than a thousand
species and varieties of plants. That the number of diseases
described in plants was far greater than the number of known
plant viruses, was probably recognized by many investigators.
This situation was partly resolved with the knowledge that a
virus may infect other species of plants and induce the appearance of diverse symptoms and that strains of the same
virus may cause different degrees of disease. Beginning in 1925,
the well-known attribute of animal viruses to form variants
was reported also for plant viruses. These findings, together
with reports on virus mutants and attenuated viruses, helped
to explain some of the variety of symptoms observed in diseased plants that had been described previously as distinct
entities.*

*The discovery of "mixed infections" helped further to clarify
some of the puzzling symptoms observed in virus-infected
plants. Mixed infections, the simultaneous occurrence of two
viruses within a host plant acting together to produce a distinct severe disease in plants, was first reported by Vanterpool.
He showed that the severe disease "streak" or "winter blight"
of tomatoes was due to the combined effect of the tomato mosaic virus and a potato mosaic virus. Only mild signs of disease were manifested in the tomato plant infected with either
virus, alone. Later, it was discovered that some diseases of the*

[1] Abridged and reprinted by permission of the author and publisher from Phytopathology. **16:** (5) 311-331 (1926).

[2] The writer is indebted to Dr. B. T. Dickson for many helpful suggestions, and for
his kindness in affording field and greenhouse facilities.

potato are caused by simultaneous infection with two distinct viruses. Vanterpool's demonstration was a significant contribution to the understanding of these unique plant virus disorders.

An outbreak of streak, stripe, or winter blight of tomato, which was characterised by its sudden onset and virulent nature and which resulted in a loss of one-third of the crop, occurred on the tomato crop in the commercial greenhouses at Macdonald College in the spring of 1923.

Diseases of the tomato with apparently identical symptoms have been reported under a variety of names from widely separated parts of the world, and there seems to be considerable difference of opinion among investigators regarding their etiology. In view of this and the increasing importance of the greenhouse tomato industry in Quebec, a study of the disease under both field and greenhouse conditions was undertaken.

EXPERIMENTAL STUDIES

The experimental investigations upon which this paper is based were conducted under field conditions during the summers of 1924 and 1925, and in the hothouse during the intervening winter. Space did not permit of dealing with large numbers of plants and, to overcome this difficulty, the experiments were carried out on a small number of plants on three, four, or more, separate occasions. Further, by conducting the experiments both in the greenhouse and in the field, results of comparative value from an environmental standpoint have been added. Therefore the writer thinks that the paucity in the number of plants was overcome, and that the results are actualities.

All field inoculations were made just before dusk and on rainy evenings whenever possible. If no rain had fallen, the plants were thoroughly drenched with water before inoculation. Inoculations in the greenhouse were performed at any time during the day.

The soil in the experimental field plots was a loam which had received a dressing of farmyard manure the previous autumn; that used in pots in the greenhouse was a rich sod soil, to which farmyard manure was added.

In all experiments conducted in the greenhouse care was given to the control of aphids and white flies.

NATURE AND PROPERTIES OF STREAK TOMATO JUICE

The effect of filtration on streak juice.—Expressed juices from leaves, stems and fruit of streak tomato plants were passed through sterile Chamberland F filters into sterile flasks. Under aseptic conditions this filtered juice was put into sterile test tubes from which it could be used at once as a source of inoculum, or kept until required.

Stained preparations of this filtered juice were examined carefully for any microorganisms. As a further check on the freedom of the filtered juice from bacteria, nutrient agar slopes and nutrient broth tubes were also inoculated in duplicate, and incubated at 22° to 26°C. No growth resulted from such filtered juice.

A portion of the unfiltered juice was always saved and inoculated into healthy tomato plants so as to serve as a check on the viability of the streak juice before passage through the filter. The results of the inoculations are given in table 1.

TABLE 1. *Results of inoculating healthy tomato plants with expressed streak tomato juice which had passed through a Chamberland F filter*

No. of tomato plants inoculated	Inoculum	Results		
		Streak	Mosaic only	No positive results
Greenhouse 1924				
11	Filtered streak juice (bacteria free), plants wounded	7	4	0
1	Filtered juice sprayed on plant (without wounding)	0	0	1
1	Filtered juice poured on soil	0	0	1
Field 1924 and 1925				
11	Filtered streak juice (bacteria free), plants wounded	11	0	0

In every case where streak developed the incubation period varied from 11 to 15 days. The results show conclusively that streak of tomato in Quebec belongs to the filterable-virus group of plant diseases.

INSECT TRANSMISSION

Transmission of streak by aphids was readily demonstrated under controlled conditions by allowing aphids, ordinarily found on tomato, to suck the juices of streak tomato plants for a few days and then placing them carefully with a camel-hair brush on vigorously-growing healthy tomato plants. In over 75 per cent of the plants streak symptoms appeared after the usual incubation period.

Three attempts to ascertain whether white flies transmitted the disease were made, but in every case the plants remained healthy.

EFFECT OF INOCULATING TOMATO WITH COMBINATION VIRUSES

The fact that mosaic is invariably present on streak tomato plants, and that streak material which has been dried for months produces mosaic only, when inoculated into tomato, suggested that there might be some other factor, possibly another infective agent which, together with tomato mosaic, produced the disease known as streak. This other factor presumably could not withstand prolonged drying. To show that true streak was not a severe manifestation of tomato mosaic only, the author subjected tomato plants showing pronounced mosaic symptoms to those conditions which had been shown to favor the development of streak most, and in no single case did true streak symptoms appear.

The publication of Johnson's findings (13) substantiated this view. This investigator, by inoculating a combination of potato mosaic and tobacco mosaic virus into tobacco and tomato, obtained leaf spots and blotches which sometimes killed entire leaves. This suggested the possibility that the other factor for which the present author had been searching was potato mosaic.

Tomato mosaic and potato mosaic combined. Juices were expressed from potato plants infested with mosaic and from mosaic tomato plants. Healthy, vigorously-growing tomato plants were inoculated, some with potato mosaic virus, some with tomato mosaic, and others again with a mixture of these two juices. The complete series which has been tested twice in the field and twice in the greenhouse is summarized in table 6 [tables 2-5 have been deleted–Ed.].

The symptoms obtained when tomato mosaic and potato mosaic viruses were used were identical with those of tomato streak produced under similar conditions. Such symptoms did not develop in plants inoculated with tomato mosaic alone or potato mosaic alone. This streak derived from the combination virus could thereafter be transmitted to tomato plants.

These results at once opened up a new field of study. Since tomato and tobacco mosaic were known to be interchangeable, the latter was mixed with potato mosaic and the combination virus inoculated into tomato, with similar results as shown in table 6, exp. 3.

It also suggested the possibility of obtaining streak by inoculating mosaic tomato plants with potato mosaic, or, conversely, inoculating tomato mosaic into tomato plants which had three weeks previously been inoculated with potato mosaic. Accordingly, one of the plants of inoculation exp. 4, and one of exp. 5, table 6, were inoculated with potato mosaic three weeks after their first inoculation. At this time both plants showed definite mosaic symptoms only. Similarly, three weeks after the first inoculation, one of the plants of table 6, exp. 6, was inoculated with tomato mosaic. In all of these cases streak symptoms invariably developed 10-15 days after the second inoculation (table 6, exp. 8 and 9).

Further evidence that streak was caused by the combined viruses of tomato and potato mosaic was adduced when streak was obtained in mosaic tomato plants on which aphids from mosaic potato plants had been placed two to three weeks previously.

TABLE 6. *Effect of inoculating healthy tomato plants with a combination of potato and tomato viruses*

Experiment no.	No. of tomato plants inoculated	Inoculum	Results 11-15 days after inoculation[a]
1	2	Tomato streak	Mosaic + streak
2	4	Tomato mosaic + potato mosaic	Mosaic + streak
3	4	Tobacco mosaic + potato mosaic	Mosaic + streak
4	2		· Mosaic
5	2	Tobacco mosaic	Mosaic
6	2	Potato mosaic	No positive results
7	2	Control plants	Healthy throughout
8	2 mosaic plants	Potato mosaic	Mosaic + streak
9	2 plants inoculated 3 weeks previously with potato mosaic	Tomato or tobacco mosaic	Mosaic + streak

[a] Observations 4 weeks after inoculation showed no change.

Dried tomato streak material combined with potato mosaic. When streak tomato tissue, which was highly infectious when fresh, was dried for several months, then macerated and inoculated into tomato plants, mosaic only was produced. Potato mosaic virus was mixed with some of the macerated material and then inoculated into healthy tomato plants. This experiment was conducted both in the field and in the greenhouse with the results shown in table 7.

The symptoms which developed in all of the plants in table 7, exp. 2, were apparently identical with those produced on tomato plants with the fresh streak tomato material several months previously. From the above results it would appear, therefore, that the potato mosaic virus is the "factor" in the streak tomato material which was destroyed by drying.

Potato streak combined with tomato mosaic. In some recent preliminary experiments to ascertain if any relationship existed between potato and tomato streak, 8 tomato plants were inoculated with potato streak (from Spaulding Rose variety obtained from the Province of New Bruns-

TABLE 7. *Results of inoculating healthy tomato plants with macerated dried streak tomato tissue combined with potato mosaic*

Experiment number	Number of tomato plants inoculated	Inoculum	Results
1	4	Macerated dried streak tomato tissue	Severe mosaic only produced
2	4	Do + potato mosaic	Mosaic + spots on leaves and streaks on stem (streak)
3	2	Potato mosaic	A peculiar mottling, distinct from tomato mosaic, was evident in some cases

wick) and 8 with the combined viruses of potato streak and tomato mosaic. In the former case 5 of the plants produced a peculiar mottling distinct from true tomato mosaic, and 3 showed no apparent changes, whereas in the latter case, streak developed in all the plants. All controls remained healthy. Although only a few preliminary experiments have been attempted, the writer has been unable to produce streak in tomato from potato streak alone. The relationship between streak of potato and streak of tomato needs further elucidation.

A single series of inoculations have revealed the fact that the combined viruses of tomato and potato mosaic may be passed through tobacco and pepper, in both of which mosaic only develops, and yet produce streak on tomato. In other words, tobacco and pepper can act as intermediate hosts. Similar experiments with other Solanaceous plants are now in progress.

DISCUSSION

The results of the experiments embodied in this paper lead to the conclusion that streak disease of tomato at Macdonald College belongs to the "filterable virus" group of plant diseases.

The results show plainly that the disease is of a systemic nature, since leaves and fruit, themselves not visibly affected but coming from otherwise diseased plants, can be carriers of the inoculum. The presence of bacteria in the lesions could never be demonstrated definitely in stained sections. That bacteria are frequently found associated with mosaic tissue has been observed by other writers (14). A yellow bacterial organism, which is apparently identical with *Bacillus lathyri,* has repeatedly been isolated from streak lesions, but no further evidence has been obtained to show that it is other than secondary.

The fact that streak juice is still infectious after being passed through a bacteria-proof Chamberland F filter; after being subjected to a temperature of 70°C. for ten minutes; and finally, after being treated with strengths of mercuric chloride injurious to bacteria, for one to two days, definitely demonstrates that streak disease of tomato in Quebec is not of bacterial origin.

That the disease is not solely a physiological or malnutritional one is shown by its infectious nature. Even if tomato plants are grown under conditions which are recommended as preventive measures, and then inoculated with streak juice, streak will develop in nearly 100 per cent of these plants, although only minor symptoms will be evident in some cases. To date, all attempts on the part of the writer to produce the disease in healthy plants by manipulating the environment have failed. In cases where others have produced the disease at will, it is possible that the infective agent was latent in those plants only to become potent when conditions were favorable for its development.

All previous experimental work indicated that tomato mosaic was one of the chief, though apparently not the only, contributing cause of streak. On this continent the two diseases were invariably mentioned as being present in the same plant. The results of the experiments with the combination viruses reported herein very strongly indicate that potato mosaic is the other contributing factor. More work is necessary to determine whether other mosaic diseases may function as potato mosaic.

SUMMARY

The experimental studies reported herein, under both field and greenhouse conditions, show that:

(1) Bacteria, which are found associated with diseased lesions, are not the cause of tomato streak.

(2) The disease is highly infectious and can be transmitted from plant to plant by rubbing the leaves of healthy plants with the macerated tissue of diseased plants.

(3) The disease is of a systemic nature, since leaves not visibly affected are infectious.

(4) Streak tomato juice is still infectious after passage through a bacteria-proof filter, can usually withstand a temperature of 70°C. for 10 minutes without losing its infectivity, and can withstand concentration of mercuric chloride which readily destroys bacteria and fungous spores.

(5) Air-dried material soon becomes non-infectious.

(6) Fertilizer treatments alone cannot prevent the disease under all greenhouse conditions.

(7) Streak in Quebec has not been transmitted through the seed.

(8) Transmission by aphids has been proved.

(9) Failure has attended all attempts to induce the disease by manipulation of environmental factors.

(10) Excessive humidity, high temperature, and succulent growth are predisposing factors. Therefore control measures should consist of guarding against all predisposing factors, keeping the greenhouse free from all

volunteer Solanaceous plants, and treating regularly for insect carriers.

(11) Tobacco may serve as a carrier of streak.

(12) A combination of potato mosaic and tomato mosaic viruses, when inoculated into tomato, produces symptoms identical with those of true streak, and all evidence indicates that these combined viruses are the true cause of the trouble.

DEPARTMENT OF BOTANY,
MACDONALD COLLEGE,
McGILL UNIVERSITY,
P. Q., CANADA.

LITERATURE CITED

1. Allard, H. A. 1916. Some properties of the virus of the mosaic disease of tobacco. J. Agr. Res. 6: 649-674.

2. Atanasoff, D. 1925. New studies on stipple-streak disease of potato. Phytopathology. 15: 171-177.

3. Bailey, L. H. 1892. Some troubles of winter tomatoes. I. Winter blight. Cornell Univ. Agr. Exp. Sta. Bull. 43: 149-158.

4. Brittlebank, C. C. 1919. A new tomato disease. J. Dept. Agr. Victoria. 17: 231-235.

5. Clinton, G. P. 1915. Chlorosis of plants with special reference to calico of tobacco. Conn. Agr. Exp. Sta. Rept. 1914: 357-424.

6. Doolittle, S. P. 1920. The mosaic disease of cucurbits. U.S. Dept. Agr. Bull. 879: 1-69.

7. Gardner, Max W., and Kendrick, James W. 1922. Tomato mosaic. Indiana Agr. Exp. Sta. Bull. 261: 1-24.

8. Hamblin, C. O. 1921. Spotted wilt of tomatoes. Agr. Gaz. N. S. Wales. 32: 50.

9. Howitt, J. E., and Stone, R. E. 1916. A troublesome disease of winter tomatoes. Phytopathology. 6: 162-166.

10. Jackson, H. S. 1917. Tomato diseases. Purdue Univ. Agr. Exp. Sta. Ann. Rept. 30: 23.

11. Johnson, James. 1921. The relation of air temperature to certain plant diseases. Phytopathology. 11: 446-458.

12. Johnson, James. 1922. The relation of air temperature to the mosaic disease of potatoes and other plants. Phytopathology. 12: 438-440.

13. Johnson, James. 1925. A virus from potato transmissible to tobacco. Phytopathology. 15: 46. (Abstract.)

14. Melhus, I. E. 1922. Mosaic studies (Abstract). Phytopathology. 12: 42.

15. Orton, C. R. 1923. Seed-borne diseases. Amer. Seed Trade Assoc. 75-82.

16. Orton, C. R., and McKinney, W. H., Jr. 1915. Winter blight of the tomato. Ann. Rept. Pa. Agr. Exp. Sta. 1914-1915: 235-246.

17. Osborne, T. G. B. 1919. Two serious new wilt diseases. J. Dept. Agr. So. Australia 23: 437.

18. Paine, Sydney G., and Bewley, W. F. 1919. Studies in bacteriosis. IV. "Stripe" disease of tomato. Ann. Appl. Biol. **6:** 183-203.

19. Selby, A. D. 1896. A blight of forced tomatoes. Ohio Agr. Exp. Sta. Bull. **73:** 237-241.

20. Stone, R. E. December, 1924. Winter blight or streak of tomatoes. Paper read before the Canadian Phytopathological Society. (Unpublished.)

21. Taylor, W. H. 1923. Black stripe and its control. New Zeal. J. Agr. **26:** 101-103. (Abs. in Rev. Appl. Myc. **2:** 430.)

22. Tomkins, C. M. 1925. Effect of intermittent temperatures on potato mosaic (Abstract). Phytopathology. **15:** 46.

1926

On a New Disease of the Nucleus
or Jaundice of the Larvae
of *Pieris Brassicae* and a New Group
# of Parasitic Microorganisms[1]

Note[2] of A. Paillot, presented by P. Marchal

This paper represents one of many reports by Paillot who contributed much fundamental information on the nature and pathology of insect virus diseases. He describes for the first time a new group of diseases, the granuloses, which are characterized by the formation of virus inclusion bodies called "granules" within tissues of the infected insect. The characteristic pathological condition was discovered in virus-infected larva of the European cabbage butterfly, Pieris brassicae. *Because the disease, in some aspects, reminded him of the polyhedral disease, silkworm jaundice, he referred to it as* grasserie. *Later, Paillot reported the discovery of granules in larvae of the cutworm* Agrotis segetum *and in other insects.*[3]

The granuloses were recognized as a major category of insect diseases with the discovery of granules in the variegated cutworm, Peridroma margaritosa *by Steinhaus.*[4] *The viral etiology of the granuloses was established by Bergold who demonstrated also that the granular virus inclusions were actually capsular in shape.*[5] *The term "capsular diseases" has been used now synonymously with granuloses.*

---

[1] Translated and reprinted by publisher's permission from Compt. Rend. Acad. Sci. **182:** 180-182 (1926).

[2] Session of 4 January 1926.

[3] Paillot, C. R. Acad. Sci. **198:** 204 (1934); **205:** 1264 (1937).

[4] Science. **106:** 323 (1947).

[5] Bergold, Z. Naturforsch. **36:** 388 (1948).

$\mathbb{W}$e described in 1924 [6] a new disease of the larva of *Pieris brassicae* characterized, from the cytological point of view, by the destruction of certain cell nuclei and the transformation of refractivity of the chondrin substance, without definite structure and of very irregular shapes; we showed that this disease was caused by microorganisms visible only in the ultramicroscope and similar to the one of silkworm jaundice.

We discovered recently a new disease of Pieride larva that is related to the nuclear diseases by its characteristic etiology and histo-cytopathological lesions. Diseased larva are identified by the whitish-yellow color of the ventral part of the body; at the time of death, the skin tears very easily and milky liquid flows out similar in aspect to that of the silkworm stricken with jaundice. The blood of larva is a little turbid in the advance state of infection and of very distinct fluorescence; if one examines it with the ultramicroscope, one sees numerous very brilliant granules kept in motion by Brownian movement. These granules are seen in the most extreme strength of the microscope; but, after dyeing with Ziehl's hot phenolic fuchsin, one distinguishes them very readily, at the same strength of 1000 diameters; they appear as very small cocci 0.2 to 0.3 microns in diameter; they multiply like ordinary micrococci and present certain morphological analogies with the pleuropneumonia organism of cattle that were considered, up to now, like some filterable viruses which are actually accessible to microscopic investigation.

The virus of Pierides does not appear to multiply in the blood, but only in the cytoplasm of adipose cells and hypodermis where it is easy to see with the ultramicroscope.

Histo-cytopathological studies of the lesions from pieces fixed by Duboscq-Brasil mixture, or, by the methods for fixing mitachondria, allows easy differentiation of the disease infecting larva from other diseases of the same type. After fixation with Duboscq-Brasil mixture and dyeing with eosin-hematin or with Heidenhain's iron-hematoxylin, adipose cells and hypodermis show the following characteristics; the nucleus is very hypertrophied; the chondrin takes on a lacquered appearance; and the nucleoli break up into bodies of very irregular form and size and are forced out to the periphery of the nucleus; to end the process of disorganization, the nucleus appears as a dot without apparent structure, hardly dyed to pale grey by iron-hematoxylin.

After fixation with Regaud's mixture or with hot formal saline, postchromatinization and dyeing according to Kull's method, one sees similar nuclear changes; the chondrin, little changed, invade the whole nuclear region.

Jaundice of Pierides is very contagious; transmission from individual

[6] Compt. Rend. Acad. Sci. **179:** 1353 (1924).

to individual is caused through the digestive passage. It does not appear to play an important part in the destruction of Pierides in nature.

The characteristic pathology of the jaundice of Pierides allows this illness to rank in the category of nuclear diseases of which one knows of two other types; the polyhedral diseases of *Bombycides* and the nuclear diseases of *Pieris brassicae*. The conspicuousness of the parasite by ordinary means constitutes a new argument in favor of the thesis that we continue to identify the ultramicroscopic granules seen in silkworm jaundice and in the nuclear disease of Pierides, with the parasitic elements of these diseases. These different microorganisms are characterized by their very reduced dimensions, by their great parasitic specificity that is exercised, not only with respect to the host, but also to the cells of the latter. They are all endocellular parasites; they are closer thus to the Sporozoa, but the existence of different stages of development has not been demonstrated. They are able, like the bacteria, on inoculation in the general cavity, to incite the morbid process characteristic of the disease; but they are differentiated by their method of existence. We believe it is possible to rank them in an intermediate group between the bacteria and the protozoa and we proposed to give the genera the name *Borrellina*. The parasite of silkworm jaundice was named *B. bombycis;* the one of Pierides jaundice, *B. brassicae* and the one of the other nuclear disease of the same insect, *B. pieris.* Prowazek believed erroneously that the endonuclear parasites seen in the silkworm stricken with jaundice ought to be in the group of Protozoa to which he gave the name Chlamydozoa; but our observations in the ultramicroscope nullify certain of the most important observations of Prowazek. The parasite of Pierides jaundice, no more than any of the other nuclear diseases, is not justified for inclusion in the Chlamydozoa group.

The specific characteristics of *Borrellina* are the following: *B. bombycis:* elements less than 0.1 micron diameter, intranuclear, provokes the transformation of chromatin into polyhedral bodies of a general hexagonal form.

B. pieris: elements less than 0.1 micron diameter, intracytoplasmic, provokes the formation, at the expense of chondrin, hylaine bodies of irregular shape and size.

B. brassicae: cocciform elements of 0.2 to 0.3 micron diameter, intracytoplasmic, causing hypertrophy of nucleus and its destruction without provoking characteristic changes of the nucleus.

1929

Observations on
a Permanently Lysogenic Strain
of *B. Enteritidis Gaertner*[1]

by F. M. Burnet and Margot McKie

(From the Walter and Eliza Hall Institute, Melbourne)

One of the first descriptions of lysogeny, later defined as the hereditary power to produce bacteriophage in the absence of infection, was reported by Bordet and Ciuca.[2] They used the term "lysogenic" to describe bacteria which released bacteriophage and give rise to lysis of sensitive bacteria. Strains of bacteria were established, subsequently, which maintained the lysogenic property in the absence of free bacteriophage. The true nature of lysogeny and its significance was not realized for many years although it was the subject of intense polemics.

An insight into the basic mechanism of lysogeny was advanced by Burnet and McKie. They attributed the permanency of the lysogenic character in bacteria to the presence of a unit called "anlage" which is capable of liberating bacteriophage. The anlage or lytic principle is a normal hereditary constituent of lysogenic bacteria and, unless activated, no liberation of bacteriophage results from the disruption of the host cell. This important concept was confirmed with the rediscovery of lysogeny by Lwoff and Gutmann.[3] The hereditary determinant of lysogeny was established as a "prophage" or "provirus" which is a reduced state of the phage genome on integration into the host nucleus. The realization that lysogeny involved an intimate interaction between viruses and host cells was rapidly exploited as a new mechanism for genetic studies at the molecular level.

[1] Reprinted by permission of the author and publisher from The Australian J. Exper. Biol. Med. Sci. **6:** 277-284 (1929).

[2] C. R. Soc. Biol. **84:** 276 (1921).

[3] Ann. Inst. Pasteur. **78:** 711 (1950).

The most disputed points in the current controversies as to the nature of bacteriophage are probably (1) the possibility of procuring phage from normal bacteria, and (2) the status of permanently lysogenic bacteria. The two subjects are obviously closely related. According to some writers there is no sharp line to be drawn between normal and lysogenic strains, all bacteria being potentially lysogenic, and differing only in the ease with which a liberated phage can be recognized. In his most recent discussion of phage theory Bordet (1928) lays great stress on the significance of naturally lysogenic strains, which he regards as primitive forms, producing more or less accidentally a principle which, innocuous to the producing strain, provokes typical bacteriophage lysis when it comes into contact with certain other more sensitive bacteria. The present note is concerned with one of these naturally and permanently lysogenic strains of bacteria.

The strain (B.T.M.) has been fully described previously (Burnet, 1929). It was received as a rough motile strain of *B. enteritidis,* showing the typical antigenic constitution of such strains, though in its physical characteristics less typically "rough" than usual. By methods which have been described previously, a large range of variants was derived from this culture, including forms with the four chief antigenic structures smooth motile (HO), smooth non-motile (O), rough motile (HR), and rough non-motile (R).

The original HR form produced in broth cultures a phage that could be detected by its action on a smooth strain of *B. sanguinarium* (NCTC 398S). In most experiments a 24-hour broth culture of the lysogenic strain was heated to 57° for 30 minutes, and the heated culture was then titrated by spreading known dilutions on an agar plate previously inoculated with *B. sanguinarium.* Perfectly typical bacteriophage lysis occurred, and the phage produced could be carried on indefinitely in broth cultures of strain 398S.

If a single colony of the original strain was added to a tube of broth, and incubated for 24 hours, titration showed approximately 2×10^6 plaques per c.cm. The smooth derivatives were considerably less active, showing roughly 2-3,000 plaques per c.cm. These estimations were made in England in 1927. Eighteen months later a fresh series of experiments was commenced in Australia. Despite numerous subcultures the two types still showed the same general activity.

The four stock cultures (HO, HR, O, and R) were replated from broth. The HO plate showed some irregularities amongst the colonies, and five more or less distinguishable types were picked off. The other plates appeared uniform, and two colonies of each were isolated. Amongst the cultures from HO, one was a rough non-motile variant, and one showed open lysogenicity by producing nibbled colonies. These were dis-

carded. All the other cultures showed permanent characters of the type
to be expected from their antigenic constitution.

The lysogenic power of seven such cultures (three HO forms, two O
forms, and one each of HR and R) was tested for six successive generations. An isolated colony was picked off into broth. From this a fresh
plating was made immediately, and the broth tube then incubated for
20 hours. The culture was then heated to 55° for 30 minutes, and titrated
on plates spread with *B. sanguinarium*. The process was then repeated
with each replating.

The successive titrations are combined in figure 1, which shows the
number of plaques per c.cm. produced at each generation. The two O
strains behaved in almost identical fashion, and one is omitted to avoid
choking the figure.

It can be seen at once that the cultures fall into two groups. The
rough strains and one smooth motile strain produce around 10⁷ plaques
per c.cm. at each generation. The bulk of the smooth strains give rise to

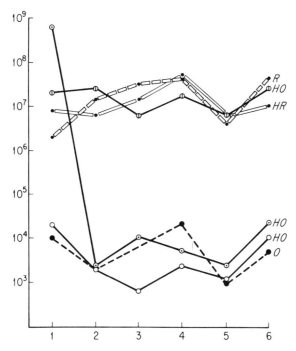

Fig. 1. The production of phage by successive generations of the various antigenic types of strain
B.T.M. The number of phage particles per c.cm. of
a 24-hour broth culture is shown for six successive
isolations from single colonies of six variants of the
antigenic constitutions shown.

only a few thousand plaques per c.cm. The findings are practically constant at each isolation.

The aberrant behaviour of the strain HO₃ is clearly due to the fact that the first colony tested was in an unstable actively lysogenic state. Subsequent generations were composed of organisms in the stable condition. The actively lysogenic nibbled colony included in the first isolation and discarded had a still higher titre, showing over 10^{10} plaques per c.cm.

In addition to the four classical antigenic varieties described, an extensive series of other variants of this strain was tested for lysogenic power. The following strains gave in broth culture titres around 10^7 per c.cm.:

(a) Eight specifically resistant rough strains derived by the action of various phages.
(b) A cohesive variant, giving tough, dry, wrinkled, colonies on agar, and forming a pellicle in broth, antigenically HR.
(c) A mucoid variant antigenically R.
(d) Another mucoid variant showing a secondary lysogenic power (see below).

The following showed the lower degree of lysogenesis (10^3 to 10^4 plaques per c.cm.):

(e) Two smooth specifically resistant variants produced by phage action.
(f) A cohesive pellicle-forming variant antigenically HO.
(g) Smooth HO and O forms recovered after animal passage.

The strains tested therefore include practically every variant type that has ever been described amongst the Salmonella group. Every single colony that has been tested has shown definite lysogenic activity. It is evident that the lysogenic function in this case is characteristic of every cell in the culture, and presumably is intimately related to some of the most permanent of the cell's activities.

THE LIBERATION OF PHAGE FROM A LYSOGENIC CULTURE

The phage produced by this strain can be propagated only at the expense of certain smooth Salmonella strains. It has never shown the slightest activity on any rough culture. Yet the rough form of BTM produces much more of the phage than the average smooth form. This suggests at once that the liberation of phage is by some totally different process from that occurring in ordinary lysis.

There is not much work reported on this subject. Gildemeister and Herzberg (1924) found with their strain Coli 88 that phage was produced more or less parallel with the growth of the culture, except at low temperatures. At 9°C. growth of the organism took place, but no liberation of phage. Flu (1925), however, working with the same strain, found that phage was produced to some degree under all conditions that allowed growth of the lysogenic strain to occur. Both would agree that any phage production that occurs takes place during bacterial multiplication. The following experiments show that this is not necessarily the case with the lysogenic strain BTM-HR.

Experiment 1: Two agar plate cultures of BTM-HR, grown for 20 hours at 37°, were scraped off with a glass rod and emulsified in 12 c.cm. of normal saline. Five c.cm. of the emulsion were measured into each of two centrifuge tubes, and the tubes centrifuged for 20 minutes at about 2,500 revolutions. The supernatant fluid was removed and set aside for titration. The deposit, drained as completely as possible of fluid, was then re-emulsified in 5 c.cm. of the liquid to be tested, which had been previously warmed to 37°. The mixtures were placed in the incubator for half an hour, and were stirred at intervals. They were then centrifuged for 20 minutes, the supernatant fluid put aside for titration, and the whole process repeated as often as required.

The supernatant fluids as they were obtained were heated to 55° in a water-bath for 30 minutes, cooled rapidly, and titrated in duplicate by plating suitable dilutions on agar, spread with the sensitive indicator strain 398S. Plaque counts were made on the following day. The results of two experiments, in which distilled water, 2% sodium chloride solution, and 2% calcium chloride solution were used, are tabulated. The figures are calculated from the average of two counts at the most convenient dilution. The duplicates agreed in nearly all cases to within 10%.

TABLE 1. *Showing number of phage particles per c.cm. liberated at successive washings of BTM-HR*

A.

1st washing	Normal saline	16,700,000		
2nd washing	Distilled water	9,760,000	2% saline	4,300,000
3rd washing	Distilled water	2,510,000	2% saline	750,000
4th washing	Distilled water	521,000	2% saline	708,000
5th washing	Distilled water	148,000	2% saline	751,000

B.

1st washing	Normal saline	56,800,000		
2nd washing	2% saline	2,290,000	2% CaCl₂	4,590,000
3rd washing	2% saline	1,540,000	2% CaCl₂	2,466,000
4th washing	2% saline	418,000	2% CaCl₂	609,000
5th washing	Distilled water	4,100,000	Distilled water	1,620,000

Somewhat larger amounts of phage were liberated when the bacteria were washed in the same way with broth, but since in these experiments there was a possibility of multiplication occurring no stress can be laid on the finding. But the findings tabulated show unequivocally that phage can be liberated in considerable amount by resting bacteria in non-nutritive media. An examination of the table, particularly of Experiment B, suggests that there is only a limited proportion of the bacteria present that can liberate phage under these conditions. Omitting the first washing from consideration, the four subsequent washings gave in each case between 40 and 50 million particles. The smaller initial liberation by the sodium chloride solution was balanced by the larger yield with the final washing in distilled water.

If the phage particles are pre-existent within the lysogenic bacteria one might expect them to be liberated when lysis by some unrelated phage occurred. It was possible to investigate this with the strain BTM-R, since a phage (No. 13) was available, capable of lysing this strain, but completely without action on the indicator strain, *B. sanguinarium,* used to detect the homologous phage.

Experiment 2. The following cultures were grown in broth:

(a) BTM-R alone.
(b) BTM-R plus a loopful of phage 13.
(c) A rough non-lysogenic strain (Wa R), also sensitive to phage 13, plus a loopful of this phage.

These were incubated overnight, and then heated to 55° for half an hour. They were then titrated for phage content on a rough strain sensitive to phage 13, and on the smooth *B. sanguinarium.* The titres on the smooth strain were:

(a) BTM-R alone: 2,200,000 particles.
(b) BTM-R + phage 13: 530,000 particles.
(c) Wa R + phage 13: Nil.

Both (b) and (c) showed the presence of phage 13 in its usual amount.

Lysis by an unrelated phage thus diminishes the amount of homologous phage liberated, and there is no evidence that the intrinsic phage exists within the lysogenic bacteria as an independent unit.

Amongst the resistant colonies obtained after lysis of strain BTM-R by phage 13 was a mucoid lysogenic variant. If this was subcultured directly on McConkey's medium it remained fairly stable, but when transferred to broth and plated after incubation gave a mixture of smooth and rough colonies. The broth contained a large amount of phage 13, and when titrated on *B. sanguinarium* showed 1,900,000 particles per c.cm. The mucoid colonies were thus doubly lysogenic, but the coexistence of another lysogenic function made no appreciable difference to the "normal" lysogenic activity.

DISCUSSION

The chief interest of the present observations concerns the rather striking differences in the production of phage on the one hand by permanently lysogenic strains, and on the other by normal strains under the influence of extrinsic lysis.

The strain described maintains its lysogenic power unaffected through almost all the variations of antigenic structure and mode of growth possible for its species. If the lysogenic power is quantitatively estimated the variants fall into two groups. All the rough strains tested and one smooth culture produced a large amount of phage (around 10^7 particles per c.cm.). The rest of the smooth strains all gave a few thousand particles per c.cm., with the exception of one culture, which was unstable, and showed evidence of frank lysogenesis (nibbled colonies). This naturally gave a very high titre of liberated phage. When the specific phage involved is tested for its action on a wide range of bacteria it is found to lyse actively, smooth *sanguinarium* and *pullorum* strains, and less regularly many smooth *typhosus* and *enteritidis* cultures. No derivative of the phage has ever shown the slightest action on any rough strain.

If we consider only the smooth phase the strain behaves exactly as the lysogenic coli strain L, originally described by Lisbonne and Carrère (1922), and extensively studied by Bordet and Renaux (1928). There is a more or less standard degree of lysogenesis, but individual colonies vary considerably, some producing so much phage as to cause frank lysis of part of the culture. Such results are compatible with the view that there is an unstably balanced struggle between phage and bacterium, a very small proportion of the bacteria always undergoing lysis of the ordinary type. But the relatively high lysogenic capacity of rough strains cannot be explained on this view, since the phage produced is incapable of lysing any rough cultures. The liberation of phage here must be determined entirely by internal factors uninfluenced by the presence of phage in the medium. It is a natural corollary from this to assume that the phage production of smooth cultures in the stable state is also a manifestation of internal conditions, rather than the result of a balanced external antagonism.

The permanence of the lysogenic character makes it necessary to assume the presence of bacteriophage or its *anlage* in every cell of the culture, i.e., it is part of the hereditary constitution of the strain. The conditions under which this *anlage* is liberated or activated are extremely obscure. The experiments described above, in which phage was obtained by washing bacteria with non-nutrient solutions, show that the liberation is not necessarily associated with growth. Distilled water was particularly effective in liberating phage, even after the bacteria had been four times washed with saline solutions. This suggests that the phage particles are preformed within the bacteria, and diffuse out when the bacteria are swollen or disrupted by imbibition of water. Against this view is the fact that no excess of the intrinsic phage is liberated when the bacteria are lysed by an unrelated extrinsic phage. The numbers of bacteria used in the washing experiments were, however, very much greater than those involved in the second type of experiment, and it is likely that only a small percentage of the bacteria (about 0.1% from the data available) are capable of liberating phage when treated with distilled water. Even if all this was liberated by extrinsic lysis the experimental methods available would probably fail to show any definite increase.

The conclusion we arrive at, therefore, is somewhat as follows: All bacteria of this permanently lysogenic type contain in their hereditary constitution a unit potentially capable of liberating phage. In a proportion (perhaps about 0.1% in day-old agar cultures) phage is actually present within the bacteria, and can be liberated by treatment with distilled water. Phage may also be liberated, presumably from bacteria of this group, during the normal processes of growth. The evidence further suggests that unless the activation of the heritable *anlage* takes place spontaneously, disruption of the cell by any means will not liberate phage. The essentials of the process seem to take place entirely within the cell. There seems to be no evidence available as to what determines whether or not intracellular activation will occur. The conditions are probably analogous to those concerned in such inorganic processes as monomolecular reactions or radioactive disintegrations.

These observations are in entire accord with the view put forward by Bordet and Renaux, that in these cases the lytic principle (or its *anlage*) is a normal (i.e., physiologically co-ordinated) constituent of the bacterium, which spontaneously secretes it without injury to itself. But as Bordet and Renaux also point out, its must not be assumed from this that the ordinary process of phage multiplication on sensitive bacteria is of the same nature.

Liberation of phage from a permanently lysogenic strain depends entirely on intracellular changes; it is essentially uninfluenced by changes in the antigenic structure of the strain or by lysis with extrinsic phages. In a strictly limited sense it is possible to liberate phage in considerable amount from bacteria that are not growing.

Classical bacteriophage lysis, on the other hand, is primarily dependent on the nature of the phage used, it is greatly influenced by changes in the antigenic structure of the bacterial strain, and liberation of phage can only be obtained with actively growing bacteria.

In the first case we have the bacteriophage unit physiologically co-ordinated in the hereditary constitution of the bacterial strain, but liberated into the medium under certain obscure conditions. Toward a sensitive bacterium this same unit behaves as a predatory entity, which becomes specifically adsorbed to the surface, and multiplies genetically within the bacterial cell, which it eventually destroys.

The difficulty of reconciling these two aspects of bacteriophage phenomena has been responsible for all the current controversy on the intimate nature of phage, whether it is an independent parasite or a pathologically altered constituent of normal bacteria. In our view both these contentions have been completely proved, and the current attitude on both sides of regarding them as irreconcilable alternatives is quite unjustified. According to the particular type of bacterium that is reacting with the phage concerned, it may be useful and convenient to regard the phage as an independent parasite or as a unit liberated from the hereditary constitution of some bacterium, the usage being determined wholly by its functional activity at the time.

SUMMARY

1. A permanently lysogenic strain of *B. enteritidis* Gaertner is described.

2. Practically every known variant of this species was tested, and all showed characteristic lysogenic activity.

3. Rough strains liberated more phage than the majority of smooth cultures.

4. Successive amounts of phage can be liberated from washed lysogenic bacteria in the presumed absence of bacterial multiplication.

REFERENCES

Bordet, J., and Renaux, E. 1928. Ann. Inst. Pasteur. **42:** 1283.

Burnet, F. M. 1929. J. Path. and Bact. **32:** 15.

Flu, P. C. 1925. Centralbl. f. Bakt., &c., I Orig. **97:** 1.

Gildemeister, E., and Herzberg, K. 1924. Centralbl. f. Bakt., I Orig. **93:** 402.

Lisbonne, M., and Carrère, L. 1922. C.R. Soc. Biol. **86:** 569.

1929

Local Lesions in Tobacco Mosaic[1]

by Francis O. Holmes[2]

The demonstration of a rational method for the quantitation of plant virus infectivity was a powerful tool that facilitated progress on plant viruses. Although McKinney[3] described a means of measuring the concentration of tobacco mosaic virus by using single tobacco plants as units of infection, the technique demonstrated by Holmes had the qualities of practicality and accuracy. Holmes suggested the use of local lesions for measuring virus infectivity which permitted several assays to be performed on one plant. These lesions are visible injuries caused by virus particles entering an inoculated leaf, infecting it, and multiplying around the point of entry. He demonstrated that the number of lesions developing on the plant leaves was dependent on the virus concentration of the inoculum. The local lesion became the principal unit for measuring virus infectivity. The method was relied on heavily by plant virus investigators, and it proved particularly valuable in work on virus purification.

INTRODUCTION

The literature concerned with the virus diseases of plants repeatedly emphasizes the systemic nature of these infections. Mayer (6), in his original description of tobacco mosaic in

[1] Contributions from the Boyce Thompson Institute for Plant Research, Inc., Yonkers, N.Y., published at the expense of the Institute out of the order determined by the date of receipt of the manuscript.

[2] Reprinted by permission of the author and the publisher, University of Chicago Press, from Bot. Gaz. 87 (1): 39-55 (1929). This paper appeared also in Contributions from Boyce Thompson Institute. 1: 504-520 (1929).

[3] J. Agr. Res. 35: 13 (1927).

1886, stated that symptoms do not develop on the leaf inoculated, but appear on all of the young developing leaves. Essentially the same account of the course of the disease was given by *Beijerinck* (2) in 1898, by *Iwanowski* (5) in 1903, by *Allard* (1) in 1914, and by others in more recent years.

No detailed descriptions of local lesions developing at the points where tobacco mosaic virus has been introduced have been published. This has probably been due in part to the fact that the local lesions are not conspicuous in commercial tobacco, *Nicotiana tabacum,* which has been used extensively. Another factor which has made the recognition of the local development of the disease more difficult has been the practice of inoculation by scratching and severe wounding. This tends to obscure the primary lesions by producing dead areas mechanically.

A few references in the literature indicate that local lesions have been observed, although their real nature has not been understood. *Allard* (1) referred to *N. langsdorffii* as follows:

Plants of this species when inoculated through the stalk and petioles seem particularly susceptible to a very destructive and progressive rot, which begins at the point of inoculation and finally kills the plant by slowly involving the surrounding tissues. *Nicotiana viscosum* (*N. glutinosa*) is sometimes killed in exactly the same manner. *Fernow* (3) said of *N. rustica:* "The leaves generally turn yellow and then brown near each point of inoculation." The briefness of these references to the local lesions developing at the site of inoculation with tobacco mosaic virus indicates that these lesions were not recognized as symptoms of the disease.

There is in the literature one account of a plant virus which produces lesions at the point of inoculation. This is the virus of ring-spot of tobacco, which *Priode* (7) describes as forming typical rings of necrotic tissues around needle punctures used to introduce it into tobacco and petunia. These local lesions are exactly like the lesions later produced when the disease becomes systemic; but tobacco mosaic has never been shown to act in this way. Most writers have specifically stated or implied that the inoculated leaf if fully developed never shows symptoms of the infection.

In the present paper the local lesions caused by the introduction of tobacco mosaic virus into the tissues of a number of *Nicotiana* species will be described, and the usefulness of these lesions in measuring the concentration of mosaic virus samples will be shown.

In a former paper (4) the writer has described a method of inoculating plants by means of very small needle punctures. This method is well suited to the demonstration of the occurrence of local lesions. The absence of extensive dead tissue around such needle punctures when transmission does not take place makes the slightest deviation from the normal condition of the leaf tissues conspicuous. The present study was undertaken because evidence was obtained that changes take place at the site of inoculation of tobacco mosaic virus into *N. tabacum*. In this plant it was noticed that pale yellow areas sometimes develop around one or more of the five pin pricks made in each plant. Since in some cases a very dilute virus was being measured, not many plants were expected to take the disease. This fact made the pale yellow areas particularly noticeable, and led to a later examination of the plants which showed them. It was found that every plant which showed such local changes around one or more of the pin pricks developed mottling within a few days. Most of the plants which did not show pale yellow areas near the inoculation punctures remained healthy. This suggested that these yellow areas might represent localized symptoms of a primary infection, since they were consistently followed by the familiar systemic symptoms. Unfortunately the pale yellow areas were very inconspicuous and could not be detected in all cases in which systemic symptoms developed.

It seemed possible that some species of *Nicotiana* might show local symptoms more conspicuously and more consistently than *N. tabacum*. A survey of a number of species[4] was therefore made. These were *N. rustica, N. trigonophylla, N. plumbaginifolia, N. longiflora, N. tomentosa, N. suaveolens, N. quadrivalvis, N. paniculata, N. sylvestris, N. sanderae, N. glutinosa, N. nudicaulis, N. langsdorffii, N. clevelandii, N. acuminata, N. glauca,* and *N. multivalvis*. Of these species, five showed pronounced necrotic local lesions instead of pale yellow areas. These species were *N. rustica, N. langsdorffii, N. acuminata, N. sanderae,* and *N. glutinosa*. A description of the local lesions in each of these five species follows.

In *N. rustica*, as in all of the species studies, pin pricks which fail to transmit the virus heal perfectly with no macroscopic trace of necrosis; successful transfers, on the other hand, are marked by necrotic spots. These are easily counted eight to ten days after the time of inoculation, and may be distinguished even when many are on the same leaf (fig. 1). These necrotic spots on *N. rustica* are brown in color, circular in some cases, but frequently irregular in outline. They increase slowly in size during the first week after they appear. Later they spread rapidly, especially in young leaves. They may involve a considerable area of the leaf surface before the leaf concerned becomes old and drops off.

The lesions on *N. langsdorffii* (fig. 2) and *N. sanderae* (fig. 3) are more conspicuous than those on *N. rustica*, because they are blackish with concentric rings of dead tissue. They grow larger day by day after their first appearance, and may become very extensive. Sometimes veins and

[4] Thanks are due to Dr. S. A. Wingard of the Virginia Agricultural Experiment Station, Dr. R. E. Clausen of the University of California, and Dr. E. M. East of the Bussey Institution, Forest Hills, Massachusetts, for their kindness in supplying seeds of these species.

even the stem of the plant are involved in the slowly spreading necrosis of the tissues.

In *N. acuminata* (fig. 4) the lesions are irregular in outline and brown in color. They appear one or two weeks after the introduction of the virus, and increase in size rather more slowly than is the case in the other species.

N. glutinosa exhibits a very different response (fig. 5). The lesions begin to be noticeable on the second or third day and are all completely formed by the fifth day, when in other species the first indications of breakdown appear. These rapidly developing necrotic lesions appear first

Figs. 1-5. Local necrotic lesions in (1) *N. rustica,* (2) *N. langsdorffii,* (3) *N. sanderae,* (4) *N. acuminata,* (5) *N. glutinosa*. Lesions in *N. rustica* and *N. acuminata* are brown, in *N. langsdorffii* and *N. sanderae* almost black, and in *N. glutinosa* pale brown surrounded by rings of darker brown.

as tiny glistening dark spots. The centers soon dry down and develop a light brown color. Around them darker brown rings form concentrically. This gives the lesions an easily recognized appearance not to be confused with other dead spots in the leaves.

In order to discover whether these necrotic local lesions consistently appear whenever a successful transfer of the mosaic virus is accomplished, a test with small *N. rustica* plants was arranged. In a number of experiments each plant was inoculated with a single pin prick in a young leaf. The inoculation was carried out with a no. 00 black enamel insect pin previously wet with juice from a mosaic leaf of commercial tobacco. Altogether 582 plants were thus inoculated. Of these, 136 took the disease, as shown by the development of the severe systemic symptoms characteristic for this species. Every one of these plants showed a local necrotic lesion at the site of inoculation. These lesions were similar to those shown in fig. 1, except that there was but one on each plant. The fact that every plant which took the disease showed a local lesion is evidence that the local lesion is a definite symptom of the mosaic. Six plants in the series showed local lesions without a later development of the systemic disease. Apparently the virus was not able to spread in these individual cases. Their number is so small, however, that the diagnosis of transfer of the disease is not much changed if local lesions are taken as evidence of the transfer without waiting to examine the later systemic symptoms. Later experiments, in which more than one pin prick was used for each plant, have substantiated these conclusions.

Further evidence that the successful transfer of virus can be detected by examination of the local necrotic lesions is afforded by the fact that concentrated virus samples cause the development of large numbers of these local lesions when they are used as inoculum, whereas known dilutions of the virus samples in water cause the development of smaller numbers of the lesions. Graphs showing the accuracy with which the numbers of lesions are dependent upon the known concentrations of virus samples will be presented later in this paper, when the use of the local lesions in measuring virus concentrations is discussed.

No bacteria or other visible microorganisms have been found upon microscopical examination of the local lesions. Fluids from plants not affected with mosaic do not produce the lesions when used as inoculum. Yet it appeared that formal experiments ought to be carried out with virus suspensions free of bacteria to show that the production of the lesions was not due to the introduction of foreign organisms. Three samples of virus were therefore prepared by adding large numbers of a small bacterium, *Aplanobacter michiganensis,* to virus previously diluted with seven volumes of water. These three samples were then passed through Berkefeld W filter candles. The bacteria were entirely removed from the mixture, as was shown by plating from the filtrates. The virus passed through the filter with no observable decrease in its concentration. The lesions developing on *N. glutinosa* plants inoculated with these sterile filtrates were identical in appearance with those produced by the use of unfiltered samples of virus.

In further support of the view that the virus of mosaic itself is responsible for the production of these local lesions, it may be stated that exactly similar lesions have been produced by the use of a virus sample which had been frozen solid for three years, and by the use of several field samples of virus collected at widely separated points. It is improbable that any sound virus or any other organism would be so closely associated with tobacco mosaic virus as to be present in each of these cases.

In order to prove beyond doubt that the lesions are not caused by any foreign organism, they should be produced in a sterile plant by the use of virus freed from bacteria. But the fact that the test plants are grown in sterilized soil from seeds seems sufficient protection against the presence of any organisms on their surface, especially as the individual plants are invariably capable of showing the lesions.

USE OF LOCAL LESIONS IN MEASURING VIRUS CONCENTRATIONS

It has long been the custom to use the appearance of the systemic disease in *N. tabacum* plants as an indicator of the successful transfer of virus from mosaic plants or extracts from them. Several methods of this kind are in use for the more or less accurate measurement of the relative concentrations of mosaic virus in different samples. In such work a whole plant is necessary for each successful transfer. As the accuracy of the measurement depends largely upon the number of successful transfers, the numbers of plants required usually prove a limiting factor in the number of measurements which can be made. Obviously it would be a great advantage if many successful transfers could be distinguished on a single plant or even on a single leaf. This advantage is given by the use of the local necrotic lesions here described.

It has been found that the number of successful transmissions of virus can be learned by counting the local necrotic spots at the points of inoculation in such species as *N. rustica* and *N. glutinosa* as well as by using whole plants as indicators. Moreover, since the lesions appear locally before systemic symptoms appear, economy of time is secured.

Since *N. rustica* offers the advantage of very large leaves, a method of using it for measuring virus concentrations will first be described. Dilution curves and a discussion of the accuracy attainable will be given. *N. glutinosa* has proved of great value, because on it necrotic lesions, which can readily be counted, appear very soon after inoculation. The disease may be transmitted by wiping the leaf surface gently with a cloth saturated in virus extract.

In *N. rustica* lesions are most readily counted when produced by pin prick punctures. A set of five insect pins held in a temporary handle has usually been used by the writer for introducing the virus. The pins are alternately dipped in a sample of virus and used to puncture the test plant leaf. In this way large numbers of punctures are rapidly made in a series of leaves. Usually each leaf will accommodate 250 or 500 punctures. The number of necrotic lesions developing is small in comparison with the number of punctures, but is sufficient to allow a fairly accurate reading of virus strength to be made with a few plants. In fig. 1 a leaf inoculated as described is shown. It is necessary to make inoculations of samples on opposite sides of the midvein of the same leaf or to use a large number of leaves for a single test. This is because leaves of different ages have been found to differ somewhat in susceptibility. In general the younger leaves are the more susceptible.

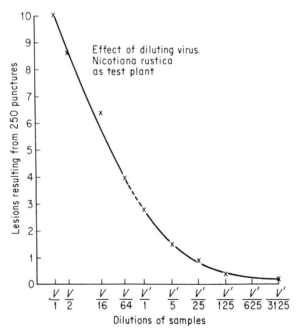

Fig. 6. Effect of diluting virus when *N. rustica* is used as test plant. Two samples of virus, V and V', used in obtaining the data represented. Virus V was more concentrated than virus V', which was exceptionally weak. The lesions resulting from 38,000 pin prick punctures are represented by the nine points determining the curve.

A curve showing the effect of dilution over a considerable range of virus concentrations is presented in fig. 6. The graph is based upon two series of experiments, one with a mosaic virus of usual strength and one with a weak sample. Thirty-eight thousand punctures were made to obtain the transfers represented by the figure. It will be observed that in the region in which four to ten lesions were obtained in each set of 250 punctures, the line appears nearly straight as drawn to a semilogarithmic scale. This part of the curve is similar to that known from earlier work with commercial tobacco. It is interesting to note the direction of the line when more dilute virus is used. With *N. rustica* it has been possible to study the lower range, because greater numbers of measurements can be made by the use of local lesions than by the use of the systemic disease as an indicator of successful transmission. The upper range is the portion most frequently dealt with, and the range in which the greatest accuracy can be obtained.

NICOTIANA GLUTINOSA AS TEST PLANT

The characteristics of *N. glutinosa* make it a very useful test plant for measuring virus concentrations. It has a low virus content when diseased, which gives it an advantage over *N. tabacum,* in that contaminations do not readily occur when the plants are handled. The rapidity of development of the local lesions makes it possible to have preliminary results of measurements on the second or third day after inoculation, according to the season. On the fourth or fifth day final results may be noted and the plants discarded. Large numbers of lesions can be distinguished on individual leaves; thus a high degree of accuracy may be obtained in comparing virus concentrations. The use of pin punctures is unnecessarily slow in the use of this species as a test plant. In its stead a much more rapid method of inoculation may be used, allowing tobacco mosaic virus to be measured as readily and as rapidly as bacteria are counted by plating methods.

The procedure is as follows. *N. glutinosa* plants are grown in 4-inch clay pots until flower buds begin to appear. At this stage at least five leaves on each plant are of good size. These five leaves are used for the inoculation; and for convenience in manipulation all the remaining leaves of the plant, as well as the growing point, are pinched off. This leaves a sturdy stem supporting five large leaves. Virus from any source to be tested is now taken up on a small piece of white cheesecloth and rubbed once firmly but gently over the entire upper surface of the five leaves. A full stream of tap water is used to wash away excess virus at once after this inoculation. After a little practice the operations become quite uniform. The results justify the belief that approximate uniformity of inoculation can thus be obtained. Undiluted tobacco mosaic extracts result in the production of about 300-600 lesions on each test plant when applied in this way. If they are diluted with water, the decrease in the number of lesions is at first very rapid, later more gradual. A wide range of concentrations can be studied accurately.

As an illustration of the effectiveness of this method of inoculation, a series of leaves showing the decrease in the number of lesions appearing with decreasing concentrations of virus in the inoculum is shown in fig. 7. A dilution curve showing the effect more accurately is shown in fig. 8. Fig. 9 shows the lower range of this curve more clearly. A curve showing the probable errors of counts of lesions on single test plants is shown in fig. 10. By reference to these curves it will be observed that a very slight dilution, as by a single volume of water, can be detected with satisfactory accuracy by the use of a small number of test plants. In most preliminary measurements a single test plant is sufficient to give an excellent idea of the strength of the virus sample in hand. Even the most important measurements are usually made accurately enough if sixteen test plants are used. Fig. 11 shows two test plants, one five days after inoculation, the other one day after inoculation.

Fig. 7. Live leaves from plants of *N. glutinosa* used to measure the effect of dilutions (1:1, 1:3.16, 1:10, 1:100, 1:1000). Numbers of lesions do not correspond to the more exact averages shown in dilution graph in fig. 8, but decrease in lesions with serial dilution is plainly shown.

The value of this method of measuring the concentration of tobacco mosaic extracts can best be appreciated when it is compared with the old method for estimating the strength of a sample by inoculating potted plants of *N. tabacum*. Ten plants of this species were frequently used in a single test. On the average five successful inoculations and five failures would be observed on this number of test plants. On an equal number of *N. glutinosa* test plants in a typical case 5000 successful inoculations would be observed because of the localized nature of the lesions counted. The accuracy of both methods depends largely on the number of successful inoculations counted. It is estimated that in the average case for the same accuracy one test plant of *N. glutinosa* used as described serves the purpose for which at least several hundred *N. tabacum* plants are required with the customary methods of using that species.

N. glutinosa differs from the other species of *Nicotiana* in two ways. It produces very little virus when successfully inoculated, and symptoms appear on the upper parts of the plant to a very limited extent. Measurements of the amounts of virus produced by this plant have shown that the concentration present does not exceed the strength of an ordinary sample of commercial tobacco mosaic virus diluted with water to one-five hundredths of its original strength. The systemic course of the disease is not like that of most species. Generally the growing tip soon shows the same type of symptoms which have occurred where the virus was introduced. The writer has never seen a case in which the developing leaves of *N. glutinosa* were affected with necrotic spots. The local lesions enlarge day by day, laying down ring after ring of dead tissue. After a week or so new secondary spots are sometimes formed on the peripheries of the extended primary lesions. Later lesions may appear on leaves younger than those inoculated, but they do not affect the developing leaves. Sometimes veins and portions of

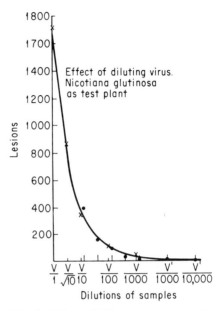

Fig. 8. Effect of diluting virus sample, *N. glutinosa* as test plant. Counts of lesions in every case represent average number of lesions appearing for each test plant, when five leaves of each plant had been wiped with the virus sample in question. Accuracy attained may be noted by closeness of determined points to the smooth curve. Nine plants used for each determination; probable error of each point as determined is therefore one-third the error shown in fig. 10 for single observations of similar numbers of lesions.

the stem are killed by the extending lesions. The green portions of the leaves between the primary lesions are not suitable sources of virus. No successful transfers have been secured when juice from them has been used as inoculum. The virus seems to be confined to the visible lesions.

N. glutinosa, like *N. rustica,* shows a gradient of susceptibility when successively older leaves are considered. The younger leaves tend to produce more local lesions when inoculated with the same source of virus as neighboring older leaves. This condition is partially remedied by removing the growing point of the plant, as is done in using the plant for measurements. In two series of plants, one with the growing tops attached, the other with the tops removed, this condition of affairs was demonstrated. In the first series, in which the growing points remained attached, the totals from top leaf to lowest leaf were 6066, 5117, 4292, 3222, and

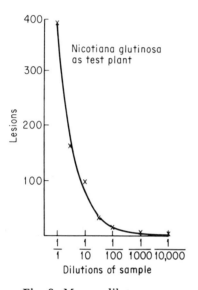

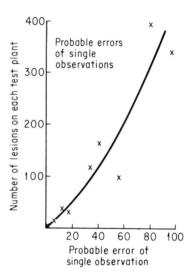

Fig. 9. More dilute range of curve shown in fig. 8, drawn to such a scale that readings may be made accurately (see fig. 10 for probable errors of single observations in this range of measurements).

Fig. 10. Probable errors of single observations for test plants having numbers of lesions between 0 and 400. The error in determining these probable errors is naturally large, and information was insufficient to extend curve beyond 400. At 1714, however, the probable error of a single observation has been found to be 414.

3198. The gradient is very marked. In the second series, in which the growing points were removed, the totals were 4795, 4778, 4227, 4320, and 4343. The gradient is much less. The practice of removing the tops insures less error in comparing leaves of different age, since the chance choice of an older or a younger leaf in any plant will introduce less variation when the difference in the susceptibility is decreased.

DISCUSSION

The recognition of symptoms which appear at the site of inoculation opens a new field of investigation in connection with tobacco mosaic.

The first development of the disease seems to be very strictly localized. It is only the later course of the infection which is marked by changes in appearance of the developing leaves. The species of *Nicotiana* differ markedly in the conspicuousness of their local symptoms. In some cases

Fig. 11. Test plant of *N. glutinosa* (at left) as used to determine virus concentrations, inoculated five days before it was photographed. Similar plant (at right) inoculated one day before it was photographed. Lesions had not yet appeared on this recently inoculated plant.

necrotic spots are formed, in others a pale yellow area marks the point of entrance and early development of the virus.

Most of what is known regarding virus diseases of plants has been learned from inoculation studies. The behavior of the virus under experimental conditions, such as filtration, purification by chemical processes, and contact with disinfectants has always been judged by its reinoculation into living plants. Such tests have been difficult to carry on with a high degree of accuracy, because of the large numbers of plants required for each determination. The use of local necrotic lesions makes it possible to recognize very large numbers of successful transmissions on single plants. This reduces the amount of labor in many experiments. A degree of accuracy never before possible can be attained in this way with the use of moderate numbers of plants. *N. glutinosa* lends itself particularly to use in measuring virus concentrations, since the necrotic lesions in this plant develop in from two to five days. These lesions are easily counted and their relative numbers show variations in the concentrations of samples with great clearness.

When very small numbers of lesions develop on *N. glutinosa* because of the use of highly diluted samples of virus, there occur many cases in which a plant shows a single local lesion. Under such circumstances it seems possible that the infection has resulted from the entrance of a single virus particle. Transfers from this type of plant may be assumed to develop virus produced from this single particle. The process of isolation may be repeated if desired. Possibly a pure line of the causal agent is thus secured. Such single particle strains have not yet been carefully studied; their isolation and use may be expected to furnish material for future work. The use of *Nicotiana* species which show local necrotic lesions is as helpful in the study of tobacco mosaic virus as Koch's plate method is in the study of bacterial cultures.

SUMMARY

1. Five *Nicotiana* species were found to develop necrotic lesions wherever virus of the common field type of tobacco mosaic successfully entered leaf tissues. These species were *N. rustica, N. langsdorffii, N. sanderae, N. acuminata,* and *N. glutinosa.*

2. The local lesions developing in *N. rustica* can be used to measure accurately the potency of tobacco mosaic virus.

3. The local lesions in *N. glutinosa* are exceptional in the rapidity of their development. They sometimes begin to appear thirty hours after inoculation. In four or five days they are well developed. Large numbers of them may be distinguished on a single plant. This allows comparisons to be made between virus samples, since the number of lesions developing depends on the virus concentration of the inoculum.

4. A standardized method for using *N. glutinosa* as a test plant for measuring the concentration of mosaic virus gives as rapid and as accurate results as the determination of bacterial numbers by plating methods.

Boyce Thompson Institute for Plant Research, Inc.
Yonkers, N.Y.

LITERATURE CITED

1. Allard, H. A. 1914. The mosaic disease of tobacco. U.S. Dept. Agr. Bull. **40.**

2. Beijerinck, M. W. 1898. Über ein Contagium vivum fluidum als Ursache der Fleckenkrankheit der Tabaksblätter. Verhandelingen der Koninklijke Akademie van Wetenschappen te Amsterdam, Sect. 2. **6:** 3-22.

3. Fernow, K. H. 1925. Interspecific transmission of mosaic diseases of plants. Cornell Agr. Exp. Sta. Memoir 96.

4. Holmes, F. O. 1928. Accuracy in quantitative work with tobacco mosaic virus. Bot. Gaz. **86:** 67-81.

5. Iwanowski, D. 1903. Über die Mosaikkrankheit der Tabakspflanze. Zeitschr. Pflanzenk. **13:** 1-41.

6. Mayer, A. 1886. Über die Mosaikkrankheit des Tabaks. Die Landwirthschaft-lichen Versuchs-Stationen **32:** 451-467.

7. Priode, C. N. 1928. Further studies in the ring-spot disease of tobacco. Am. J. Bot. **15:** 88-93.

1930

Studies on the Action
of Yellow Fever Virus in Mice[1]

by Max Theiler

(From the Department of Tropical Medicine,
Harvard Medical School, Boston, Mass.)

A significant factor which enhanced the progress of research on animal viruses was the introduction of mice in the 1930's as an experimental host in virus studies. In 1929, Andervont reported on the susceptibility of mice to infection with herpes virus, but the extensive usefulness of the animal in virus research was established by Theiler in experiments with yellow fever virus. He demonstrated that mice succumbed to the disease after intracerebral inoculation with the virus which provided a distinct criteria for quantitating virus potency. Furthermore, he demonstrated the feasibility of employing the mouse as an indicator host for measuring serum antibody levels by the virus-serum neutralization reaction. The successful development of a yellow fever vaccine by Theiler was greatly facilitated by the use of mice in fundamental experiments. The detection, isolation, and characterization of a wide variety of viruses, particularly those of the arthropod-borne group, may be attributed to the susceptibility of mice to experimental infection with these viruses.

The study of the etiology of a disease is greatly facilitated by the discovery of an experimental animal susceptible to the virus of that disease. The finding by the West African Yellow Fever Commission of the Rockefeller Foundation (1928) that the Indian

---

[1] Abridged and reprinted by permission of the author and publisher from the Annals Trop. Med. Parasit. **24**: 247-272 (1930).

monkey *Macacus rhesus* is susceptible to the virus of yellow fever has been productive of a great deal of research with fruitful results. Rhesus monkeys, however, are rather expensive and at times the supply is limited. The finding of a common laboratory animal susceptible to the virus of yellow fever would be a great advantage.

It is generally conceded by all workers that the common laboratory animals,—rabbits, guinea pigs, rats and mice, are not susceptible to the virus of yellow fever when injected by the usual routes.

The French workers Lasnet (1929) and Laigret noted in yellow fever patients neurological symptoms. Laigret suggested that the central nervous system of yellow fever patients should be tested for the presence of virus.

It was decided to test the common laboratory animals by intracerebral injection. Familiarity with the work of Andervont (1929) with herpes virus and mice, and the simplicity of his technique suggested mice as the first choice.

PRELIMINARY EXPERIMENTS

In the preliminary experiments material from three different rhesus monkeys dying of yellow fever was employed. In every case mice were injected intracerebrally and in two cases the same material was injected intraperitoneally. The results of these experiments are summarized in Table I. The material used consisted of brain from one monkey, citrated blood and brain from another, and brain from a third. All the mice which received an intraperitoneal injection remained well and are not included in the table. Of the mice which received an intracerebral infection of citrated blood, only one survived the injection, as citrate appears to be very toxic when injected by this route. Examination of the table shows that quite a number of the mice became ill. Furthermore, the virus could be propagated in other mice by brain to brain passage. In three out of four cases in which this was tried the mice became infected and died after an appreciably shorter course of the disease. Two of these strains were stopped after the second passage and the third died out for some unknown reason in the fourth generation.

Pathological study was made of brains from five mice, injected with virus from the second and third monkeys. Three of these brains showed an acute encephalitis and two were normal. It is significant that one of these which was negative pathologically was also negative on passage to other mice. No brains were preserved from mice injected with material from the first monkey. The results of these preliminary experiments were sufficiently encouraging to warrant a more exhaustive study. The remainder of this article is concerned with the work done with a fourth strain established in mice.

TABLE 1. *Mice injected intracerebrally with yellow fever virus from rhesus monkeys. Preliminary experiments.*

Number of rhesus	Material injected	Number of mice	Result	Remarks	Microscopic pathology
I	Brain.	1	Killed, 8th day.	No lesions.	No tissues saved.
		2	Ill, 10th day.	Ether. Brain proved infective to four mice which all died on 8th and 9th days.	No tissues saved.
		3	Ill, 19th day.	Ether. No lesion.	No tissues saved.
		4	Found dead, 21st day.	. . .	No tissues saved.
II	Citrated blood.	1	Ill, 11th day.	Ether. Brain proved infective to two mice, dying on 8th and 9th days.	No tissues saved.
	Brain.	1	Ill, 12th day.	Ether. Brain proved infective to two mice, both dying on 8th day.	Encephalitis.
		2	Dying, 23rd day.	. . .	No tissues saved.
		3	Remained well.	. . .	. . .
		4	Remained well.	. . .	. . .
		5	Remained well.	. . .	. . .
III	Brain.	1	Died, 1st day.	. . .	No tissues saved.
		2	Ill, 5th day.	Ether.	Negative.
		3	Ill, 6th day.	Ether. Passed to five mice which all remained well.	Negative.
		4	Found dead, 18th day.	. . .	No tissues saved.
		5	Ill, 21st day.	Ether.	Encephalitis.
		6	Ill, 22nd day.	Ether.	Encephalitis.
		7	Found dead, 25th day.	. . .	No tissues saved.
		8	Found dead, 25th day.	. . .	No tissues saved.
		9	Ill, 25th day.	Ether.	No tissues saved.
		10	Ill, 30th day.	Ether.	No tissues saved.
		11	Remained well.	. . .	. . .
		12	Remained well.	. . .	. . .

ESTABLISHMENT OF THE VIRUS OF YELLOW FEVER IN MICE

I am indebted to Dr. A. W. Sellards for the strain of yellow fever virus used in these experiments. This virus originated in Senegal and is known as the "French Strain" in medical literature.

Six mice were injected intracerebrally with the serum of a monkey which was dying from yellow fever. One of these mice was found dead the following day. Of the five remaining mice, one was definitely ill on the eighth day, one was found dead on the tenth day, one was ill on the fourteenth day and two remained well. The brain of the mouse which was ill on the fourteenth day proved non-infectious for other mice. The mouse which appeared ill on the eighth day was killed by means of ether and the brain used for passage of the virus to other mice and for pathological study. Microscopical examination showed an encephalitis and the presence of eosinophilic intranuclear bodies. Five mice were injected intracerebrally with a portion of this brain and all were dead or dying and were killed from the seventh to the ninth day. The virus has since been kept continuously in mice for more than seventy-five passages, over a period of fourteen months.

In this paper, whenever the term "virus" is used, the strain established in mice is meant, unless definitely indicated otherwise.

TECHNIQUE

The methods employed were simplified as much as possible. For the preparation of the virus for passage the brain is removed from an infected mouse by reflecting the skin over the head, then searing the surface of the cranium and opening the skull by means of sterile scissors. The brain is removed and cut up into small pieces, saline is added, usually about 5 c.c. per brain, and a suspension is made by forcibly drawing the brain substance in and out of a syringe through a rather coarse needle. This suspension is allowed to stand for several minutes in order that the larger particles may settle. The supernatant fluid is used for injection purposes. Two drops of this is the usual dose and 0.5 c.c. is the maximum that can be injected intracerebrally with safety. The skin of the head is washed with alcohol and the injections are made through the skin and bone at the posterior end of the skull, a little to one side of the mid-line. After an intracranial injection some mice show great excitement, others lie very quiet as if dying. These conditions may last for several hours, but the following day the mice appear to be perfectly well and remain so until they become ill as a result of the infection. Crude as this method is, it is remarkable how few secondary infections occur.

COURSE OF INFECTION

After the shock due to the injection has passed off the mice appear perfectly normal. The first sign of illness is generally a roughening of the fur and a loss of activity. The next day the mouse is usually very ill remaining in one spot and in many cases showing paralysis of the hind legs. This condition increases until death occurs the same day or the next. In the early passages, the time of onset of illness until the death of the animal was usually two or three days, but sometimes the mouse would linger on in a moribund condition for two or three days longer. In the later passages the mice usually appeared ill on one day and died later the same day or early on the next. It would often occur that all the passage mice were perfectly well in the morning and all dead or dying in the evening of the same day.

At autopsy there are no constant macroscopic changes on which the diagnosis of infection with the yellow fever virus can be based. The only sure means of diagnosis is the examination of sections of brain, which invariably show an encephalitis and specific nuclear changes.

VIRULENCE OF MOUSE VIRUS FOR RHESUS MONKEYS

The pathogenicity of the mouse virus was tested on three different occasions. In each case the amount injected was approximately the same, namely the entire brains of three mice ill or dying of the infection. The first monkey was injected intraperitoneally with the third passage twenty-four days after the virus had been established in mice. This monkey was dying on the fifth day and was etherized. Autopsy revealed the typical lesions of experimental yellow fever and the diagnosis was confirmed by the microscopic examination of sections.

The second monkey was injected with virus from three mice dying after the twenty-ninth passage, 189 days since the establishment of the virus in mice. This monkey had been used before but there was every reason to believe that he was normal. He showed a temperature on the sixth and seventh days of 104.8°F. and 104.2°F., and thereafter was normal. Twenty-two days after the injection of mouse virus this monkey was given an immunity test with virulent monkey yellow fever virus. He showed a rise of temperature to 104.2°F. on the third day and thereafter was normal.

The third monkey was injected with material from the forty-second passage in mice 273 days after the establishment of the mouse strain. There was no rise of temperature and the monkey remained well until the forty-seventh day, when he appeared to be ill. He was found dead on the morning of the next day. The autopsy findings were consistent with, though not typical of experimental yellow fever in monkeys. There was no jaundice. The lymphatic glands were enlarged and appeared haemorrhagic. The liver was yellow and fatty, but did not have the typical boxwood colour. The left lung showed a massive pneumonic process.

Microscopical examination of the liver showed a fatty infiltration, particularly in the periphery of the lobules. There were occasional necrotic cells scattered throughout the organ. No intranuclear changes such as have been described as inclusions by Torres (1929) and Cowdry and Kitchen (1929) were found. The appearance of the liver changes are not typical of yellow fever but this disease cannot be excluded.

Mice injected intracerebrally with material from this monkey (blood and liver) either died from a bacterial infection or remained well. Passage to other mice did not result in any infection. All the mice which survived the injection of monkey material, as well as those used in subinoculations, were later given an immunity test with passage mouse virus and all died in the regular time. All the evidence, therefore, pathological and experimental, tends to indicate that this monkey did not die of yellow fever, but of some intercurrent infection.

The number of monkey experiments are obviously too few to be of much significance. On account of the fact that one of the monkeys had been used before, only two are of any value. The only legitimate interpretation that can be drawn from the death of the first monkey, is that some of the original yellow fever virus was carried through three mouse passages, and not that proliferation of the virus in the mice had occurred. The development of immunity in the second monkey is significant, though here one cannot be sure that the immunity was produced by the injection of mouse virus. There was every reason to believe that this monkey, though used before, was normal. Assuming that the virus in mice is yellow fever, and the serum experiments leave very little doubt that this is actually the case, the fact that the third monkey lived for forty-seven days after an injection of mouse virus, whether he died from yellow fever or not, warrants the conclusion that continuous passage of the virus through mice leads to an attenuation for monkeys. This opens the interesting speculation whether continuous passage of yellow fever virus through monkeys or mice would also lead to an attenuation for man.[2]

ACTION OF IMMUNE HUMAN SERUM ON MOUSE VIRUS

(A) LABORATORY INFECTION

The serum "T" employed in this experiment was that of a laboratory worker who, during the course of these experiments, developed an attack of fever which was at first thought to be a relapse of malaria. This illness was characterised by an irregular temperature ranging from 101°F. to 103°F., and lasting for five days; a trace of albumin in the urine; a pulse slow in proportion to the temperature; a low blood pressure and a marked leucopenia. The source of infection was in all probability from the mouse virus in about the thirty-second passage, as there was very little chance of acquiring the infection in any other way.

Serum taken a week before onset of the illness was available as control to the convalescent serum. The procedure adopted was the same as that of the second experiment above, except that in the preparation of the virus the infective brain suspension was centrifuged at low speed for

[2] I am indebted to the De Lamay Mobile Research Fund for the purchase of the three monkeys used in these experiments.

twenty minutes. Virus (brain from fortieth mouse passage) and sera were mixed and injected immediately into the brains of mice. The results were as follows:—

1. Of five mice which received the mixture of serum obtained before the illness and virus, all were dead or dying by the seventh day.

2. Of six mice injected with the mixture of convalescent serum and virus, one died on the second day, one died on the tenth day and four remained well.

3. Of five mice injected with a mixture of immune monkey serum (also used in the two experiments reported above) and virus, two died on the tenth day and three remained well.

If we exclude the mouse which died on the second day it will be seen that of five mice which received the mixture of convalescent serum and virus, four were protected and one died after a rather prolonged incubation period.

(B) Convalescent serum from a Naturally Acquired Case in Liberia

The serum of this patient, "V" who had passed through an attack of yellow fever in Liberia, West Africa, was tested in the same manner as described above. The virus (brain from fifty-third mouse passage) was centrifuged for thirty minutes, and equal parts of serum and virus were mixed and injected immediately into the brains of six mice. Similar mixtures were prepared with "T" serum and normal human serum, and each injected into six mice. The results were as follows:—

1. Six mice injected intracerebrally with a mixture of normal serum and virus were all dead on the sixth day except one which, by accident, received a very small injection and which died on the seventh day.

2. Of six mice injected intracerebrally with a mixture of serum "V" and virus, one died on the fifth day, one died on the sixth day, one died on the eighth day, one died on the tenth day and two remained well.

3. Of six mice injected with a mixture of "T" serum and virus, one died on the second day and one on the third day (both probably due to intercurrent disease), one died on the eighth day, two died on the eleventh day, and one remained well.

It is obvious that in this experiment the virus used was rather virulent, as manifested by the death on the sixth day of all the mice which received the mixture of normal serum and virus, and by the survival of only one mouse which received the mixture of "T" serum and virus. In repeated neutralization tests with one serum and various preparations of virus obtained from different mice, the number of mice which survived varied, due probably to the difference of virus content in the mouse brains used.

Protection tests similar to the above have been carried out with convalescent yellow fever sera from Africa, Brazil and Colombia, and all with possibly one exception have shown some protection. It is hoped that the results of these tests, some of which are still in progress, will be published in a separate article in the near future.

SUMMARY

Mice were injected intracerebrally with yellow fever virus from four different rhesus monkeys. In every experiment some of the mice became ill and died. The virus can be propagated indefinitely in mice by mouse brain to brain inoculations.

The virus of yellow fever is highly neurotropic in mice, being present at death in high concentration in the brain, spinal cord, sciatic nerve and adrenal. The virus is either entirely absent, or is present in very small amounts in the blood, liver, spleen, kidney, and testis.

Injection of the virus into the nervous system, e.g. eye, brain, spinal cord, results in infection. Injection of the virus subcutaneously, intra-dermally, intramuscularly, intraperitoneally, very seldom indeed results in infection and death but often produces an immunity to a subsequent intracerebral injection of passage virus.

Evidence is presented that in mice the virus travels along the nerve paths, both centripetally and centrifugally.

Young mice less than two weeks of age are susceptible to an injection of the virus into the subcutaneous tissues and the peritoneal cavity as well as to intracerebral injection. The distribution of virus in the body of a young mouse dying after an intraperitoneal injection is the same as that in an adult mouse after an intracerebral injection—viz., the nervous system is highly infective, whereas the blood and abdominal organs (with the exception of the adrenal) are either free from virus or contain very little. Virus injected into the abdominal cavity of a young mouse cannot be demonstrated in the blood or abdominal organs (liver, spleen, kidney) forty-eight hours after the injection. The brain at this time is already highly infective.

The serum of a monkey immune to yellow fever, human serum from a laboratory infection as well as human sera from naturally acquired infections neutralize the mouse virus partially or completely. This effect can be shown by mixing the immune serum and virus *in vitro* and then injecting the mixture intracerebrally into mice.

Infective mouse brain stored in the freezing room at $-8°C$. retains its virulence for at least 160 days. Kept in 50 per cent glycerine at $2°-4°C$. brain proved infective after fifty-eight days but not after 100 days.

Passage of the yellow fever virus through mice leads to a loss of virulence of the virus for monkeys. A rhesus monkey injected with the third mouse passage died of typical experimental yellow fever in five days. A monkey injected with material from the forty-second mouse passage remained well for forty-seven days. This monkey was found dead on the forty-eighth day—death in all probability being due to intercurrent disease.

The brains of all mice, no matter how infected, show an encephalitis which in well-marked cases is highly reminiscent of encephalitis lethargica. In addition to the vascular changes there are present almost invariably nuclear changes in the ganglion cells, which resemble those present in human and monkey yellow fever livers and which have been described as inclusions by Torres (1929) and Cowdry and Kitchen (1929).

CONCLUSIONS

1. Mice are susceptible to the virus of yellow fever when injected into the brain. The strain can be maintained indefinitely by brain to brain passages.

2. The virus established in mice is highly neurotropic for these animals.

3. The action of immune yellow fever sera can be demonstrated by injecting a mixture of immune serum and virus into the brains of mice.

4. Passage of yellow fever virus through mice leads to a loss of virulence for monkeys.

5. Yellow fever virus produces an encephalitis in mice. In addition there are specific eosinophilic nuclear changes in the ganglion cells.

6. The neurotropic character of the virus as well as the pathological changes induced, afford strong evidence that the etiological agent of yellow fever should be classified with the filterable viruses.

REFERENCES

Andervont, H. B. 1929. Activity of herpetic virus in mice. J. Infect. Dis. 44: 383-393.

Cowdry, E. V., and Kitchen, S. F. 1929. Intranuclear inclusions in yellow fever. Science. 69: 252-253.

Cowdry, E. V. 1930. Intranuclear inclusions in yellow fever. Amer. J. Hyg. 11: 227-299.

Kleine, F. K. 1905. Neue Beobachtungen zur Hühnerpest. Zeitschr J. Hyg. 51: 177-182.

Kraus, R., and Doerr, R. 1908. Ueber das Verhalten des Hühnerpestvirus im Zentralnervensystem empfänglicher, natürlich und künstlich unempfänglicher Tiere. Centralbl. f. Bakt. Orig. 46: 709-715.

Kraus, R., and Schiffmann, J. 1907. Studien über Immunisierung gegen das Virus der Hühnerpest. Centralbl. f. Bakt. Orig. 43: 825-832.

Laigret. Personal communication to Dr. A. W. Sellards.

Lasnet. 1929. African Conference of the Yellow Fever, 1929, p. 30. Imprimerie Militaire Universelle L. Fournier. Paris.

Rosenthal, W. 1906. Ueber Beziehungen zwischen Hühnerpest und Lyssa. Centralbl. f. Bakt. Orig. **40**: 204-206.

Stokes, A., Bauer, J. H., and Hudson, N. P. 1928. Experimental transmission of yellow fever to laboratory animals. Am. J. Trop. Med. **8**: 103-164.

Torres, C. M. 1929. Intranuclear inclusions in experimental yellow fever. Instituto Oswaldo Cruz, Supplemento das Memorias, No. 6, 69-71.

1931

The Susceptibility of the Chorio-Allantoic Membrane of Chick Embryos to Infection with the Fowl-Pox Virus[1]

by Alice Miles Woodruff, Ph.D., and
Ernest W. Goodpasture, M.D.

(From the Department of Pathology, Vanderbilt University
School of Medicine, Nashville, Tenn.)

*The susceptibility of the developing chick embryo to virus in-
fection was shown initially by Rous and Murphy in 1911 with
the inoculation of cell filtrates of Rous sarcoma. Almost two
decades later the tremendous potential of this host for experimental and practical studies with animal viruses was realized
largely through the efforts of Ernest W. Goodpasture and his
associates. Woodruff and Goodpasture described a technique
for the inoculation of the developing chick embryo and demonstrated that fowl-pox virus forms distinct lesions on the chorio-
allantoic membrane that are characteristic of the disease. The
value of this host for the cultivation of other viruses was exploited rapidly. The chick embryo as an experimental host in
virus research offered several advantages; availability, low cost,
absence from viral antibodies, comparative freedom from latent viruses (exception of the fowl leukosis complex), and a
variety of extraembryonic cell layers which enlarged its susceptibility to many viral agents. The usefulness of the host
was greatly extended by Burnet and his workers who developed improved methods of inoculation and correlated the
reactions of different viruses in the egg with infectivity. Some
notable applications which evolved from the use of the chick
embryo were the detection and isolation of a wide variety of*

[1] Abridged and reprinted by permission of the author and publisher from Am. J.
Path. 1931, 7: 209-222 (1931).

viruses, development of a quantitative method for measuring virus infectivity, and the production of antigens and virus vaccines.

For studying a representative of the pox group of virus diseases, fowl-pox has many advantages, among them being the fact that infectious material is readily obtained and easily handled, since the disease is limited to fowls. It is believed that knowledge gained concerning this disease may be serviceable in the study of other members of the pox group. Hence, this virus has been the subject of several problems investigated in this laboratory during the last three years.

Fowl-pox, like the other pox diseases, is characterized by the appearance of eruptive skin lesions. The spontaneous fowl-pox nodules appear especially on the unfeathered parts of chickens, although experimental lesions may be easily induced in specialized epidermal structures such as cornea, feather follicles and oil gland. The lesions consist of a hyperplasia of the epithelial cells, with inclusion bodies in their cytoplasm. It has been shown that these inclusions are composed of groups or colonies of minute (Borrel) bodies (1). While the presence of inclusions has always been considered pathognomonic of the disease, recent experimental work has given much evidence in favor of the theory that the Borrel body, one component of the inclusion, is the etiological agent of the disease (2, 3, 4). Heretofore, fowl-pox has been studied only in the grown or newly hatched chicks, or in tissue culture. Tissue culture experiments with this virus have, however, been few and inconclusive (5, 6). The present paper deals with the inoculation of the virus into embryonic tissues in the incubating egg.

The chorio-allantoic membrane of the chick embryo has been used by a number of investigators for the study of the growth of various implanted tissues. Rous and Murphy (7) were the first to use this technique for the study of tumors. Danchakoff (8) has used the method to grow embryonic chick tissues. Since the publication of these two papers the technique has been used frequently in experiments with auto- and heteroplastic grafts, as well as in those with auto- and heterogeneous tumors. The production of experimental infection in the chorio-allantoic membrane has, however, been done only in the one instance where Rous and Murphy grew the virus of the Rous sarcoma (7).[2]

[2] Mention is made by Askanazy[15] of the production of tuberculous chicks by the infection of fertile eggs.

TECHNIQUE FOR INOCULATION OF CHICK EMBRYOS

The technique for opening the eggs used in our experiments was based on that described by Clark (10). We omitted the use of a hot box, but kept the air sac immersed in water at 39°C. Keeping the air sac thus immersed prevented sagging of the egg contents when the egg was opened. We found that a piece of plasticene molded to fit the egg was a convenient support. The top surface of the egg was sterilized by bathing in alcohol and flaming. Then, proceeding with sterile precautions, a window, 7 to 10 mm. square was made by cutting or scraping with a sharp point. We found the sharp end of a scissors blade very convenient for this. After the shell was removed, the shell membrane was cut away carefully in order to expose the chorio-allantoic membrane.

For purposes of clarity in the description of the inoculation of chick embryos and the chorio-allantoic membrane, a diagram of the 12 day chick with its membranes has been reproduced from Lillie (11) (Text-Fig. 1). One label designating the chorio-allantoic membrane (the membrane

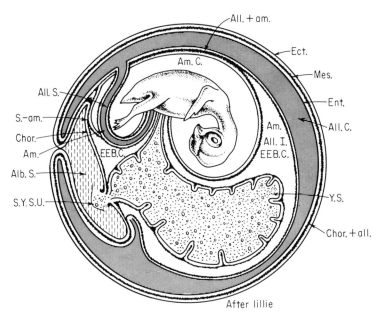

After lillie

Fig. 1. Alb. S., albumin-sac. All. I., inner wall of the allantois. All. C., cavity of allantois. All. S., stalk of allantois. All. + Am., fusion of allantois and amnion. Chor. + All., fusion of chorion and outer wall of allantois. Am., amnion. Am. C., amniotic cavity. Chor., chorion. Ect., ectoderm. E.E.B.C., extra-embryonic body cavity. Ent., entoderm. Mes., mesoderm. S.-Am., sero-amniotic connection. S.Y.S.U., sac of the yolk-sac umbilicus. Y.S., yolk-sac.

formed by the fusion of chorion or serosa with the outer wall of the allantoic sac), has been added to the original diagram.

Two sorts of inoculation were attempted. The simpler procedure consisted in slightly injuring the chorio-allantoic membrane by pricking with
a needle and applying a drop of an uncontaminated virus suspension
(Method I) to the injured area. In the second and more difficult operation, the skin of the embryo itself was inoculated. This involved cutting
the chorio-allantoic membrane and amnion and slightly abrading the
skin of the embryo, since some injury to epithelial cells favors the invasion of the virus.

In most of the techniques described in the literature the original piece
of shell is replaced following the operative procedure and parafined, so
that the egg can be turned daily to continue normal development. Since
we desired to watch the effects of the virus and to get sections at once if
the chick should die, we substituted a glass cover slip for the original
shell, fixing it upon a ring of vaseline, and returned the egg to the incubator immediately after the operation. This technique necessitated keeping the window uppermost during the rest of embryonic growth. The
lack of turning caused usually an oval depression and fold in the membrane directly below the opening. No other abnormality due to lack of
turning appeared to occur, for a number of chicks hatched normally from
eggs which had been subjected to this treatment.

Embryos at various stages of development were used. Since it takes
about four days for a well defined fowl-pox lesion to appear after inoculation, it was necessary to inoculate at least that many days before hatching. The most extensive lesions were obtained six to seven days after
inoculation, so that 10 to 15 day embryos were used most frequently.
Occasionally, a contamination occurred in the inoculation of the egg.
Sometimes a mould grew symbiotically with the virus in the embryonic
membrane. Such contaminated eggs were discarded. Except as a contaminating organism is introduced upon inoculation, the eggs are relatively free from infection and remain, according to Rettger (12), a sterile
medium, unless subjected to moisture and dirt.

RESULTS OF INOCULATION OF EMBRYO CHICK
AND MEMBRANES

Fowl-pox infection of the chorio-allantoic membrane occurred as the
result of inoculation in every case where the embryo survived for at least
four days. Infections were first noted when thickened areas on the chorio-
allantoic membrane were detected after several days' incubation. That a
fowl-pox infection was definitely present was proved by three tests. The
tissue, removed with sterile precautions and inoculated onto the scarified
epithelium of adult hens, produced a massive fowl-pox lesion. Smears of

the lesions, stained by Morosow's method (13), showed Borrel bodies present in great numbers. Histological sections of the tissue showed the typical picture of the fowl-pox lesion (Figs. 2 and 9). These lesions are characterized by a marked hyperplasia of the ectodermal layer and an accompanying thickening of mesoderm as well. (Compare with normal membrane (Fig. 1).) Frequently hyperplasia of the entoderm occurs also. In the cells of the ectodermal layer many large inclusions are present, while in the entodermal layer, when occasionally a definite infection is present, inclusions are few and small. The lack of an inflammatory exudate, even in an advanced stage of the infection, should be noted.

In order to show the gross appearance of the infected areas several infected eggs were fixed in Zenker's fluid with the membranes intact. Sometimes the infection occurred in just a few areas, presumably at the site of the original inoculation (Fig. 6), but more often the infected area covered half the surface of the serosa (Fig. 5), and frequently small isolated areas of infection were found at a distance from the large primary lesion.

Upon the discovery that the outer embryonic membrane always developed this large area of infection directly below the window in the egg, it was decided to attempt the removal, with sterile precautions, of pieces of the infected membrane. By flaming the whole egg and carefully removing the coverslip, the infected tissue was exposed. Pieces of the infected membrane were cut away and washed in sterile Tyrode's solution. A sample of the tissue was inoculated into glucose yeast broth, and it was found that uncontaminated material could be obtained readily in most cases. The infected tissue in Tyrode's solution was then stored at 4°C until needed. Virus thus prepared was used generally within two weeks, although samples stored for several months were shown to be still virulent. Uncontaminated virus was obtained by this fourth method in much larger quantities than any other means so far devised. Consequently this method was used in subsequent experiments where such virus was required. The virus obtained by Method IV is convenient for almost any type of fowl-pox problem, if uncontaminated virus is needed, for the material can be used in a number of ways—as bits of infected tissue, as free inclusions which can be teased out from it, or as a Borrel body suspension, made by grinding the tissue with saline.

The inoculation of the embryonic skin caused considerably more trauma than the inoculation of the chorio-allantoic membrane. The percentage mortality was so great that this operation was soon abandoned, since the membrane inoculations proved very satisfactory. Several successful embryo inoculations were made, however. One infection of an embryo foot was produced (Fig. 7), and other infections were obtained, notably at the umbilicus. Although it was not intended to inoculate at this point, injury to the umbilical region must have occurred during the operation, for, with the inoculation of chorio-allantoic membrane alone, umbilical lesions were not obtained except on chicks which hatched and survived for several days.

Concerning the effect of fowl-pox on embryonic development and ability to hatch, our information is scant since most of the embryos were sacrificed before hatching. A few chicks, however, were hatched from eggs with infected membranes. These chicks were apparently normal, though they must have carried the virus, since all of those that were not sacrificed immediately developed fowl-pox lesions six to eight days later. The nodules appeared most frequently at the base of the beak or about the umbilicus. This infection may have been the result of autoinoculation during the process of pecking through the shell and escaping from the infected membranes. A second possibility is that the cells at the beak and umbilicus, injured during hatching, were infected by virus in the blood stream. The extreme vascularity of the chorio-allantoic membrane would make it seem highly improbable that the blood would remain virus free. Proof of the presence of virus in the circulation was obtained from a series of experiments in which pieces of liver were removed with sterile precautions from chicks which had either hatched from or died in eggs with infected membranes. In the majority of cases where liver material was inoculated onto the scarified epithelium of chicks a small lesion was obtained. In one case out of six, the inoculation of liver material produced no lesion. The lack of massive lesions as a result of these inoculations seemed to us to indicate that though the virus is present in small quantities in the blood stream, it is not actively proliferating there. This observation is in accordance with an accepted view concerning the virus present in the circulation of infected adult hens (14).

Following the successful inoculation of the membranes of 10 to 15 day embryos, the question arose as to how early in the development of the embryo a successful inoculation could be made. Danchakoff (8) working with embryonic grafts on the allantois states that embryos younger than 7 days could not be used because of the small size of the allantois at that stage. Whether or not the absence of the chorio-allantoic membrane made our inoculations of membranes of embryos younger than 6 days more difficult, it was found that such inoculations were not generally successful. The chorio-allantoic membrane of 6 day embryos was infected with no difficulty, and on one occasion we succeeded in infecting this membrane in an embryo which was inoculated at the 4 day stage (Fig. 8). In younger embryos, the injury caused by opening the egg and pricking the membranes seemed to be greater, for the embryos usually died too soon after inoculation for a lesion to develop. The technical difficulties involved caused us to abandon an attempt to determine the susceptibility of embryos of less than 4 days' development. It is not intended, therefore, to imply that younger embryos could not be infected.

Detailed study of a number of histological sections of infected chorio-allantoic membrane revealed the fact that entodermal as well as ecto-dermal epithelium could be infected. Inclusion bodies were usually less numerous, and hyperplasia was less marked than in infected ectoderm (Figs. 9, 10 and 11). Entoderm seems to be much less susceptible than ectoderm since entodermal infection did not occur in every case of suc-cessful ectodermal infection. A somewhat similar retarded response of entoderm was found by Huxley and Murray in work with chorio-allantoic grafts (15). The stimulus in this case, however, was an operative one rather than one caused by an infection.

It should be mentioned in passing that occasionally the membrane was torn at inoculation, and at this point infected ectodermal cells had fused with cells of the entodermal layer. For the identification of a true entodermal infection, however, we were able to obtain sections of isolated nodules at a distance from the point of inoculation, where there was no possibility of ectodermal cells being present in the entodermal layer.

A further indication that entoderm is less susceptible than ectoderm to fowl-pox infection is seen in the fact that entodermal derivatives of the adult hen are rarely infected. Instances of spontaneous lesions in the crop have occasionally been observed. Two instances of spontaneous le-sions of the trachea have also been seen. These lesions were not isolated nodules, but part of massive lesions of the throat. Though the infected areas appeared to be in columnar epithelium, the lesions were not con-sidered to be complete proof of the susceptibility of tracheal epithelium (*i.e.* epithelium of entodermal origin), since they were not isolated from epithelium of ectodermal derivation. Using uncontaminated virus (Method IV), an attempt to corroborate the experimental infection of embryonic entoderm by the production of a fowl-pox lesion in adult tracheas was made.

With sterile precautions, the tracheas of two hens were cut, scarified and inoculated. The hens were sacrificed eleven and thirteen days respec-tively after inoculation. In both cases a gross infection of the skin of the neck occurred but there were no adhesions to the trachea. In each experi-ment the mucous membrane of the trachea contained a number of small nodules, sections of which showed the typical fowl-pox lesion (Figs. 12 and 13). The infection of entodermal tissues, both adult and embryonic, is thus shown to be possible under experimental conditions. Uncontami-nated virus may prove useful in other experiments of this type. Using such virus, intracerebral inoculations might prove interesting, as well as further inoculations of entodermal derivatives such as the mucous mem-brane of the intestine, or of mesodermal epithelium, *e.g.*, that in the kidney.

The position of the capillaries in some of the sections of infected chorio-allantoic membrane corroborates Danchakoff's theory concerning the development of the respiratory net of the allantois (16). The allantois is both the respiratory and excretory organ of the embryo. By the thirteenth to fifteenth day its capillary network has in some manner become the outermost layer of living cells. This is contrary to the usual belief that the mesodermal cells of the embryo must always be bounded by two germ layers. This phenomenon was explained by Füllborn (17) as being due to the degeneration of the epithelial cells of the chorion. Danchakoff, however, holds that the final position of the capillary net is due to a migration of the capillaries. She proved that ectodermal cells were still present, by subjecting them to the pressure of grafted tissue, after which keratinization occurred.

Our sections indicate that migration of capillaries rather than degeneration of epithelial cells has occurred in the change of position of the respiratory net. The ectodermal layer can be distinguished because of the infected epithelium in at least part of the section. If the fowl-pox lesion had developed before the migration of the capillary net, this migration was prevented either wholly or partially. Some sections (Fig. 2) show the capillary net entirely below the ectoderm in the heavily infected area, while it occupies a midplace in the ectoderm of the same lesion where the infection is less (Fig. 3), and is found on the surface with ectodermal cells below when it reaches a non-infected area (Fig. 4).

In a number of the sections of infected serosa, epithelial pearls were noted, suggesting the possibility that rapid passage of the infection from one embryo to another might result in massive hyperplasia resembling an epithelial tumor. Accordingly a series of experiments was begun in which it was attempted to graft bits of infected tissue from the chorio-allantoic membrane on normal membranes. After a period of four to seven days, the original explant plus the newly infected area surrounding it was removed. Part of the block was used for sections and part for transplantation. The explants varied in size from 0.5 to 1.5 c.mm. It was found that identification of the transplant in the gross was difficult, due to its inclusion in the fresh growth of infected tissue. By dipping the transplants in a suspension of India ink in saline, however, enough carbon adhered to the tissue so that the transplant could be identified even after it had produced a heavy infection in the host membrane. Since it was thought that the ink might injure the cells of the transplant, both plain and inked transplants were tried, and several of each type were identified in sections. The series was terminated with the third transplant. Study of the sections obtained showed that in neither inked nor plain transplants had a true graft occurred. Apparently the infected cells degenerated too rapidly for them to become established in the new location. Though hyperplasia was evident, the type of lesion in the second and third transplants was not different from that obtained after the first inoculation. It was concluded that the epithelial pearls were probably due to mechanical displacement of the epithelium in the membrane.

DISCUSSION

Experiments upon fowls have shown the great susceptibility of ectodermal cells to infection with the virus of fowl-pox. When the virus is injected intravenously the resulting lesions are almost entirely confined to the skin. Sometimes, however, the epithelium of the esophagus, crop and trachea are affected, showing the ability of the virus to multiply in epithelium having an entodermal derivation. From the fact of the infrequent occurrence of spontaneous gastro-intestinal and tracheal lesions, and from the characteristics of these lesions whether spontaneous or experimental, it seems evident that the virus of fowl-pox affects ectodermal epithelium much more readily than entodermal, and increases more abundantly in the former. In common with certain other cytotropic viruses, that of fowl-pox seems thus to possess a high degree of cellular specificity.

The experiments recorded in this paper show that the same specificity obtains when this virus is brought into contact with the tissues of chick embryos, and in similar degree. That is to say, in the embryo as in the adult fowl, ectodermal squamous epithelium is more susceptible, while entoderm of the allantois is less readily affected, and in the latter cells, virus regenerates much less abundantly, judging from the number and size of cellular inclusions.

This susceptibility appears very early in the cellular differentiation of the embryo. With the technical methods at our disposal it was not determined how early the embryonic cells acquire this susceptibility, or, to state it differently, how soon certain embryonic cells lose their susceptibility, supposing that the earliest undifferentiated cells from the ovum are all susceptible to the virus. It would be of great interest to know whether or not ectodermal and entodermal epithelium acquire their susceptibility as a result of cellular differentiation.

By the use of the chorio-allantoic membrane of chick embryos for the production of the infection, the preparation of non-contaminated concentrated virus in fairly large quantities is made possible. This virus, being the infected tissue grown in and obtained from a sterile medium, can thus be used in whatever form desired, i.e., as infected tissue, inclusion bodies, or a suspension of Borrel bodies. This method and also Method I, described in this paper, have an advantage over any other known preparations of non-contaminated fowl-pox virus, in that, since the cells in which the virus has developed have never been contaminated, the virus should be free from antigens not directly associated with the disease. This fact should make it especially useful in immunological experiments.

One of the uses of such a virus preparation has been demonstrated in the successful inoculation of adult chicken trachea with fowl-pox virus. Inoculations of such virus into the internal organs of the chicken, especially those with epithelial surfaces such as the kidney, might give valuable information.

The use of embryonic chick membranes as a medium for the production of other virus infections, *e.g.*, vaccinia, might prove advantageous in the study of the etiology and development of these diseases.

SUMMARY

1. Ectodermal and entodermal cells of the chorio-allantoic membrane of the chick, as well as embryonic chick skin, are susceptible to infection with the virus of fowl-pox at an early stage in the development of the embryo. Whether or not this specific susceptibility is acquired as a result of cellular differentiation has not been determined.

2. Four methods for the isolation of uncontaminated fowl-pox virus are described.

3. In two of these methods the virus is developed in tissue that has never been contaminated by extraneous microörganisms.

4. Fowl-pox infection in the trachea of the adult hen has been induced by means of inoculation with uncontaminated virus.

REFERENCES

1. Borrel, A. 1904. Sur les inclusions de l'épithélioma contagieux des oiseaux. Compt. Rend. Soc. de Biol. **57:** 642.

2. Woodruff, C. Eugene, and Goodpasture, Ernest W. 1929. The infectivity of isolated inclusion bodies of fowl-pox. Am. J. Path. **5:** 1.

3. Woodruff, C. Eugene, and Goodpasture, Ernest W. 1930. The relation of the virus of fowl-pox to the specific cellular inclusions of the disease. Am. J. Path. **6:** 713.

4. Goodpasture, Ernest W., and Woodruff, Alice Miles. 1930. The nature of fowl-pox virus as indicated by its reaction to treatment with potassium hydroxide and other chemicals. Am. J. Path. **6:** 699.

5. Findlay, G. Marshall. 1928. A note on the cultivation of the virus of fowlpox. Brit. J. Exper. Path. **9:** 28.

6. Loewenthal, H. 1928. Über die Kultur unsichtbarer Krankheitserreger. (Züchtung des Vogelpockenvirus.) Klin. Wchnschr. **7:** 349.

7. Rous, Peyton, and Murphy, J. B. 1911. Tumor implantations in the developing embryo. Experiments with a transmissible sarcoma of the fowl. J. Am. Med. Assoc. **56:** 741.

8. Danchakoff, V. 1916. Equivalence of different hematopoietic anlages. I. Spleen. Am. J. Anat. **20:** 255.

9. Friedberger, E., and Hoder, F. 1927. Ueber Trennung invisibler Vira von

den Begleitbakterien mittels der Friedbergerschen. Kapillarsteigmethode. Deutsche med. Wchnschr. **53**: 1008.

10. Clark, Eliot R. 1920. Technique of operating on chick embryos. Science. **51**: 371.

11. Lillie, F. R. 1908. The development of the chick. Henry Holt & Co., New York. 220.

12. Rettger, L. F. 1913-14. The bacteriology of the hen's egg with special reference to its freedom from microbic invasion. Centralbl. f. Bakt., Pt. II. **39**: 611.

13. Morosow, M. A. 1926. Die Färbung der Paschenschen Körperchen durch Versilberung. Centralbl. f. Bakt., Pt. I, Orig. **100**: 385.

14. Goodpasture, E. W. 1928. Filterable Viruses, Rivers, T. M. Williams & Wilkins, Baltimore. 235-277.

15. Huxley, J. S., and Murray, P. D. F. 1924. A note on the reactions of chick chorio-allantois to grafting. Anat. Rec. **28**: 385.

16. Danchakoff, V. 1917. The position of the respiratory vascular net in the allantois of the chick. Am. J. Anat. **21**: 407.

17. Füllborn, Fried. 1895. Beiträge zur Entwicklung der Allantois der Vögel. Inaugural dissertation, Berlin.

18. Askanazy, M. 1923. Pathologische Anatomie, Aschoff, L. Gustav Fischer, Jena. 187.

DESCRIPTION OF PLATES

PLATE 40

FIG. 1. Normal chorio-allantoic membrane from hatching chick. × 50.

FIG. 2. Ectoderm of chorio-allantoic membrane of chick embryo showing fowl-pox infection, and the position of the capillary net below a heavily infected area. Section taken five days after inoculation. Note absence of inflammatory exudate. × 200.

FIG. 3. An intermediate position of capillary net in the hyperplastic ectodermal epithelium adjacent to massive fowl-pox infection of embryonic membrane (Fig. 2). × 200.

FIG. 4. Position of capillaries on surface of non-infected ectoderm adjacent to area (Fig. 3) of hyperplastic epithelium in fowl-pox infected membrane. × 200.

PLATE 41

FIG. 5. Massive fowl-pox infection in chorio-allantoic membrane of 15 day embryo, seven days after inoculation.

FIG. 6. Isolated areas of fowl-pox infection in chorio-allantoic membrane of 16 day embryo, seven days after inoculation (shown at right).

FIG. 7. Fowl-pox infection in epithelium of foot of 21 day embryo, seven days after inoculation. × 50.

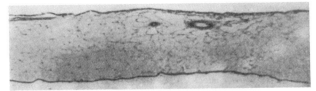

1

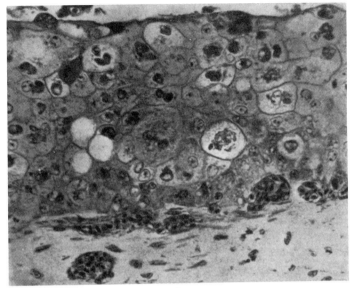

2

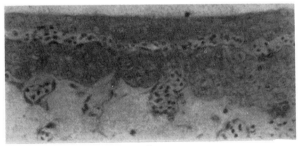

3

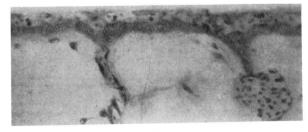

4

Plate 40.

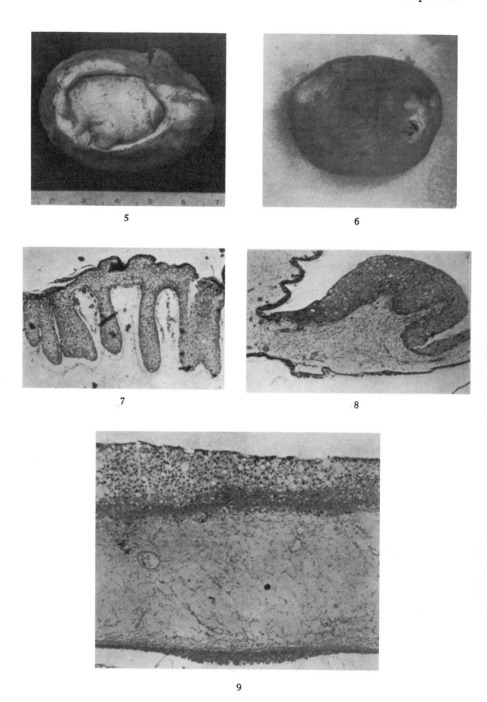

5

6

7

8

9

Plate 41.

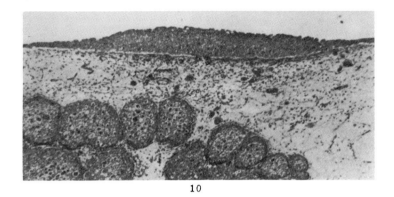

10

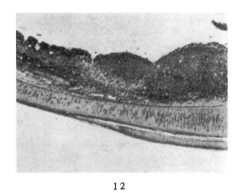

11

12

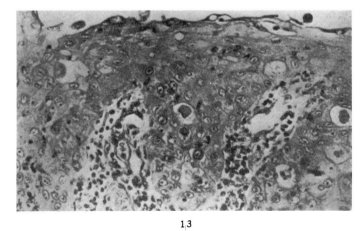

1,3

Plate 42.

Fig. 8. Fowl-pox infection in ectoderm of chorio-allantoic membrane resulting from inoculation at 4 day stage. × 50.

Fig. 9. Fowl-pox infection in chorio-allantoic membrane showing massive lesion in ectoderm and hyperplasia of entoderm. × 50.

Plate 42

Fig. 10. Isolated area of fowl-pox infection in entoderm of chorio-allantoic membrane, six days after inoculation. Note small size of inclusions and cells as compared with those of epithelial nodules from ectodermal layer in lower portion of picture. × 50.

Fig. 11. A portion of Fig. 10 under higher magnification, showing fowl-pox infection in entoderm of chorio-allantoic membrane. Note that inclusions are smaller and hyperplasia less than in infected ectoderm of Fig. 2. × 200.

Fig. 12. Experimental fowl-pox infection of mucous membrane of trachea. Cf. normal epithelium at left with infected area at right. × 50.

Fig. 13. A portion of Fig. 12 under higher magnification, showing experimental fowl-pox infection of mucous membrane of trachea. Note metaplasia of epithelium and relatively few inclusions. × 200.

1932

The Sizes of Different Bacteriophages[1]

by W. J. Elford and C. H. Andrews

From the National Institute for Medical Research,
Hampstead, London.

*Elford's development of a series of graded collodion mem-
branes provided a means for estimating the sizes of viruses by
filtration and proved an invaluable aid for general experimental studies with viruses. Many of the values for virus diameters obtained by this technique compared favorably with subsequent measurements determined with the electron microscope. In this study it was established that different strains of
bacterial viruses have different sizes. Furthermore, the diameter of the plaques produced by a virus is a function of its size.
Elford's filtration technique was a contributing factor to the
early comprehension of the nature of viruses.*

There are many references in the lit-
erature to work on the size of "the bacteriophage": it would be as reasonable to talk of the size of "a bacterium," for there can be very few
workers to-day who would agree with d'Herelle that all races of bacteriophage are representatives of a single species, the *"Bacteriophagum in-
testinale."* Some writers on the subject have not even recorded what
bacteria were attacked by the particular bactcriophage whose size they
were estimating. Very few have considered the possibility that different
bacteriophages might be of differing sizes. Biemond (1924), however,
found evidence that one Shiga-phage studied by him was larger than another one; and Burnet and McKie (1930, *b*) thought that their anomalous
Salmonella phage S 13 was smaller than most others.
  The earlier workers compared phages with other substances as regards

[1] Abridged and reprinted by the publisher's permission from the Brit. J. of Exp.
Path. **13** (5): 446-456 (1932).

their filterability through collodion membranes; most of them reached untrustworthy conclusions through neglect of the fact that the presence of phage can be detected in far lower concentrations than is possible with the substances with which they were comparing it. It has thus been concluded that "the phage" is smaller than albumin (Bürgers and Bachmann, 1924), than strychnine nitrate (Stassano and de Beaufort, 1925), than hæmoglobin and serum-albumin (Eliava and Suarez, 1927), than nucleoprotein and albumin (Jermoljewa, Bujanowskaja and Severin, 1932).

The majority of workers have, however, agreed more or less with d'Herelle's estimate of $20\text{-}30\mu\mu$ as the diameter of "the bacteriophage." This conclusion has been reached mainly on the basis of filtration experiments through acetic collodion membranes; such membranes are, however, far from ideal for the purpose, as discussed by one of us elsewhere (Elford, 1931). Optical methods have been used by Bechhold and Villa (1925-6), who consider that "the phage" has a diameter of over $35\mu\mu$. Hetler and Bronfenbrenner (1931) estimated the size of a coli-phage by a diffusion method. They believe that phage in broth filtrates is adsorbed to particles of bacterial protein of varying size, but that the ultimate units of purified phage may be as small as $1.2\mu\mu$ in diameter. Reasons for doubting the validity of their conclusions will appear in the subsequent discussion.

EXPERIMENTAL METHODS

The material studied has consisted of filtrates of lysed broth cultures of organisms. Experiments with "purified" phage will also be described. Most of the phages are amongst those studied by Dr. F. M. Burnet (1930, *a*); we are much indebted to him and to Prof. Topley for strains of these and other phages; also to Dr. A. P. Krueger för a strain of staphylococcal phage. Care was taken by repeated plating out and picking of single plaques to ensure that all the phages studied were really pure. Titres of phage were estimated by means of plaque-counts on agar plates; despite its defects, this seemed to us the best method available.

We confined our attention to phages which could be obtained in high titre—at least 10^7 particles per c.c.—and we were careful to ensure in the course of our work that they were maintained at their maximum titre and filtered at a pH of 7.4 to 7.6. The effect of variations in titre on the filterability of a virus had been forcibly brought home to us during earlier work with vaccinia (Elford and Andrewes, 1932); we took care, therefore, that our results with phages were not vitiated by fallacies arising in this quarter.

The several phages have been filtered through graded collodion membranes of the new type described by Elford (1931). (For convenience these membranes are referred to as gradocol membranes.) The form of ultrafilter employed was the same as in previous experiments (see Barnard and

Elford, 1931). The membrane was supported on a perforated plate, and filtration conducted under positive nitrogen pressure of 76 cm. mercury. The experimental conditions were carefully controlled: the temperature was 18-20°C., the area of membrane surface (*i.e.* total area of holes in plate supporting the membrane) was 1.05 sq. cm., while the membrane thickness ranged from 0.12-0.15 mm. The analytical procedure consisted in collecting measured samples of filtrate, which were then tested quantitatively for the presence of phage by the method already indicated.

EXPERIMENTAL RESULTS

UNIFORMITY OF SIZE OF PHAGE PARTICLES

The forms of the filtration curves (Chart I) and their clean separation suggest that the phage particles in any particular preparation are of a relatively uniform and characteristic order of size. For instance, in the case of S 13 phage, a $25\mu\mu$ membrane completely retained the phage, a $30\mu\mu$

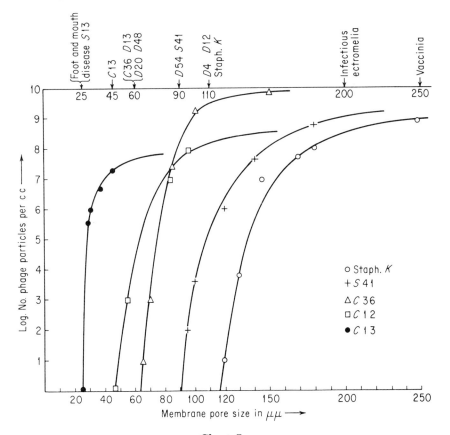

Chart I.

membrane permitted 1 per cent. to pass, a $35\mu\mu$ membrane 50-75 per cent., while grades $45\mu\mu$ and upwards yielded filtrates equivalent in titre to the original. These facts, particularly when one remembers that the membranes are not ideal filters with pores all exactly of the same dimension, provide strong evidence that the phage particles are very uniform in size. Bronfenbrenner (1927) considers that the active principle in bacteriophage preparations is not in its elementary form, but is attached to carrier particles. We think it very probable that some phage may be adsorbed to bacterial fragments, in view of the observed fact that dead bacteria can adsorb phage irreversibly (Krueger, 1931). However, were all the phage attached to bacterial or broth proteins of varying sizes, then a gradual loss of activity would be expected as progressively less permeable membranes were employed. Further, all the strains of phage, particularly those developed in the same organism, might be expected to have the same apparent size. The results obtained in our studies are in contradiction to both these implications, different phages being retained by membranes of widely differing permeabilities.

PROBABLE SIZES OF PHAGES

Their filtration curves having been determined and analysed under strictly comparable conditions, the phages were arranged in order of their relative sizes. Thus—

$$
\left.\begin{array}{l} \textit{Staph. k.} \\ \text{D 4} \\ \text{D 12} \end{array}\right\} > \left\{\begin{array}{l} \text{D 54} \\ \text{S 41} \end{array}\right\} > \left\{\begin{array}{l} \text{C 36} \\ \text{D 13} \\ \text{D 20} \\ \text{D 48} \end{array}\right\} > \text{C 13} > \text{S 13.}
$$

The difficulties in assigning values for actual sizes from filtration data have been fully discussed by one of us elsewhere (Elford, 1932). The probable sizes of the phages (see Table II) have been deduced from the end-point determinations on the basis presented in that paper.

TABLE II. *Probable sizes of phages*

Phage	End-point	Probable size
Staph. K D 4 D 12	$110\mu\mu$	$50\text{-}75\mu\mu$
D 54 S 41	$90\mu\mu$	$30\text{-}45\mu\mu$
C 36 D 13 D 20 D 48	$60\mu\mu$	$20\text{-}30\mu\mu$
C 13	$45\mu\mu$	$15\text{-}20\mu\mu$
S 13	$25\mu\mu$	$8\text{-}12\mu\mu$

PHAGE-SIZE AND PLAQUE-SIZE

Early in our work we were struck by the facts that a phage, S 13 which seemed by filtration experiments to be very small, produced very large plaques on agar, while our staphylococcal phage, the largest we then had, gave rise to minute plaques, and our coli-phage (C 36), which was apparently between them in size, produced plaques of intermediate size. A possible relationship between size of phage and size of plaque seemed accordingly to be worth some inquiry.

MEASUREMENT OF PLAQUE-SIZES

Many factors determine the size of plaque which any given phage will produce on agar. When several phages are being compared it is necessary to standardize the conditions of the measurements in order to obtain comparable results. The technique we used was as follows: exactly 15 c.c. of 2 per cent. agar were poured into Petri dishes 8 cm. in diameter; plates were dried in the incubator, spread with organisms, and at the same time with a suitable dilution of phage; they were then again dried off. Readings were taken after 20 hours at 37°C. For the smaller plaques measurements were taken by the aid of a low power of a microscope with a micrometer eye-piece. Twenty plaques were measured and an average taken of the values obtained. As a general rule the heaviness of the seeding of bacteria and the time of taking the measurements were not factors greatly affecting the results; but the depth of agar in the plates and the concentration of the agar were most important. In most instances we also made measurements on plates poured with 20 c.c. of 1 per cent. agar, and the plaques obtained were very considerably larger than on the 15 c.c. 2 per cent. agar plates. Measurement of the smaller plaques was thus made easier, but it was found very hard to obtain reproducible results with the phages producing large plaques; probably we did not control sufficiently the drying of the plates.

With this exception the phages under study produced plaques of which the *average* diameter varied very little, though of course there was considerable variation around the mean on every plate. If, however, a phage was active against two different organisms, it commonly gave rise to different-sized plaques according to the organism attacked. Thus, a number of phages studied by us attacked a Flexner dysentery bacillus (rough W) as well as a rough *B. coli*. Almost all these phages produced larger plaques when acting on the dysentery than when attacking the *B. coli*. As mentioned earlier, the diameter of a phage particle is apparently irrespective of the organism attacked. In Chart II one phage (D 12) is recorded as giving 0-sized plaques—plaques too small to measure. Such phages when tested undiluted could inhibit growth on a plate, but yet they could not produce discrete plaques when diluted and tested on

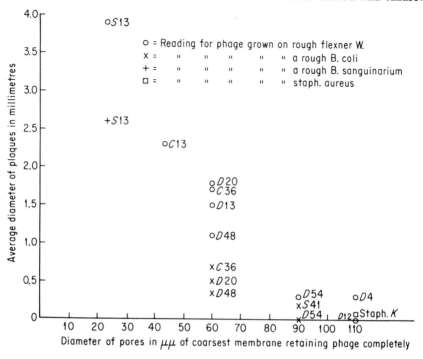

Chart II.

2 per cent.—or even 1 per cent.—agar. On still more dilute agar, however, (0.67 per cent.) one such phage could produce *tiny* plaques.

RELATION OF PHAGE-SIZE TO PLAQUE-SIZE

The relations we found to exist between phage-size and plaque-size are shown in Chart II. Four phages all producing plaques of intermediate size were retained by membranes with pores $60\mu\mu$ in diameter. Two phages (C 13 and S 13) giving rise to larger plaques appeared from the filtration experiments to be distinctly smaller, while our five largest phages all produced very small plaques. We are anxious not to draw too sweeping conclusions from these results. A relationship between plaque-size and phage-size certainly exists, and is particularly striking when one considers phages acting on a single organism (compare all the circles in Chart II); but we deemed it unwise to attempt to draw curves on the graph to illustrate the relationship, since the diameter of a phage-particle is certainly not the only factor affecting plaque-size under our standardized conditions. A small phage can probably travel by diffusion, and perhaps other means also, more rapidly than can larger ones, and thus tend to produce a large plaque; but the rate of its multiplication and other factors will certainly come into play as well. It may be mentioned that when tested on Flexner WR on 2 per cent. agar, phage C 13, a definitely larger phage than S 13, regularly produced smaller plaques than did S 13 (see Chart II); but on 1 per cent. agar its plaques were larger on the average than were S 13's.

DISCUSSION

The bacteriophages studied by us appear to be of the same order of size as the viruses attacking animals. For purposes of comparison the filtration endpoints of three of these viruses are charted at the top of Chart I. But while most of the animal viruses so far measured seem to be greater than $75\mu\mu$ in diameter, all our phages are probably smaller than this. It is of interest, however, that the smallest phage we have encountered (S 13) seems to be of almost exactly the same size as the smallest known virus, that of foot-and-mouth disease (*cf.* Galloway and Elford, 1931). While many animal viruses are now proving visible by more refined optical methods, our largest phages have apparently a diameter which does not bring them within the limits of optical resolution at present available.

Our observation that small phages tend to produce large plaques on agar, and conversely, may be of help to workers on the physical properties of phages, who may wish for any reason to study a very large or a very small phage.

SUMMARY

1. The sizes of a number of bacteriophages have been estimated by the help of graded collodion membranes. Different phages appear to differ from one another in size, but the particles of any one phage seem to be very uniform in size, and not to vary even when the phage is grown on different organisms. The estimated diameter of the smallest phage we have studied (S 13) is $8\text{-}12\mu\mu$, that of the largest is probably between 50 and $75\mu\mu$.

2. Our conclusions as to the relative sizes of three phages have been confirmed by diffusion experiments.

3. Phages "purified" by two different methods show no evidence of change in size.

4. Size of a phage is an important factor in controlling the size of plaque produced. Small phages tend to give rise to large plaques on agar, and conversely.

REFERENCES

Barnard, J. E., and Elford, W. J. 1931. Proc. Roy. Soc. B. **109**: 360.

Bechhold, H., and Villa, L. 1926. Zeitschr. Hyg. Infektskr. **105**: 601.

Biemond, A. G. (Jun.). 1924. *Ibid.* **103**: 681.

Bronfenbrenner, J. 1927. J. Exp. Med. **45**: 873.

Bürgers, and Bachmann, W. 1924. Zeitschr. Hyg. Infektskr. **101**: 350.

Burnet, F. M., and McKie, M. 1930, *a*. J. Path. Bact. **33**: 637; 1930, *b*. Austral. J. Exp. Biol. Med. Sci., **7**: 199.

Elford, W. J. 1931. J. Path. Bact. **34**: 505; 1932. In the Press.

Idem and Andrewes, C. H. 1932. Brit. J. Exp. Path. **13**: 36.

Eliava, G., and Suarez, E. 1927. C. R. Soc. Biol. **96**: 462.

Galloway, I. A., and Elford, W. J. 1931. Brit. J. Exp. Path. **12**: 407.

Hetler, D. M., and Bronfenbrenner, J. 1931. J. Gen. Physiol. **14**: 547.

Jermoljewa, Z. W., Bujanowskaja, I. S., and Severin, W. A. 1932. Z. Immun-Forsch. **73**: 360.

Krueger, A. P. 1931. J. Gen. Physiol. **14**: 493.

Idem and Tamada, H. T. 1929, *a*. *Ibid*. **13**: 145; 1929, *b*. Proc. Soc. Exp. Biol. Med. **26**: 530.

Loeb, J. 1922. J. Gen. Physiol. **5**: 109.

McBain, J. W., and Liu, T. H. 1931. J. Amer. Chem. Soc. **53**: 59.

Stassano, H., and de Beaufort, A. C. 1925. C. R. Soc. Biol. **93**: 1378.

1933

Transmission of the Virus through the Eggs of an Insect Vector[1]

by Teikichi Fukushi

Botanical Institute, Faculty of Agriculture, Hokkaido Imperial University, Sapporo. (Comm. by S. Ikena, M.I.A., Oct. 12, 1933.)

One of the most complex, yet challenging, areas of virology is the insect transmission of plant viruses. Its significance is unquestioned with the knowledge that no other group of diseases is so generally dependent upon insects for dissemination of the infectious causal entity. Japanese investigators are credited with much of the historical studies on the transmission of plant virus diseases by insects. Hatsuzo Hashimoto in 1883, a rice grower in Japan, was the first to prove experimentally the relation of leafhoppers to the stunt disease of rice. Because of his failure to publish the results of his experiments, he remains scientifically unknown, though his historical contribution was an important step toward the recognition of the role of insects in virus diseases. The first publication concerned with insects as vectors of a plant virus disease, dwarf disease of rice, appeared in Japan but was unknown to the Western World for almost 40 years.[2] In the interim during its rediscovery, insect transmission of virus diseases was recognized and verified experimentally by other researchers for both plant and animal viruses.

Insects may acquire a virus and transmit it immediately to a susceptible plant or a lengthy incubation period may ensue before the vector can transmit the virus. This latter mechanism has been the subject of intense interest because it implies that the plant virus multiplies in the insect host. The

---

[1] Reprinted by permission of the author and publisher from the Proc. Imp. Acad. Tokyo. **9**: 457-460 (1933).

[2] Takata, J. Jap. Agr. **171**: 1 (1895).

work of Fukushi in the late 1930's provided the first experimental evidence of plant virus multiplication in insects which was demonstrated by transovarial passage. One of his publications, reprinted here, describes the passage of rice stunt virus through the eggs of infective female leafhoppers to their progeny. The virus was not passed to offspring by the infective male. This was the first authentic transmission of a plant virus through the eggs of the vector. Later, Fukushi reported on the transovarial passage of the virus in the insect vector for six generations.[3] By a similar procedure, Black[4] passed clover clubleaf virus for 21 generations and was able to demonstrate infectivity of the last offspring. It was calculated that the original virus inoculum was diluted by a factor of 10^{26}. The evidence strongly suggested that some plant viruses multiplied in their insect vectors.

In the course of study on the special relationship which exists between the virus of dwarf disease of rice plant and its insect carrier, *Nephotettix apicalis* Motsch. var. *cincticeps* Uhl., the writer obtained evidence to indicate that the virus may be transmitted through the eggs of the leafhopper, by breeding successive generations from infective parents or from crosses between infective females and non-infective males and vice versa. A brief description of the disease was given in the writer's previous paper (1931) and repetition in this short article would be superfluous. A more detailed account will be given in another publication presenting the results of transmission experiments and discussions on the etiology of the disease.

The experimental procedure adopted is as follows. A pair of male and female leafhoppers, either one or both infective, were confined to a young healthy rice plant in a glass tube[5] and allowed to remain there for one day, transferring to a new healthy plant every day. Precaution was taken to confine single nymphs to rice plants in separate glass tubes and to allow them to remain there until they grew into adults in order to obtain female leafhoppers which had never copulated. The eggs are laid in the leafsheath at a few spots near the ground and thrust transversely into the tissue lying one under the other. A few days after oviposition the spot where the eggs are deposited becomes easily discernible by its slightly discolored and

[3] J. Fac. Agr. Hokkaido Imperial Univ. **48**: 85 (1940).

[4] Nature. **166**: 852 (1950).

[5] The glass tube was 30-40 cm. long by 3 cm. in diameter closed at the upper end by a thin cotton cloth and put on a rice plant.

more or less raised surface. The eggs hatch in about ten days. The tiny nymphs just emerged from eggs were transferred to healthy rice plants taking the necessary precautions so that they had no opportunity to feed upon plants on which the eggs had been deposited and which might have been affected by the disease in consequence of the infestation of the infective parents. Daily observations were continued as the hatching of eggs approached and the nymphs which had just emerged from eggs were transferred singly by means of a small camel's hair brush to a young healthy rice plant and a glass tube was put on it. The leafhoppers were allowed to remain there and were kept under observation for two months or longer. The results of experiments will be shown in the following table.

TABLE I. *Virulence of the Progeny of infective leafhoppers*

Parents		No. of progeny tested	No. of viruliferous progeny
Female	Male		
infective female × infective male			
e279-4-3(♀)	e279-4-4(♂)	7	5
e'34(♀)	e'29(♂)	14	13
e'39(♀)	e'36(♂)	8	8
e'49(♀)	e'68(♂)	4	4
e'53(♀)	e'58(♂)	1	1
infective female × uninfective male			
e279(♀)	a(♂)	13	13
e151-4(♀)	b(♂)	16	15
e151-1(♀)	c(♂)	26	17
e151-4-4(♀)	d(♂)	6	0
e279-4(♀)	e(♂)	35	33
e279-1(♀)	f(♂)	27	0
e151-1-16(♀)	g(♂)	30	0
e'51(♀)	h(♂)	8	8
e279-4-5-3-3(♀)	i(♂)	5	5
e'62(♀)	j(♂)	2	2
e'69(♀)	k(♂)	2	0
e'65(♀)	l(♂)	1	1
e'61(♀)	m(♂)	12	6
uninfective female × infective male			
a(♀)	e151-1-22(♂)	9	0
b(♀)	e151-1-13(♂)	19	0
c(♀)	e151-1-13(♂)	5	0
d(♀)	e'47(♂)	9	0
e(♀)	e279-4-32(♂)	14	0
f(♀)	e'64(♂)	4	0
g(♀)	e'72(♂)	3	0

(♀ and ♂ denote infective male and female respectively while ♀ and ♂ stand for uninfective male and female.)

As shown above the majority of the offspring from the infective parents proved to be viruliferous and the progeny from the crosses between non-infective females and infective males were entirely free from virus whereas those from the crosses between infective females and non-infective males were either viruliferous or free from virus. It appears that the eggs are not affected by the virus after they have been deposited in the leafsheaths but probably at an early stage of their development in the ovary of the maternal insect body, because in no case has it been observed that the infective progeny emerged out of the eggs from non-infective females which had been laid in the leafsheaths of diseased plants. It is worthy of note that some individuals of the progeny from the infective females were viruliferous while others from the same parents were apparently free from virus. This appears to indicate that all the ova produced in an ovary are not always affected by the virus.

Although a number of virus diseases of plants have been demonstrated to be transmissible by the agency of certain insects, in no case has it been shown that the virus is transmitted through the eggs of an insect carrier. McClintock and Smith (1918) reported that the virus of spinach blight (or spinach mosaic) is transmitted from infective aphids to their vivipariously produced progeny up to the fourth generation. This was the only evidence yet recorded that indicates the possible transmission of virus from infective insect vectors to their offspring. Hoggan (1933), however, has been unable to confirm their conclusion.

Dwarf disease of rice plant, therefore, occupies a unique position among the virus diseases of plants for the reason of its transmission through the eggs of the insect vector.

According to Murata (1915, 1931), Onuki and Murata, formerly entomologists in the Imperial Agricultural Experiment Station were probably the first to notice that the offspring from infective leafhoppers are capable of producing dwarf disease in healthy rice plants. In 1902? they found that certain leafhoppers emerged from the eggs which had been taken from the Prefecture of Shiga where this trouble was prevalent at that time produced infections in healthy rice plants. However, they gave no detailed account of it. The idea generally prevailing at that time was that the disease was due to the infestation of leafhoppers and these entomologists considered the capability of producing dwarf disease to be a characteristic specific to the leafhoppers native to the Prefecture of Shiga, because all the leafhoppers of the same species taken in the vicinity of Tokyo failed to produce infections in healthy rice plants. Subsequently they found that even non-infective leafhoppers from Tokyo became infective after feeding upon dwarf diseased rice plants. Murata briefly stated that the capability of producing dwarf disease was transmitted from infective parents to their progeny through 3 or 4 generations but he presented no experimental procedures nor results which are considered to be indispensable to induce such very significant conclusions.

At any rate these entomologists were evidently in ignorance of the fact that they were dealing with a virus disease in dwarf disease of rice plant and that the virus may be transmitted through the eggs of the leaf-hopper, Nephotettix apicalis Motsch. var. cincticeps Uhl.

1935

Isolation of a Crystalline Protein Possessing the Properties of Tobacco-Mosaic Virus[1]

by Wendell M. Stanley

The Rockefeller Institute for Medical Research, Princeton, N.J.

A new era of virus research was initiated with Stanley's report of the first isolation and crystallization of a virus—tobacco mosaic. The procedure employed by Stanley for its crystallization involved a series of precipitation techniques which were used primarily in work with proteins. Although many researchers had probably obtained virus preparations of considerable purity, a decisive correlation of biological activity with the chemical entity was lacking. Stanley demonstrated that the crystals of tobacco mosaic virus at high dilutions induced the typical disease on inoculation in tobacco plants and, thereby, established conclusively the infectiousness of his preparation. This startling achievement supplied a powerful stimulus which intensified the biochemical approach to virus purification and to the chemical and structural analyses of virus particles.

A crystalline material, which has the properties of tobacco-mosaic virus, has been isolated from the juice of Turkish tobacco plants infected with this virus. The crystalline material contains 20 per cent. nitrogen and 1 per cent. ash, and a solution containing 1 milligram per cubic centimeter gives a positive test with Millon's, biuret, xanthoproteic, glyoxylic acid, and Folin's tyrosine reagents.

[1] Reprinted by permission of the author and publisher from Science. **81**: 644-645 (1935).

The Molisch and Fehlings tests are negative, even with concentrated solutions. The material is precipitated by 0.4 saturated ammonium sulfate, by saturated magnesium sulfate, or by safranine, ethyl alcohol, acetone, trichloracetic acid, tannic acid, phosphotungstic acid and lead acetate. The crystalline protein is practically insoluble in water and is soluble in dilute acid, alkali or salt solutions. Solutions containing from 0.1 per cent. to 2 per cent. of the protein are opalescent. They are fairly clear between pH 6 and 11 and between pH 1 and 4, and take on a dense whitish appearance between pH 4 and 6.

The infectivity, chemical composition and optical rotation of the crystalline protein were unchanged after 10 successive crystallizations. In a fractional crystallization experiment the activity of the first small portion of crystals to come out of solution was the same as the activity of the mother liquor. When solutions are made more alkaline than about pH 11.8 the opalescence disappears and they become clear. Such solutions are devoid of activity and it was shown by solubility tests that the protein had been denatured. The material is also denatured and its activity lost when solutions are made more acid than about pH 1. It is completely coagulated and the activity lost on heating to 94°C. Preliminary experiments, in which the amorphous form of the protein was partially digested with pepsin, or partially coagulated by heat, indicate that the loss in activity is about proportional to the loss of native protein. The molecular weight of the protein, as determined by two preliminary experiments on osmotic pressure and diffusion, is of the order of a few millions. That the molecule is quite large is also indicated by the fact that the protein is held back by collodion filters through which proteins such as egg albumin readily pass. Collodion filters which fail to allow the protein to pass also fail to allow the active agent to pass. The material readily passes a Berkefeld "W" filter.

The crystals are over 100 times more active than the suspension made by grinding up diseased Turkish tobacco leaves, and about 1,000 times more active than the twice-frozen juice from diseased plants. One cubic centimeter of a 1 to 1,000,000,000 dilution of the crystals has usually proved infectious. The disease produced by this, as well as more concentrated solutions, has proved to be typical tobacco mosaic. Activity measurements were made by comparing the number of lesions produced on one half of the leaves of plants of Early Golden Cluster bean, *Nicotiana glutinosa* L., or *N. langsdorffii* Schrank after inoculation with dilutions of a solution of the crystals, with the number of lesions produced on the other halves of the same leaves after inoculation with dilutions of a virus preparation used for comparison.

The sera of animals injected with tobacco-mosaic virus give a precipitate when mixed with a solution of the crystals diluted as high as 1 part in 100,000. The sera of animals injected with juice from healthy tobacco plants give no precipitate when mixed with a solution of the crystals. Injection of solutions of the crystals into animals causes the production of a precipitin that is active for solutions of the crystals and juice of plants containing tobacco-mosaic virus but that is inactive for juice of normal plants.

The material herein described is quite different from the active crystalline material mentioned by Vinson and Petre and by Barton-Wright and McBain, which consisted, as Caldwell has demonstrated, largely of inorganic matter having no connection with the activity. These preparations were less active than ordinary juice from diseased plants, and the activity they possessed diminished on further crystallizations.

The crystalline protein described in this paper was prepared from the juice of Turkish tobacco plants infected with tobacco-mosaic virus. The juice was brought to 0.4 saturation with ammonium sulfate and the precipitated globulin fraction thus obtained was removed by filtration. The dark brown globulin portion was repeatedly fractionated with ammonium sulfate and then most of the remaining color was removed by precipitation with a small amount of lead subacetate at pH 8.7. An inactive protein fraction was removed from the light yellow colored filtrate by adjusting to pH 4.5 and adding 2 per cent. by weight of standard celite. The celite was removed, suspended in water at pH 8, and the suspension filtered. The active protein was found in the colorless filtrate. This procedure was repeated twice in order to remove completely the inactive protein. Crystallization was accomplished by adding slowly, with stirring, a solution containing 1 cubic centimeter of glacial acetic acid in 20 cubic centimeters of 0.5 saturated ammonium sulfate to a solution of the protein containing sufficient ammonium sulfate to cause a faint turbidity. Small needles about 0.03 millimeters long appeared immediately and crystallization was completed in an hour. Crystallization may also be caused by the addition of a little saturated ammonium or magnesium sulfate to a solution of the protein in 0.001 N acid. Several attempts to obtain crystals by dialyzing solutions of the protein gave only amorphous material. To date a little more than 10 grams of the active crystalline protein have been obtained.

Although it is difficult, if not impossible, to obtain conclusive positive proof of the purity of a protein, there is strong evidence that the crystalline protein herein described is either pure or is a solid solution of proteins. As yet no evidence for the existence of a mixture of active and inactive material in the crystals has been obtained. Tobacco-mosaic virus is regarded as an autocatalytic protein which, for the present, may be assumed to require the presence of living cells for multiplication.

1935

A Protective Action of Neurotropic Against Viscerotropic Yellow Fever Virus in Macacus Rhesus

by Meredith Hoskins

From the Yellow Fever Laboratory of the International Health Division, Rockefeller Foundation, Bahia, Brazil [1]

In the 1930's and early 1940's several unique viral phenomena, namely, interference, transformation (reactivation), and hemagglutination were reported which opened new facets of research on animal viruses. Subsequent studies revealed that these phenomenon had certain practical implications, but more important, was the realization that they provided new approaches for the study of viral multiplication and for exploring virus-cell interrelationships.

Although the interference phenomenon was demonstrated first with plant viruses, classic examples of animal virus interference were first shown experimentally by Hoskins with strains of yellow fever virus, and almost at the same time, by Magrassi[2] with strains of herpes simplex virus. The elicitation of the phenomenon, which may be manifested in a variety of forms, is a complex entity that is dependent on the construction and employment of certain specific conditions. Studies on the mechanisms involved in the phenomenon have revealed many important aspects of viral multiplication at the cellular level. The practical consequences of work on animal virus interference, although not dramatic, have been applicable in veterinary science, for example, therapy against distemper in

[1] The studies and observations on which this paper is based were conducted with the support and under the auspices of the International Health Division of the Rockefeller Foundation. Reprinted by permission of the publisher from the Am. J. Trop. Med. 15: 675-680 (1935).

[2] Ztschr. f. Hyg. u. Infekt. 117: 501, 573 (1935-36).

silver foxes. In addition, the demonstration that reduced im-
munogenic effectiveness may occur when two attenuated
viruses are administered 'as mixtures in vaccines is pertinent
to current trends employing such vaccines for human immu-
nization. The interference phenomenon, in relation to chronic
and mixed viral infections, is still the subject of active investi-
gation.

It was first shown by Theiler (1) that repeated passage of the French strain of yellow fever virus through the brain tissues of white mice leads to some change in the virus so that it no longer causes the visceral lesions of yellow fever when inoculated into *Macacus rhesus*. These observations have been confirmed and extended by Sellards (2), Sawyer, Kitchen, and Lloyd (3), and Lloyd and Penna (4). On the other hand yellow fever virus of the Asibi strain is almost uniformly fatal to *M. rhesus* when inoculated into these animals.

There are here presented the results observed following inoculation of the two above mentioned viruses into *M. rhesus,* both simultaneously and at intervals up to forty-eight hours—the viscerotropic virus always being inoculated first. The details of seventeen experiments, in which forty-eight test animals were used, are set forth in table 1, and the results are summarized in table 2.

Certain explanations of table 1 are necessary. The term "viscerotropic virus" is used to designate the strain of yellow fever virus which has been carried in *M. rhesus* ever since its isolation from a human patient in 1927 and which produces visceral lesions in and is highly fatal to *M. rhesus*. The term "neurotropic virus" is used to designate yellow fever virus of the so-called "French strain," which was isolated by Sellards in Dakar and which has been carried through the central nervous tissues of white mice for more than 200 passages.

In most of the experiments the viscerotropic virus was contained in blood which had been drawn from rhesus monkeys during the highly infectious stage of yellow fever and which had been dried while in the frozen state according to the technic of Sawyer, Lloyd, and Kitchen (5). Exceptions to this were experiments 1, 2, and 17, in which the viscerotropic virus was contained in an emulsion in physiological saline of the liver of a monkey that was killed when ill or moribund with yellow fever; in the first two of these experiments the suspension of liver was subjected to a temperature of 60°C. for thirty minutes in an attempt to inactivate the virus.

The neurotropic virus was contained in an emulsion of the freshly

TABLE 1

Experiment number	Date	Viscerotropic virus	Neurotropic virus	Interval	Test monkey (m. rhesus)		Control monkey (m. rhesus)	
					Number	Fate	Number	Fate
		grams	grams	hours				
1	9/14/32	?*	0.6	0	1	Fever; survived	2	Died of yellow fever, 9th day
2	10/25/32	?*	0.6	0	3	Fever; survived	4	Died of yellow fever, 7th day
3	11/ 5/32	0.025*	0.6	0	5	Late fever; survived	6	Died of yellow fever, 4th day
4A	11/16/32	0.023	0.6	0	7	Fever; survived		
4B	11/18/32	0.03	0.6	0	9	Irregular; survived fever (tuberculosis?)	8	Died of yellow fever, 4th day
4C	11/21/32			16	10	No fever; survived		
5	11/16/32	0.023	0.3†	24	11	Died of yellow fever, 5th day		
6	11/29/32	0.04	0.2	24	12	Died of yellow fever, 5th day		
7	12/ 5/32	0.02	0.6	24	13	No fever; survived		
					14	Died of yellow fever, 7th day		
8	1/ 2/33	0.02	0.6	24	15	Fever; survived	16	Died of yellow fever, 6th day
					17	Early fever; survived		
9	1/11/33	0.02	0.6	30	18	Died of yellow fever, 5th day		
					19	Fever; survived		
10	1/26/33	0.02	0.6	48	20	No fever; survived	21	Died of yellow fever, 5th day
					22	Died of yellow fever, 7th day		
11	2/ 8/33	0.02	0.6	48	23	Died of yellow fever, 7th day		
					25	Died of yellow fever, 6th day	24	Died of yellow fever, 6th day
12	2/ 1/33	0.02	0.6	48	26	Died of yellow fever, 5th day		
					27	Died of yellow fever, 5th day		
13A	2/20/33	0.02	0.6	0	28	Died of colitis, 18th day		
13B	2/20/33			21	29	Died of yellow fever, 6th day		
13C	3/ 1/33			19	30	No fever; survived		
					31	No fever; survived		

TABLE 1. *Continued*

Experiment number	Date	Viscerotropic virus	Neurotropic virus	Interval	Test monkey (m. rhesus)		Control monkey (m. rhesus)	
					Number	Fate	Number	Fate
		grams	*grams*	*hours*				
14A	3/13/33	0.02	0.6	16	32	Slight fever; survived		
					34	Late fever; survived	33	Died of yellow fever, 9th day
14B	3/14/33	0.02*	0.6‡	0	36	No fever; survived		
15	4/10/33	0.02	0.55	24	37	No fever; survived		
					40	Died of yellow fever, 8th day		
					41	Slight fever; survived		
					42	Died of yellow fever, 8th day		
					43	Died 11th day of intercurrent infection		
					44	Died of yellow fever, 5th day	38	Died of yellow fever, 6th day
					45	Died of yellow fever, 5th day	39	Died of yellow fever, 8th day
					46	Fever; survived		
					47	Fever; survived		
					48	Died of yellow fever, 6th day		
16	4/18/33	0.02	0.6	0	49	Died of colitis, 9th day		
					51	Died of colitis, 9th day		
					52	Fever (1 day); survived	50	Died of yellow fever, 6th day
					53	Late fever; survived		
					54	Fever; survived		
					55	Fever; survived		
17	5/28/33	§	0.6	0	56	Fever; survived		
					58	Died of yellow fever, 4th day		
					59	Died 8th day with lesions of yellow fever encephalitis	57	Died of yellow fever, 7th day
					60	Fever; survived		
					61	No fever; survived		

* Intraperitoneally.   ‡ Subcutaneously.
† Dried.   § One cubic centimeter emulsion of infected monkey liver.

TABLE 2. *Summary*

Interval between inoculation of viscerotropic and neurotropic virus	Fate of test monkeys				
		Number died of:			
	Number survived	Viscero-tropic yellow fever	Yellow fever encephalitis	Intercurrent infections	Total
hours					
0	13	1	1	3	18
16	3	0	0	0	3
19	2	0	0	0	2
21	0	1	0	0	1
24	7	8	0	1	16
30	1	1	0	0	2
48	1	5	0	0	6
Total..........	27	16	1	4	48

removed brains of white mice that had been killed when sick or moribund with yellow fever encephalitis.

The route of inoculation of the two viruses, whether subcutaneous or intraperitoneal, appeared to make little difference. The viscerotropic virus was inoculated subcutaneously except in experiments 1, 2, 3, and 14B, in which it was inoculated intraperitoneally. The neurotropic virus was inoculated intraperitoneally except in experiment 14B, in which it was inoculated subcutaneously.

The amounts which were inoculated of each of the two viruses are shown in table 1. The most commonly used amounts were 0.02 gram of dried blood containing viscerotropic virus and 0.6 gram of brain emulsion containing the neurotropic virus.

The virulence of each lot of the viscerotropic virus used was controlled by inoculating a monkey with it alone. That the viscerotropic virus which was used in each of the experiments was highly potent is attested by the fact that in each experiment there died of yellow fever, with typical visceral lesions, either the control monkey which received viscerotropic virus alone or one or more of the test monkeys which received both of the viruses.

Of the forty-eight test monkeys used in these experiments (see table 2) four died of intercurrent infections without any lesions of yellow fever while under observation. These may be eliminated from consideration, as may also the one monkey (no. 59) that died with lesions in the central nervous system identical with those found in yellow fever encephalitis. It may be noted that no symptoms which might be attributable to these lesions were observed in this monkey prior to death.

From table 2 it may be seen that neurotropic virus appears to have a very definite protective effect when administered simultaneously with viscerotropic virus. Thirteen of the fifteen animals receiving the two viruses simultaneously survived, and only one of the two deaths which occurred was due to viscerotropic yellow fever. When the neurotropic virus was administered from 16 to 24 hours after the viscerotropic virus, 12 of 21 animals survived, and apparently complete protection was obtained up to the twenty-hour interval. But when the neurotropic virus was administered after an interval of forty-eight hours there appeared to be no protective effect—which is not surprising in view of the short incubation period of the disease in rhesus monkeys.

We have no adequate explanation for this apparently very definite protective effect of the neurotropic virus, especially when it is administered simultaneously with the viscerotropic virus, and to a lesser extent when it is administered up to twenty-four hours afterward. We may remark that tests for the presence of protective substances in emulsions of brains of mice killed while moribund with yellow fever encephalitis have been negative.

REFERENCES

1. Theiler, M. 1930. Ann. Trop. Med. and Parasit. **XXIV:** 249.

2. Sellards, A. W. 1931. Proc. Nat. Acad. Sci. **XVII:** 339.

3. Sawyer, W. A., Kitchen, S. F., and Lloyd, W. 1932. J. Exp. Med. **LV:** 945.

4. Lloyd, W., and Penna, H. A. 1933. Am. J. Trop. Med. **VIII:** 1.

5. Sawyer, W. A., Lloyd, W., and Kitchen, S. F. 1929. J. Exp. Med. **I:** 1.

6. Sawyer, W. A., and Lloyd, W. 1931. J. Exp. Med. **LIV:** 533.

1936

The Feulgen Reaction of
the Bacteriophage Substance[1]

by M. Schlesinger

National Institute for Medical Research, London, N.W. 3

The fundamental constituents of viruses were revealed in this brief but important report by Schlesinger. He demonstrated that "purified" preparations of bacteriophage consisted mainly of nucleic acid and protein and that the former was of the deoxyribonucleic type. Schlesinger's approach to the study of viruses in the early 1930's, which involved the purification of these agents and the subsequent biochemical analyses of the viral materials, in retrospect, were a prelusion to modern virus research.

In confirming Stanley's original findings on the crystallization of tobacco mosaic virus, Bawden and Pirie and associates[2] detected the presence of phosphorus and carbohydrates in the form of constituents of nucleic acid in their purified preparations. The nucleic acid was of the ribonucleic type which these investigators identified also in other plant viruses. These demonstrations by Schlesinger and Bawden and Pirie firmly established the nucleoprotein nature of viruses.

Three years ago, a method was described which yielded pure preparations of a *Coli* bacteriophage of large particle size (WLL) in weighable quantities.[3] The high phosphorus content (3.7 per cent) of these preparations and their high affinity for basic

[1] Reprinted by permission of the publisher from Nature. **138:** 508-509 (1936).

[2] Nature. **138:** 1051 (1936).

[3] M. Schlesinger, Biochem. Zeitscher. **264:** 6 (1933).

dyes suggested in connexion with other analytical results that the chief constituent of the particles was of nucleoprotein nature.[4]

It has now been found that they are intensively stained by Feulgen's reagent, generally regarded as a histo-chemical reagent for thymonucleic acid. Bacteria and bacterial debris (even a concentrated preparation of debris of phage-size obtained by lysing the organism with the very small phage S13 which afterwards could be removed by washing) treated in the same way remain unstained. So the phage-substance seems to be chemically different from any constituent of the bacterial cell normally present in significant amounts.

The concentrated and purified preparations of a *Staphylococcus* phage obtained recently by Dr. Elford show exactly the same staining reactions as the WLL-*Coli*-phage.

[4] M. Schlesinger, Biochem. Zeitscher. **273**: 306 (1934).

1936

A Method for Changing the Virus of Rabbit Fibroma (Shope) into that of Infectious Myxomatosis (Sanarelli) [1]

by George P. Berry and Helen M. Dedrick

University of Rochester, School of Medicine and Dentistry.

This short but intriguing report remained a virological curiosity for many years. Interest in the phenomenon was rekindled recently, and, in the wake of new research, various hypotheses have been promulgated to explain the exact mechanism of the phenomenon under the terms "transformation," "recombination," and "multiplicity of reactivation." Although it has been cited as the first example of genetic interaction between animal viruses, Fenner and associates support the view that the Berry-Dedrick phenomenon, also demonstrated in their studies with poxviruses, is essentially a process of intracellular "non-genetic reactivation." [2] These divergent views have resulted in an intensification of research on the genetic and non-genetic mechanisms of viral reactivation. In consequence, certain fundamental implications have been recognized which are pertinent to the reactivation of virus particles in vaccines and to the study of the biology of cancer.

The close immunological relationship between rabbit fibroma and infectious myxomatosis led us to explore the hypothesis that the viruses in question are but different strains of one basic virus. Our approach was suggested by Griffith's studies in 1928 on

---

[1] Reprinted by permission of the author and the American Society for Microbiology and The Williams & Wilkins Co., from the J. Bact. 31: 50-51 (1936).

[2] Brit. J. Med. 135-142 (July 21, 1962).

the transformation of pneumococcal types. We believe that we have changed the virus of rabbit fibroma into that of infectious myxomatosis.

The method consisted in inoculating domestic rabbits with a mixture of active fibroma virus and heat inactivated myxoma virus. The fibroma virus was a suspension of pooled dermal and testicular fibromata, the myxoma virus a suspension of primary skin lesions. The myxoma suspensions were inactivated for 30 minutes at 60°C., at 75°C. and at 90°C. Transformation from fibroma to myxoma virus occurred with "60°C. material" in 6 experiments, with "75°C. material" in 2, but not with "90°C. material." Test rabbits developed characteristic fatal myxomatosis, with typical histopathology. Secondary lesions yielded myxoma virus on transfer, and normal animals were infected by simple contact.

Control rabbits outnumbered test animals. Inoculations and serial transfers of heat inactivated myxoma suspensions were negative, as were the results of mixing such suspensions with a variety of viruses and other materials.

These experiments suggest that something in myxomatous material, not destroyed at 75°C., lends virulence to fibroma virus, possibly in a manner analogous to bacterial haptenes. This approach may well prove useful in exploring other virus relationships, for instance in the animal pox group, in the foot and mouth disease group, etc.

1939

An Intermediate Host for
the Swine Influenza Virus[1]

by R. E. Shope

The Rockefeller Institute for Medical Research, Princeton, N.J.

Shope had demonstrated previously that the manifestation of swine influenza disease was the result of the concerted action of a bacterium, Hemophilus influenza suis and the virus of swine influenza.[2] The complex etiology and epidemiology of swine influenza was elucidated further in the paper presented here. The survival of the virus during interepidemic periods was found to involve swine lungworm larvae which harbor the agent throughout their development in the intermediate host, the earthworm, and in the definitive host, the swine. The role of the intermediate host in perpetuating the disease was found to exist on a large scale in nature. Other viral diseases of animals in which the etiological agent depended on a intermediate host for interepidemic survival were salmon poisoning in dogs, bovine pseudorabies, and East African swine fever. Studies on the habitat and survival mechanisms of viruses in nature, exemplified by Shope's classic study, are vital to the broader understanding and effective control of virus diseases.

Swine influenza is a disease in which two infectious agents, one a virus and the other a bacterium, are etiologically essential. The disease, either as it occurs naturally in the field or as it is transmitted experimentally in the laboratory, is highly contagious, and no intermediate host is required to explain its epidemiology, once an

---

[1] Reprinted by permission of the author and publisher from Science. **89**: 441-442 (1939).

[2] J. Exp. Med. **54**: 373 (1931).

epizootic has started. However, no satisfactory explanation of how or where the disease persists during the 8 or 9 months elapsing between the yearly epizootics has yet been advanced. During much interepizootic periods the swine population in the middle western hog-raising states is, so far as can be told, free of swine influenza. The bacterial component of the etiological complex, *H. influenzae suis,* can persist apparently indefinitely in the upper respiratory tracts of some recovered swine, but similar persistence of the virus can not be demonstrated. The origin or source of swine influenza virus responsible for the fresh epizootics each autumn thus has remained obscure. It is with the epidemiology of these "first cases" of swine influenza that the experiments to be briefly outlined in the present paper are concerned.

Because the swine lungworm, a nematode parasitic in the bronchioles of the bases of the lungs of swine, enters prominently into the experiments to be described, a short account of its life cycle, as determined by the Hobmaiers[3] and by Schwartz and Alicata,[4] will be given. The cycle in brief is as follows. The embryonated lungworm ovum passed in the swine feces is swallowed by an earthworm, in which it hatches as a first-stage larva. After undergoing development within the earthworm the larva eventually reaches its third stage in which it is capable of infesting swine. It remains in this stage until its earthworm intermediate host is ingested by a swine, when it is liberated, penetrates the swine intestinal mucosa and migrates to the respiratory tract by way of the lymphatics and blood stream. The whole of this cycle can occupy a span of several years for its completion or, under the most favorable conditions, can be completed in slightly less than one month. Lungworms constitute a very common parasite in swine reared under the usual farm conditions.

In the present experiments feces and bronchial exudate, containing embryonated lungworm ova, and adult lungworms were obtained from swine that had been ill of swine influenza for from three to five days. This material, after mincing the adult lungworms with scissors to free their ova, was mixed with loamy topsoil and fed to earthworms. Beginning one month later, earthworms were removed from time to time, from the barrels of earth in which they were kept, for use in experiments. They were fed to swine intact but usually mixed with a small amount of dry grain feed. Two swine fed in this way in the first experiment remained apparently normal, and it seemed that the experiment must be interpreted as negative. These two particular swine had, prior to their earthworm feeding, been used in another experiment during the course of which they had received three intramuscular injections of a suspension of live *H. influenzae suis* at eight-day intervals. They had developed no illness. After

---

[3] A. Hobmaier and M. Hobmaier, Münch. Tier. Woch. **80:** 365 and 433 (1929).

[4] B. Schwartz and J. E. Alicata, Jour. Parasit. **16:** 105 (1929-30); **18:** 21 (1931); and U.S. Dept. Agric. Tech. Bull. No. (456) (1934).

the apparently negative result of the earthworm feeding there was occasion to inject them again intramuscularly with a suspension of live *H. influenzae suis*. On the third day following this injection they developed clinically typical swine influenza. With this fortuitous suggestion that a provocative stimulus was required to elicit infection, other similar experiments were conducted. Swine were fed the lungworm-infested earthworms and developed neither illness nor virus-neutralizing antibodies. After a period of observation of from 11 to 30 days they were injected intramuscularly with a suspension of living *H. influenzae suis*. No illness resulted from the first injection. However, when the injection was repeated eight days later, characteristic swine influenza resulted after three days.

In other experiments the procedure was varied to coincide with that of the initial experiment, and in these the swine received two preliminary intramuscular injections of suspensions of live *H. influenzae suis* at eight-day intervals before being fed lungworm-infested earthworms. After the earthworm feeding, sufficient time for the lungworms to complete their migration to the swine respiratory tract was allowed to elapse. Then the swine were again injected intramuscularly with a suspension of live *H. influenzae suis*. Swine influenza usually resulted on the third day after this injection, although in two instances its appearance was delayed until the fourth and fifth days.

In all experiments the clinical diagnosis of swine influenza was confirmed either by the direct demonstration of swine influenza virus by mouse inoculation or by the development of specific swine influenza virus-neutralizing antibodies in the sera of swine that were allowed to recover. Numerous control swine have been given series of from three to twelve intramuscular injections of suspensions of living *H. influenza suis* at eight-day intervals with entirely negative results. In like manner no swine fed the lungworm-infested earthworms has developed swine influenza without a provocative stimulus having been first applied. Earthworms that had been fed lungworm ova as long as three months earlier have been used successfully. The results of experiments over longer periods of time are not yet complete.

Swine influenza virus has not yet been demonstrated directly by mouse inoculation, either in earthworms known to be carrying infective third-stage lungworm larvae or in lungworms obtained from swine thought to be ready for provocation. If this finding is duplicated in a larger series of tests it would appear that the virus in the intermediate host is present either in very minute quantities or in a masked form. However, in a single experiment containing two swine, the animals were given the provoking stimulus and one was killed the day before the expected onset of illness. Swine influenza virus was demonstrated in or about the lungworms obtained from the bronchi at the bases of the lung of this animal but not in the anterior lobes usually involved in swine influenza. The following day the second swine in the experiment came down with typical swine influenza. It was autopsied, showed pulmonary alterations characteristic of early swine influenza, and swine influenza virus was abundantly present not only about the lungworms at the bases but in the pneumonic anterior lobes as well.

The present experiments have been conducted with known species mixtures of both lungworms and earthworms. Dr. Norman R. Stoll has kindly identified the lungworms employed as *Metastrongylus elongatus* and *Choerostrongylus pudendotectus,* while Dr. Libbie Hyman has tentatively identified the earthworms being used as *Helodrilus foetidus, Helodrilus caliginosus* var. *trapezoides, Octolasium lacteum* and *Lumbricus terrestris.* Furthermore, all experimental swine thus far employed have been carrying lungworm infestations of various degrees prior to their use. Experiments with single pure species of either lungworms or earthworms or with lungworm-free swine have not yet been completed.

The findings described are tentatively interpreted in the following way. Lungworm larvae from pigs with swine influenza harbor swine influenza virus throughout their development both in their intermediate host, the earthworm, and in their definitive host, the swine. The virus apparently lies latent within the lungworm after the parasite has finally migrated to the swine respiratory tract and is only liberated or activated to cause infection when a provocative stimulus is applied. In the experiments just outlined multiple intramuscular injections of *H. influenzae suis* are believed to have supplied the provocative stimulus. *H. influenzae suis* does not, however, appear to be specific or requisite as the provocative agent because, in a preliminary experiment, a single intrapleural injection of calcium chloride solution has served equally well in provoking the swine influenza virus infection.

1941

The Agglutination of Red Cells by Allantoic Fluid of Chick Embryos Infected with Influenza Virus[1]

by George K. Hirst

The Laboratories of the International Health Division of
The Rockefeller Foundation, New York

*The agglutination of red cells (hemagglutination) by viruses,
first noted in the process of harvesting allantoic fluid from
chick embryos infected with influenza virus, was reported by
Hirst and observed, independently, by McClelland and Hare.[2]
The long periods of obscurity that are associated often with
important discoveries before their potential is realized was
lacking, fortunately, in this circumstance. In contrast, the
fundamental and practical significance of the agglutination
phenomenon was exploited rapidly. Under varied conditions,
the reaction was reported to occur with other myxoviruses,
poxviruses, and members of the arthropod-borne group of
viruses. The hemagglutination-inhibition test, based on the
capacity of specific immune serum to inhibit agglutination of
red cells by virus, was a practical facet of the phenomenon. It
proved particularly valuable in the differentiation of virus
strains and in the diagnosis of infection by measuring the specific antibody response.*

*The heuristic value of the phenomenon is apparent from
the revealing studies that were made subsequently on the interaction between the virus particle and the cell surface. The
phenomenon proved to be an excellent model for the investigation of the early stages of virus infection without interven-*

[1] Reprinted by permission of the author and publisher from Science. 94: 22-23 (July
4, 1941).

[2] Canad. Public Hlth. J. 32: 530 (1941).

*tion from later stages of the viral growth cycle. The data that
was forthcoming from researches provided new knowledge on
the nature of the cell surface in relation to virus adsorption.
The enzymatic activity of some viruses, identification of their
substrate, the role of these substrates in virus attachment, and
the recognition of viral inhibitors were aspects of research that
supplied fruitful information for our understanding of virus
infections.*

When the allantoic fluid from chick embryos previously infected with strains of influenza A virus was being removed, it was noted that the red cells of the infected chick, coming from ruptured vessels, agglutinated in the allantoic fluid. Since red cells in the allantoic fluid of chick embryos inoculated with sterile materials did not agglutinate at all, it seemed that this agglutination phenomenon might be the result of infection with influenza virus in the chick.

To demonstrate the agglutination phenomenon in the infected chick embryos, the egg shell was opened over the air sac. The outer chorioallantoic membrane was torn away, and several large blood vessels were purposely ruptured. Fifteen to 30 seconds were allowed for the embryo to bleed into the allantoic fluid before the contents of the allantoic sac were emptied into a petri dish. If the embryo had been infected with influenza virus, macroscopic agglutination of the red cells occurred within 15 to 30 seconds in the petri dish. If the agglutination did not appear promptly, it usually did not occur at all, and the differentiation between positive and negative eggs was easy. Virus titrations and serum neutralization tests were then set up in eggs, with this agglutination phenomenon as an index of infection. Egg-passage viruses and ferret sera were used in these tests. One-tenth cc of the material was inoculated into the allantoic sac of 11-day old embryos which were then allowed to incubate for 2 days. The eggs were opened by the method described above, and positive and negative reactions were recorded. By using eggs in the same way that mice are used in serum titrations and virus titrations, it was found that serum neutralization tests and virus neutralization tests could be performed. The end points were as sharp as those obtained in the mouse test. The agglutination reaction worked equally well with strains of influenza A or B virus and with swine influenza virus. Cross-neutralization tests were then set up with these viruses, which gave results consistent with the specificity of these strains as established in mice. A neutralization test with acute and convalescent serum from a case of influenza A demonstrated a rise in antibody titer in the convalescent serum which was consistent with the rise obtained in similar tests in mice.

Throat washings have been passed in eggs, and while this phase of the work is in a preliminary stage, we have so far isolated two strains of influenza A virus directly from throat washings and obtained the agglutination phenomenon in the chick embryo on the second passage. The virus from these throat washings was set up in a neutralization test with A and B antiserum in eggs and its identity as A virus was established. In one case the total elapsed time from inoculation of the throat washings until the confirmation of the identity of the virus by specific serum was only 9 days. Whether B virus and other as yet undescribed viruses from influenza cases will behave similarly is now being determined.

At present neither the mechanism of the agglutination phenomenon nor its specificity for influenza virus infection is well understood. However, the following facts have emerged:

(a) When infected allantoic fluid, either fresh or stored at $-72°C.$ (from which the red cells had been removed by low-speed centrifugation), was mixed in a test tube with washed normal adult chick red cells, an agglutination phenomenon occurred. This *in vitro* agglutination was somewhat slower than the one previously described. Here a positive agglutination reaction was usually visible in 5 to 20 minutes. The red cells sedimented rapidly and formed a characteristic, ragged, granular pattern on the bottom of the tube. If red cells were added in the test tube to allantoic fluid from uninfected chicks, only the slow sedimentation of red cells occurred with no aggregation, and in settling out the cells formed a sharp round disk in the bottom of the tube. If the allantoic fluid from chicks infected with PR8 virus was diluted before adding the red cells, agglutination was still visible in a concentration of 1:512 (final concentration of allantoic fluid).

(b) When normal chick embryo red cells were added in sufficient numbers to allantoic fluid and allowed to settle out, over 99 per cent. of the virus disappeared from the supernatant fluid.

(c) When the allantoic fluid was centrifuged (45 minutes, 11,500 r.p.m.) the "titer" of the supernatant in terms of agglutinating capacity dropped approximately four times. This fall in agglutinating titer was consistent with the expected drop in virus titer as determined by previous tests in mice with the same fluid which showed that 70 to 90 per cent. of the virus was sedimented.

(d) If, instead of infected allantoic fluid, the supernatant from centrifuged ground mouse lung infected with PR8 mouse passage virus was used, the added red cells agglutinated in a dilution as high as 1:5000 (final concentration of mouse lung).

(e) When influenza A ferret antiserum (PR8) in dilutions as high as

1:1024 was mixed with allantoic fluid infected with homologous virus, the agglutination phenomenon was inhibited. The inhibition was specific, that is, influenza B ferret antiserum in dilutions as low as 1:8 failed to inhibit the agglutination of red cells by fluids containing influenza A virus.

(f) Such inhibition also occurred with human serum, and in Table I

TABLE I. *Comparison between in vitro inhibition of red cell agglutination and mouse neutralization tests with acute phase and convalescent serum from a case of influenza A*

Serum	Constant amount of infected allantoic fluid tested against various dilutions of serum*		Results of neutralization test in mice against uniform dose of virus†	
	Dilution of serum	Agglutination after 1 hour	No. died	No. survived
Acute	1:8	++	4	0
	1:16	++++		
	1:32	++++	4	0
	1:64	++++		
Convalescent........	1:8	—	0	4
	1:16	—		
	1:32	—	0	4
	1:64	—		
	1:128	—	0	4
	1:256	—		
	1:512	+	3	1
	1:1024	+++		
Saline control, no virus		—		
Virus control, no serum		++++		

* The W.S. strain of influenza virus was used for the infection of chick embryos.
† The PR8 strain of influenza virus was used for the protection test in mice.

is a titration of acute and convalescent serum from a proven case of influenza A. Dilutions of serum were mixed with a constant amount of W.S. infected allantoic fluid; then a constant amount of chick embryo red cell suspension was added, and the agglutination was read in 1 hour. The change of titer of this agglutination-inhibiting substance following infection is obvious and appears to be of the same order of magnitude as the rise in the patient's neutralizing titer against PR8 virus as determined in the mouse.

Such an *in vitro* test as shown in Table I will be of great advantage over the mouse neutralization tests if it can be shown that it measures influenza neutralizing antibodies. Our results so far suggest that the amount of agglutination-inhibiting substances in sera parallels the neutralizing antibody titer more closely than the complement-fixing titer. Whether this *in vitro* test will be sensitive and specific enough to replace the mouse protection method for determining serum neutralizing antibodies, is a problem at present under investigation. A more complete report will be published at a later date.

1946

Induced Mutations in Bacterial Viruses[1]

by M. Delbrück and W. T. Bailey, Jr.

The phenomenon of genetic recombination was first discovered by Delbrück and Bailey in studies on mixed infections with related bacterial viruses and, independently, by Hershey.[2] Recognition of genetic recombination depends on the presence of distinct mutant factors in parent viruses employed in mixed infection experiments and the appearance of mutant factors of both parents in progeny. Detailed studies by Hershey and Rotman[3] established the importance of this phenomenon as a method of genetic analyses. By construction of a genetic map of the phage particle, they showed through recombination tests that independent mutants occupy loci at different positions on the map and that they may be arranged in a linear fashion. Two major theories have evolved to explain genetic recombination on a molecular basis, i.e., the classical "crossing-over" and "copy-choice." [4]

The accrual of fundamental information from recombination studies with bacteriophage, a system ammenable to experiments of this nature, are directly applicable to the replication of other viruses and is, therefore, a unifying influence in general virology. That recombination may have a bearing on the cyclic occurrence of viral epidemics, the survival of the agent in the interim, and the subtle changes in antigenic structure of some viruses are some practical considerations which may be explored through studies of this phenomenon.

[1] This work was supported by grants-in-aid from The Rockefeller Foundation and from the John and Mary R. Markle Foundation. Reprinted by permission of the author and publisher from the Cold Spring Harbor Symp. Quant. Biol. **XI**: 33-37 (1946).

[2] Genetics. **31**: 620 (1946).

[3] Genetics. **34**: 44 (1949).

[4] Lederberg. J. Cell. Comp. Physiol. **45**, Suppl. 2: 75 (1955).

In another paper of this Symposium, to which ours is closely related and to which we refer the reader for a description of material and for terminology, Dr. Hershey (4) has described a variety of spontaneously occurring mutations of bacterial viruses. One class of mutations affects the type of plaque. These mutations occur in only one group of serologically related viruses, the group to which belong T2, T4, and T6. The most conspicuous of these mutations is the *r* mutation. Our observations are concerned exclusively with this *r* mutation. We have seen also some of the other mutations which affect the type of plaque and which Hershey has described, but we have not made systematic experiments concerning them.

We have infected bacteria simultaneously with mixtures of wild type and *r* mutant of the viruses T2, T4, and T6, and have investigated the yields of virus from such mixedly infected bacteria. These experiments are a sequel to previous studies of mixed infections with pairs of different viruses. The chief result of the studies to be reported here is the fact that the yield of virus from mixedly infected bacteria may contain a high proportion of one or more new types of virus—i.e., of a type that was not used for the infection. In all cases the new types exhibit combinations of the genetic markers of the infecting types.

MUTUAL EXCLUSION

We will begin with a recapitulation of earlier work on mixed infections (3, 6, 2). The chief finding of these earlier studies was the mutual-exclusion effect. It was found that any mixedly infected bacterium yields upon lysis only one of the infecting types of virus. The other virus does not multiply; even the adsorbed particles of the excluded type are not recovered upon lysis. Which one of the two types of virus used for infection is excluded and which one multiplies depends on the pair used and on the conditions of the experiment, such as timing and multiplicity of infection. For the pair T1, T2 the virus T1 is always excluded except when it is given a head start of at least four minutes (3). If T1 is added more than four minutes earlier than T2, then T2 will be excluded in an appreciable proportion of the infected bacteria. Lysis of any one bacterium always occurs after a time interval corresponding to the latent period of intracellular virus multiplication of the virus type which does multiply in that particular bacterium.

A similar situation was encountered (2) in the study of the pair T1, T7. Here, too, the mutual-exclusion mechanism operates perfectly; in practically every bacterium either one or the other of the two viruses is excluded from multiplication. The exclusion powers of these two viruses are nearly balanced. In a bacterial culture simultaneously infected with

T1 and T7 there is a clean split into T1 yielders and T7 yielders, the two types occurring with comparable frequency.

During a closer study of this pair it became evident that the excluded virus is not without effect on the course of events. The excluded virus may reduce the number of virus particles liberated upon lysis of the bacterium. This has been called the depressor effect (2).

A cursory survey of other pairs of virus particles seemed only to confirm these findings and, in particular, seemed to point to the mutual-exclusion effect as a very general phenomenon.

In these earlier investigations an attempt was made also to test whether mutual exclusion occurs when a bacterium is infected with two particles of the *same* kind. Such an assumption ("self-interference") seemed to suggest itself from the observation that bacteria infected with several particles of one kind are lysed after exactly the same latent period as are bacteria infected with only one particle. The test of mutual exclusion requires that one find out whether the yield of virus from any one bacterium is the offspring of only one or of several of the infecting particles. To make such a test one must be able to differentiate the off-spring of the various infecting particles; in other words, one has to mark the infecting particles with hereditary markers. One is thus naturally led to the study of mutual exclusion between a virus and one of its mutants.

The first attempt in this direction was made by Luria (5), who studied interference between T2 and T2*h*. The difficulty with this pair lies in the fact that no indicator strain resistant to T2*h* and sensitive to T2 is available. Luria succeeded nevertheless in showing that a large proportion of the bacteria infected with T2 *and* T2*h* did not liberate any T2*h*. At least a partial functioning of the mutual-exclusion mechanism seemed to be indicated by these results.

THE BREAKDOWN OF MUTUAL EXCLUSION FOR THE PAIRS (T2r+, T2r) AND (T4r+, T4r)

The first definite indication of a new phenomenon came in March, 1945, when Hershey tried mixed infections with a wild-type strain (T2) and its *r* mutant. Hershey observed that the mixedly infected bacteria give rise to mottled plaques, and he verified that the mottled plaques contain a mixture of the two types used for infection. Dr. Hershey communicated his discovery to us and we have since been following this promising lead.

Mixed Infections with T2r+, T2r

Hershey's finding that the majority of the mixedly infected bacteria give mixed yields was confirmed by two methods; *viz.*, (1) by plating mixedly infected bacteria before lysis, (2) by plating single bursts after lysis (1).

In these experiments the infecting doses of wild type were slightly higher than those of the *r* mutant. Each kind of virus was in at least threefold excess over the bacteria. In the case of simultaneous infection, about one-third of the bacteria gave pure wild-type bursts. Most of the remaining bursts were mixed. These mixed bursts contained wild type and mutant in all proportions. On the average, however, wild type was predominant. The predominance may be due to an inherent advantage of wild type, or it may be due to the fact that in these experiments the infecting doses of wild type were slightly greater than those of the mutant. We have found that the wild type of this strain of virus is somewhat more rapidly absorbed than its r mutant, and the predominance of wild type in the bursts may be due in part to the more rapid adsorption of the wild type.

If the two viruses are not given simultaneously, the ratios are shifted in favor of the virus which precedes. Thus, if wild type precedes by six minutes, almost all bursts are pure wild type. If the r mutant precedes by six minutes, there is a majority of pure r bursts and mixed bursts, but there is still a fair proportion of pure wild type.

MIXED INFECTIONS WITH T4r+, T4r

The results for this pair were similar to those for mixed infections with wild type and r mutant of T2, with the following minor differences:

(1) A greater proportion of the single bursts showed mixed yields (23 out of 25).

(2) The r mutants predominated in the mixed bursts, although all proportions were encountered. Fig. 1 shows the correlations between wild type and r mutant in the individual bursts of one large experiment, in which sixty samples were plated for bursts.

For this pair, too, it was found that wild type is absorbed slightly more rapidly than is its r mutant.

These experiments substantiated Hershey's findings. They showed, moreover, that in the bacteria giving

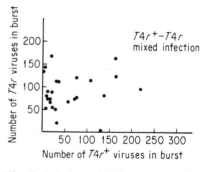

Fig. 1. T4r+ and T4r content of individual bursts of bacteria infected with these viruses. Each dot represents one burst. The abscissa is the T4r+ content, the ordinate the T4r content.

mixed yields all proportions of wild type to r mutant could be found. The results seemed to prove an almost complete breakdown of the mutual-exclusion mechanism, nearly every bacterium yielding virus particles of both the infecting types. However, modifications of the experimental set-up to be reported presently revealed unexpected new features, which throw the interpretation of Hershey's experiment into doubt.

It may be recalled that the first experiments on mixed infection had been undertaken in the hope of obtaining lysis of bacteria at an intermediate stage of intracellular virus multiplication. Our expectation had been that in mixed infection with (T1, T2) the bacteria would be lysed after 13 minutes, the latent period of T1, and that thus an intermediate stage in the multiplication of T2 would be revealed. T2 by itself does not lyse the bacteria until 21 minutes after infection. This hope had been frustrated when mutual exclusion was discovered. Hershey's discovery of an apparently complete breakdown of the mutual-exclusion mechanism for infections with the pair (T2r^+, T2r) revived the hope of studying intermediate stages of intracellular multiplication of viruses. However, the study of pairs like (T2r^+, T2r) suffers from the handicap that indicator strains are not available for obtaining separate counts of the two types. Instead, one has to rely on plaque appearance. The majority of the plaques are clearly differentiated, but there are always a few plaques whose classification is a little uncertain. These would require subculture for verification, a very laborious procedure when large numbers are involved. For this reason we eventually (October, 1945) decided to try the pairs (T2, T4), (T6, T4), and (T2, T6). These viruses are closely related to each other serologically and morphologically, but they are otherwise independent wild types, and indicator strains which sharply distinguish between them are available. The r mutation was used as an additional genetic marker.

THE BREAKDOWN OF MUTUAL EXCLUSION FOR THE PAIRS
(T4, T2), (T4, T6), AND (T2, TN)

In Hershey's case of mixed infection with wild type and r mutant, a breakdown of mutual exclusion is indicated by the appearance of mottled plaques when mixedly infected bacteria are plated. For pairs with host-range differences another criterion can be employed, the appearance of clear plaques in platings on mixed indicator strains (2). Any bacterium that liberates at least one particle of each of the infecting types can lyse both indicator strains, while any bacterium that liberates only particles of one of the infecting types will form a plaque which is overgrown by the indicator strain for the other type and which will therefore be turbid. A comparison of plaque counts on mixed indicators and on strain B gives the fraction of the bacteria with mixed yields—i.e., the fraction of the bacteria in which the mutual-exclusion mechanism failed to operate.

Table 1 lists the fraction of mixed yielders for a variety of combinations between the wild types and r mutants of T2, T4, and T6. The breakdown of the mutual-exclusion mechanism is particularly marked for the combinations involving T2. These findings would seem to fit well with Hershey's findings, and to suggest the generalization that mutual exclusion operates the more perfectly the more dissimilar the two infecting viruses.

TABLE 1. *The breakdown of the mutual-exclusion principle*

Infecting pair		% Mixed yielders
T6	T4	
r^+	r^+	Few
r	r	10
r	r^+	20
r^+	r	12
T2	T4	
r^+	r^+	60-90
r^+	r	60-90
r	r^+	80
T2	T6	
r^+	r	80

Wild type and r mutant give no mutual exclusion, serologically closely related viruses give partial mutual exclusion, and unrelated viruses give complete mutual exclusion.

The Nature of the T2 Particles Liberated by Mixedly Infected Bacteria Involving T2

A paradoxical feature occurred in all the combinations involving T2. When mixedly infected bacteria were plated, the number of *clear* plaques on mixed indicators was in all cases much greater than the number of plaques on the indicator for T2. The number of clear plaques *on mixed indicators* gives the number of bacteria which liberate a mixture of the infecting types. The number of plaques *on the T2 indicator* gives the number of bacteria which liberate T2, irrespective of whether or not such a bacterium also liberates the other type. The latter plaque count comprises two classes, the mixed yielders plus the pure T2 yielders. The mixed indicators show only one of these classes, the mixed yielders. It follows that the count on mixed indicators should always be smaller than, or at most equal to, the count on the T2 indicator, contrary to the actual finding.

The possibility was considered that the clear plaques found on mixed indicators might be due, not to a mixed yield of T2 and T4 particles, but to host-range mutants. Conceivably, host-range mutants might arise during the growth of the plaques and these mutants might be responsible for the lysis of both indicator strains. It must be realized that mixed indicators constitute an ideal enrichment medium for host-range mutants.

This possibility was ruled out by two tests. First, the viruses in question were plated separately on the same pair of mixed indicators. No clear plaques were found. This shows that host-range mutants in sufficient number to cause clear plaques on mixed indicators do not occur when the viruses are plated separately. Second, the contents of ten of the clear plaques from platings of mixedly infected bacteria on mixed indicators were analyzed for their virus content. Each of these plaques contained a mixture of particles with host ranges characteristic of the infecting types, and no particles with extended host range.

It follows that the clear plaques on mixed indicators are due to genuine mixed yields of T2 and T4 particles. The low count of T2 yielders on the indicator for T2 must mean that a considerable proportion of the putative T2 particles liberated from mixedly infected bacteria fail to form plaques on the T2 indicator. The T2 particles used for infection in these experiments do not have this property; they register with the same efficiency on the T2 indicator as on mixed indicators. The low efficiency of plating of the T2 particles in the yields from mixedly infected bacteria is not a hereditary property. Their progeny registers with the same efficiency on the T2 indicator as on mixed indicators.

It might be mentioned in passing that there are many T2 indicator strains of the type B/4 on which the normal T2 exhibits a low efficiency of plating. In fact the strain of B/4 employed in these experiments is unique in registering T2 with full efficiency of plating. This strain was isolated by Dr. Hershey. The question arose whether the low efficiency of plating of the normal T2 on the other strains of B/4 is also increased by the addition of B/2. Experiments showed that this is not the case. Therefore, low efficiency of plating of the T2 particles liberated from mixedly infected bacteria must be caused by a specific property of these particles.

The findings may be summarized as follows. A large proportion of bacteria mixedly infected with T4 and T2, or T6 and T2, give mixed yields. The liberated T2 particles have a low efficiency of plating on the T2 indicator but not on mixed indicators. The low efficiency of plating of these particles on the T2 indicator is not a hereditary property.

More experiments will be needed to clarify this situation. Specifically, the role of the second indicator strain in raising the efficiency of plating of the liberated T2 particles has to be clarified. This indicator strain by itself is totally resistant to T2. Preliminary experiments have not given any clue to the factor contributed by the second indicator strain.

INDUCED MUTATIONS

We now turn to the principal point of this paper, the occurrence in mixed infections of induced mutations at the r locus. In the experiments described in the two preceding sections, the mixedly infected bacteria were regularly plated on strain B, on each of the indicator strains separately, and on mixed indicators. In some of these experiments one of the infecting viruses was genetically marked by using the r mutant instead of the wild type. It was noted that the platings on one or the other of the indicator strains, or on both, gave a high proportion of mottled plaques.

For instance, in a mixed infection with the viruses (T2r+, T4r) the plating on B/2 gave plaques the majority of which had mottled halos, indicating that the majority of the bacteria had liberated a mixture of wild-type and r-type particles which could attack B/2. Wild-type particles able to attack B/2 had not been used in this experiment. The wild-type particles, therefore, represented a new type, created during the mixed infection.

The creation of wild-type particles with the host range characteristic of T4 was verified in three ways. First, by analyzing the contents of the mottled plaques. These analyses confirmed the assumption of the presence of a mixture of T4r+ and T4r particles. Second, by plating on B/2 after lysis. These plates, too, showed the presence of T4r+, though in smaller proportion, indicating that induced mutants occur in small numbers, though they occur in the yields of the majority of the mixedly infected bacteria. Third, by plating single bursts on B/2. Small numbers of induced mutants were found in the majority of the bursts, confirming the inference of the previous test.

A priori, this new type could have arisen as a modification of either one of the infecting types: either as a modification of T4r by a mutation

$$T4r \rightarrow T4r+ \text{ (under the influence of T2r+),}$$

or as a modification of T2r+ by a mutation

$$T2r+ \rightarrow T4r+ \text{ (under the influence of T4r).}$$

The first assumption implies a mutation at the r locus, the second assumption a mutation at the genetic site (or sites) determining host range. We prefer the first hypothesis for three reasons. First, the mutation at the r locus is known to occur spontaneously and is known to require only one step. Second, a change from the host range characteristic for T2 to that characteristic for T4, as implied in the second assumption, may be expected to require several mutational steps, since T2 and T4 are independent wild types, and since at least two phenotypic changes are involved—namely, loss of activity on B/4 and gain of activity on B/2. Third, when the new type was tested serologically, it was found to be indistinguishable from the infecting type, with the same host range. We therefore believe that the new types arise by a mutation at the r locus, without change of host range.

Table 2 is a summary of the combinations of infecting types which have been tested for the occurrence of induced mutations at the r locus. The data point to three generalizations:

(1) Mutations occur from wild type to r type or from r type to wild type.

(2) Mutations occur only if one of the infecting types is wild type, the other r type. When both the infecting types are wild type, or both r type, no mutations are found.

TABLE 2. *Mixed infections yielding induced mutations*

Infecting pair		Induced types
T6	T4	
r^+	r^+	none
r	r	none
r	r^+	T6r^+, T4r
r^+	r	T4r^+
T2	T4	
r^+	r^+	none
r^+	r	T2r, T4r^+
T2	T6	
r^+	r	T2r

(3) In the same mixed infection both infecting types may be changed, wild type to r type, and r type to wild type.

A discussion of possible theoretical interpretations of these findings does not seem warranted at this point, since our studies are far from complete. Perhaps one might dispute the propriety of calling the observed changes "induced mutations." In some respects they look more like transfers, or even exchanges, of genetic materials. We do not pretend to be able to put forward convincing arguments for either point of view.

A comment might be added with respect to Hershey's original discovery of mixed yields of wild type and r type. We now know that mutual exclusion may break down in infections with closely related viruses. Hershey's finding may therefore be interpreted as a lack of mutual exclusion. On the other hand, we know that in mixed infections with wild type and r type induced mutations do occur. To explain Hershey's findings one might assume, therefore, that only one of the infecting types multiplies while the other type induces mutations in it. A much closer study of the interrelations between the breakdown of mutual exclusion and the occurrence of induced mutations will be necessary to settle this ambiguity. For this purpose detailed studies of the contents of single bursts, and of the numerical relations between the different types of viruses in such bursts, should prove of great value.

SUMMARY

We will briefly retrace in historical order the steps that have led to our present state of knowledge regarding mixed infections of bacteria with bacterial viruses.

Mixed infections with pairs of *unrelated* viruses, like (T1, T2) or (T1, T7), results in mutual exclusion. Only one of the infecting types multiplies, the other is lost *(3, 6, 2)*.

The excluded virus may greatly reduce the yield of successful virus (depressor effect) (2).

Mixed infections with wild-type and r-type particles of the *same* strain do not, apparently, give rise to mutual exclusion (Hershey, 4).

Mixed infections with pairs of *related* viruses of the group T2, T4, T6 give partial mutual exclusion. The T2 particles liberated in mixed infections of this type exhibit certain nonheritable peculiarities, the nature of which has not yet been ascertained.

Mixed infections with pairs of the group T2, T4, T6, in which one of the pair is used in the wild-type form, the other in the r-type form, give rise to the liberation of new types, which can be characterized as mutants of the infecting types. The mutations occur at the r locus.

REFERENCES

1. Delbrück, M. 1945. The burst size distribution in the growth of bacterial viruses (bacteriophages). J. Bact. **50:** 131-135.

2. Delbrück, M. 1945. Interference between bacterial viruses. III. The mutual exclusion effect and the depressor effect. J. Bact. **50:** 151-170.

3. Delbrück, M., and Luria, S. E. 1942. Interference between bacterial viruses. I. Interference between two bacterial viruses acting upon the same host, and the mechanism of virus growth. Arch. Biochem. **1:** 111-141.

4. Hershey, A. D. 1946. Spontaneous mutations in bacterial viruses. Cold Spring Harbor Symp. Quant. Biol. **11:** 67-77.

5. Luria, S. E. 1945. Mutations of bacterial viruses affecting their host range. Genetics. **30:** 84-99.

6. Luria, S. E., and Delbrück, M. 1942. Interference between bacterial viruses. II. Interference between inactivated bacterial virus and active virus of the same strain and of a different strain. Arch. Biochem. **1:** 207-218.

1947

Isolation of the Polyheder Virus and the Nature of Polyheders[1]

by Gernot Bergold

Kaiser Wilhelm Institute of Biochemistry, Department of
Virus Research, Tübingen

*The polyhedroses are a major group of insect virus diseases
which are distinguished by the formation of many-sided crystalline bodies or polyhedra. The exact nature of the polyhedra
and their relationship to the etiological agent were the subjects of controversy since their discovery in 1856. At various
times, they were regarded either as the causative agent, crystalline accumulations of virus, or simply carriers of the virus. The
denouement was supplied by Bergold in the paper presented
here.*

*Bergold demonstrated that virus particles may be liberated
from the polyhedra after the polyhedra were treated with a
dilute solution of sodium carbonate. The virus particles were
occluded in the polyhedra, and the latter, therefore, served as
vehicles for the virus. The polyhedra per se were noninfectious.
Furthermore, by employing biophysical methods and serological tests, significant differences in the composition between
the virus particles and the polyhedra were established.*

*A point of historical interest in this report is the first
visualization of insect viruses, the agents of polyhedroses, with
the electron microscope. A capsule virus, representative of
another large group of insect virus diseases (the granuloses or
capsular diseases) was similarly illustrated, shortly thereafter.[2]*

---

[1] Abridged and reprinted by permission of the author and publisher from Zeitschr.
Naturforschg. **2b:** 122-143 (1947).

[2] Bergold Zeitschr. Naturforschg. **36:** 338 (1948).

SUMMARY

In the infectious polyheder disease of insect larvae, polyhedric protein crystals form in the nuclei of almost all cells of the body of the insects affected. The nature of these polyheders was investigated on *P. dispar, L. monacha,* and *B. mori* larvae. They were found to consist of the major part of a non-infectious, very uniform polyheder protein with a molecular weight of 276,000, 336,000, or 378,000 and to a small extent of an infectious polyheder virus protein with a particle weight of about 10^9. These infectious polyheder virus particles, which are rich in nucleic acids, could be isolated in a pure state. Electron-microscopic pictures of them could then be taken and their sedimentation constants and diffusion constants could be measured. The polyheder protein and virus protein could be split into smaller components which then reunited to form high-molecular particles. The polyheder protein and the polyheder virus were found to be related serologically.

The polyheder disease affects the larvae of certain species of moths. Investigation of this disease formed the subject of a considerable amount of research carried out already in the past century, because this infectious disease is the main factor by which the widespread occurrence of some of our principal forest and field pests such as *L. monacha, P. dispar, D. pini* is checked. The disease, which is almost always lethal, has been named after the polyheder-shaped crystal formations that are 1-10μ large and occur in the nuclei of almost all cells of the body of the insects. A comprehensive account of the knowledge on the subject acquired before and of the problems involved in this disease, which is of great importance from the economic standpoint, has been given in an earlier article (1), so that we shall only report on research carried out during the past four years.

Experiments carried out on insects showed that the polyheders themselves are etiologically related to the disease and that they do not merely represent non-infectious reaction products derived from the cell nucleus. Starting from the known fact that the polyheders are soluble in weak alkalies and that the middle intestine of the larvae which are susceptible to the polyheder virus infection has an alkaline reaction, solutions of the polyheders in weak alkali were investigated by the ultracentrifuge method and electrophoretically. It was found that after the polyheders had been dissolved under definite conditions and this solution had been purified, centrifuging resulted in the separation of a uniform protein with a constant molecular weight and a constant electric charge. The molecular weight was approximately 200,000-300,000 (1, 2, 3). The infectious dose of the polyheder solutions was according to some determinations 10^{-10}g. of protein per individual for silkworms (BM = *B. mori*), 10^{-13}g. for

Porthetria dispar (Pd), and 10^{-15}g. for *Lymantria monacha* (Lm). This high virulence, which had been established in an inadequate number of animal experiments, was not readily reproducible and showed strong fluctuations. Because the minimum infectious dose did not change significantly after 3 hours of centrifuging at 30,000 rpm (60,000 g.), the conclusion was drawn that the characteristic protein was uniform and that it presumably was identical with the infectious protein. An admixture of some other high-molecular protein could not have been present in a quantity exceeding 5%. The result obtained in an ultra-filtration experiment indicated that large molecules with a particle weight of several million could not have been present. The isolation of an infectious virus protein with a molecular weight of 200,000-300,000 was of such great fundamental importance that a thorough investigation of the problem became necessary. The investigation had three different aims:

I. Purification in as far as possible, further characterization, and determination of the molecular weight of the polyheder protein and of its components formed by splitting.

II. Improvement of the testing procedure by the use of polyhederfree insects which had been bred for a great number of years, use of a much larger number of insects, isolation of individual insects on which experiments were carried out, and statistical evaluation of the results.

III. A thorough investigation of the question as to whether the polyheder protein is identical with the infectious virus protein.

*   *   *   *

V. THE NATURE OF THE POLYHEDER AND OF THEIR COMPONENTS

Before discussing the interrelationships of the polyheder components, we shall compare the conditions pertaining to the phosphorus and nitrogen content.

Desnuelle and co-workers (16) investigated in some detail the Bm polyheders and the Bm polyheder protein, which they regarded as the infectious virus protein on the basis of our earlier publications. They found that the Bm polyheders contain 14.5% of N, 0.248% of P, and 0.920% of S and that the Bm polyheder protein contains 15.0% of N, 0.127% of P, and 0.83% of S. On the basis of the P content they assigned to the Bm polyheder protein a minimum molecular weight of 97600, i.e., almost exactly a quarter of the value of 378000 found by us on the basis of the S and D determinations. Furthermore, they gave a very interesting compilation of the amino acids of the Bm polyheder protein on the basis of their experimental results.

Our own results are listed in Table 11.*

* Tables 1 through 10 have been deleted from the article.—ed.

TABLE 11. *The nitrogen and phosphorus content of the polyheder and their constituent parts*

	Polyheder			Polyheder protein			1. Split product $\frac{6}{6}$		2. Split product $\frac{18}{18}$		Polyheder virus		
	Pd	Lm	Bm	Pd	Lm	Bm	Pd	Bm	Pd	Bm	Pd	Lm [c]	Bm
% N[a]	14.72	15.26	14.73	15.44	15.62	15.16	14.50	14.82	—	14.37	15.28	—	13.92
% P[b]	0.127[d] — 0.246	0.175[d]	0.191[d] — 0.243	0.045	0.039	0.062	0.05	0.07	—	0.07	1.33	—	1.34
N/P	116-60	87	77-60	345	400	245	290	212	—	205	11.50	—	10.40

[a] Micro-Kjeldahl determinations (precision $+1\%$); all samples were dried in high vacuum over P_2O_5 for several days.
[b] Determined with a precision of $+2$-3% by applying the strychnine molybdate method.
[c] The Lm virus values could not be determined because only a small quantity of the substance was available.
[d] The values of the P-determinations on different polyheder preparations showed that there were variations in the P-content of the polyheders.

We found that the polyheders, the polyheder protein and the products of splitting of the polyheder protein as well as the polyheder virus have the same nitrogen content, whereas the phosphorus content varies greatly. The highest P content was found for the pure polyheder virus, which contained approximately 1.33% of P (See Note), and the lowest for the polyheder protein, which contained 0.039-0.062%, i.e., approximately half of the content found by Desnuelle, et al.

Note: On the basis of preliminary quantitative nucleic acid determinations with the Dische reagent, which had been carried out according to the method of F. B. Seiber and A. L. Dounce, the total quantity of phosphorus is presumably present in the form of thymonucleic acid phosphorus.

A comparison of the high N/P ratios (Table 11.) of the intact polyheders with the much lower values for the polyheder viruses (10.4 and 11.5) indicates that the polyheders cannot consist of virus protein only and that the polyheder protein does not in any case arise as a secondary splitting product of the polyheder virus following dissolution of the polyheders in alkali. We therefore have two different proteins with respect to their particle weight and their P or nucleic acid content. Both of these proteins are originally contained in the polyheders. A proof of this can be seen in Figure 52. which shows that one can discern by means

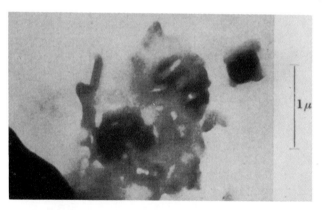

Fig. 52. Portion of a *P. dispar*-polyheder with virus miss-ing, dissolved in weak sodium carbonate solution.

of an electron microscope vacant sections having the approximate shape of a Pd virus particle in Pd polyheders which had partly dissolved. In other words, the virus particle has been dissolved out of these polyheders.

Because a more detailed characterization by physico-chemical methods was impossible and a relationship between the two proteins could not be established by other means, an attempt was made in collaboration with Dr. Friedrich-Freksa to establish a relationship by means of a serological investigation. A Bm virus protein solution (0.15%) which had been purified and concentrated and a polyheder protein solution (0.15%), both of which had been derived from the same polyheder solution, were used for this purpose. The polyheder protein solution was purified for a second time by one hour centrifuging at 25000 rpm (45000 g) in order to remove virus protein which may have been present. Dr. Friedrich-Freksa had already been able to establish before that even small quantities of the polyheder protein exert an extremely strong antigenic action. A rabbit was immunized with the polyheder virus and another rabbit with the polyheder protein by injecting them with 15. mg three times at intervals of 5 days. Seven days after the last injection, immune serum was taken from the animals and reacted with the homologous and non-homologous antigen. The immune serum of the polyheder virus formed a precipitate with the polyheder protein and the immune serum of the polyheder protein formed a precipitate with the virus. This clear result could be checked further by establishing that the immune serum of the polyheder virus, on being exhausted by precipitation with the polyheder protein, yielded a second, distinct precipitation on addition of the polyheder virus. The whole test was repeated and gave the same result. The result of this experiment, which was carried out by Dr. Friedrich-Freksa with approximately 7.5 mg of the polyheder virus, demonstrates clearly that the polyheder protein is related to the polyheder virus serologically and the latter contains additional antigenically active centers.

Gratia and Paillot (17) were able to establish in 1939 that polyheder solutions, about the complex nature of which they did not yet know anything, have no serological similarity with the lymph liquid and tissue extracts of silkworms. One must conclude on the basis of this that the polyheder protein is totally or at least partially a component part of the polyheder virus.

Three possibilities then exist:

1. The polyheder protein is a component of the polyheder virus which can no longer associate to a large virus particle because it has been deprived of the nucleic acid.

2. The polyheder protein is a decomposition product of the virus protein, a view which is supported by its complete insolubility in water.

3. The polyheder protein is a product of a reaction which takes place in the host's cell (18) and crystallizes around the virus, forming the polyheders.

It is most likely that the polyheder protein resembles the so-called "soluble antigens" of other viruses, particularly the smallpox virus. In the case of the latter, one obtains similarly by careful splitting of the elementary particles with alkali a nucleoprotein and also a protein which is related serologically to the nucleoprotein.

To summarize, we established in our investigation that the water-insoluble polyheders, which according to work by Brill and von Kratky (unpublished) are genuine protein crystals, consist to the extent of about 82% of their weight (cf. Table 12) of a water-insoluble, P-poor non-

TABLE 12. *Distribution of the polyheder components with respect to weight and the N and P content*

	mg	Nitrogen		Phosphorus	
		mg	%	mg	%
Bm-Polyheder	100	14.73	100	0.214	100
Undissolved Polyheder					
Residues	1.00	0.14	0.96	0.004	1.8
Polyheder-Protein	82.20	12.42	84.40	0.023	10.7
Virus Protein	5.00	0.69	4.70	0.056	26.2
Undissolved Virus Protein	0.22	0.03	0.21	0.003	1.4
Low-molecular Fractions					
Losses during precipitation	11.58	1.45	9.73	0.129	60.2

infectious polyheder protein with a molecular weight of 276000 for Pd, 336000 for Lm, and 378000 for Bm and in addition to that contain approximately 5% of a water-soluble phosphorus and nucleic acid-rich, infectious polyheder virus with a particle weight of $1\text{-}2 \times 10^9$.

One can see from Table 12 that the polyheder proteins contains approximately 85% and the virus protein approximately 5% of the total nitrogen. On the other hand, the polyheder protein contains only 11% of the total phosphorus as compared with a content of about 26% in the virus protein. The missing 10% of N are lost in precipitation and washing, whereas the balance of 60% of P is recovered almost completely as dialyzable, free phosphate. The solution of the polyheders and the separation of the two proteins can be carried out only in weak alkali solutions and is accomplished best by centrifuging. According to the sedimentation and diffusion tests and the direct measurement of dimensions in electronomicrographs, the virus particles, which resemble bacteria as far as their shape is concerned, have a length of about 350 mμ and a diameter of about 87 mμ in the case of Bm larvae and the dimensions of 415 and 160 mμ in the case of Pd larvae. Particles of this size are still discernible in the dark field of a visible light microscope, so that one may assume that the "Chlamydozoa" originally observed by Prowazek (18) in the illuminated field after staining are perhaps actually identical with the infectious virus particles, which have later also been described by Komarek and Breindl (19), Paillot and Gratia (20), and Letje (21). The pictures published by me (1), which show minute vibrating particles inside the thin polyheder membrane or outside of the membrane after they have been released in the form of a cloud, presumably represent the polyheder virus itself or low aggregation stages of this virus rather than

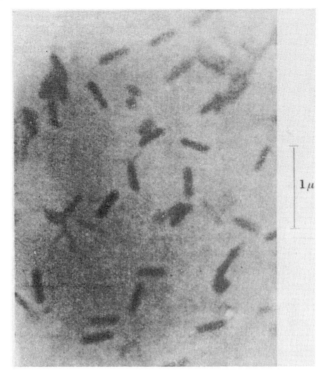

B. mori-Polyheder-Virus, 5×10^{-5} g/ccm in H_2O.

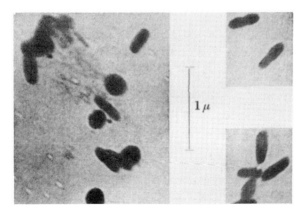

P. dispar-Polyheder-Virus, 2×10^{-5} g/ccm in H_2O.

undissolved aggregation stages of the polyheder protein, as has been assumed originally. A rough estimate of the number of the vibrating particles, which become visible on solution in alkali, leads to a quantity of several hundred, which is in good agreement with respect to the order of magnitude with the values derived from the ratio of weights and the number calculated on the basis of the particle weight. A further argument in favor of the assumption that these particles, which are barely visible in the dark field, are actually polyheder virus particles is the finding that when centrifuged solutions which have a low infectious capacity are observed under the microscope, only a few of these particles are seen as compared with the cloud-like swarms which are seen when non-centrifuged, active solutions are observed. This had already been established by Paillot and Gratia (20).

In the course of the investigation described, 434 analytical ultracentrifuge tests and 92 diffusion measurements were carried out during 4 years. Equipment which has been described elsewhere (4) was used for this purpose.

I wish to thank Dr. Friedrich-Freksa for many suggestions and valuable advice.

I am grateful to my assistants, Miss M. Vialon, Miss L. Pister, Mrs. U. John, and Miss E. Engelhart for their tireless work.

BIBLIOGRAPHY

1. Bergold, G. 1943. Biol. Zbl. 63: 1.

2. Bergold, G. 1942. G. Schramm, Biol. Zbl. 62: 105.

3. Bergold, G. 1942. u. J. Hengstenberg, Kolloid-Z. 98: 304.

4. Bergold, G. 1946. Zeitschr. Naturforsch. 1: 100.

5. Markham, R., Smith, K. M., and Lea, D. 1942. Parasitology. 34: 315.

6. Glaser, R. W. 1915. J. Agr. Res. 4: 101.

7. Bergold, G. 1941. Biol. Zbl. 61: 158.

8. Schelling, H. v. 1939. Arb. Staatsenst. exp. Therap. Georg-Speyer-Haus, Frankfurt a. M., No. 37: 28-54.

9. Glaser and Stanley. 1943. J. Exp. Med. 77: 451, acc. to Bull. Analytique. 7 (7/115): 902 (1946).

10. Lauffer, M. A. 1943. Proc. Soc. Exp. Biol. Med. 52: 330, acc. to Ann. Rev. Biochem. (1946.)

11. Taylor, A. R. 1944. J. Biol. Chem. 153: 675-88.

12. Melchers, G., Schramm, G., Trurnit, and Friedrich-Freksa, H. 1940. Biol. Zbl. 60: 524.

13. Ruska, H. 1943. Atch. ges. Virusforschg. 2: 480.

14. Eyer, H., and Ruska, H. 1944. Z. Hyg. Infekt.-Krankh. 125: 483.

15. Weyer, F., Friedrich-Freksa, H., and Bergold, G. 1944. Naturwiss. 32: 361.

16. Desnuelle, P., Chi-tan, Chang, and Formageot, C. 1943. Ann. Inst. Pasteur, 69: 75 and 248.

17. Gratia, A., and Paillot, A. 1939. Arch. ges. Virusforschg. 1: 130.

18. Prowazek, S. v. 1907. Arch. Protistenkunde. **10**: 358.

19. Komarek, J., and Breindl, V. 1924. Z. angew. Entomol. **10**: 99.

20. Paillot, A., and Gratia, A. 1939. Arch. ges. Virusterschg. **1**: 120.

21. Letje, W. 1939. Seidenbauforschg. **1**: 1.

1949

Cultivation of the Lansing Strain
of Poliomyelitis Virus in Cultures
of Various Human Embryonic Tissues[1]

by John F. Enders, Thomas H. Weller,[2] and
Frederick C. Robbins[3]

Research Division of Infectious Diseases, Children's Hospital,
and Departments of Bacteriology, Comparative Pathology,
and Pediatrics, Harvard Medical School, Boston

*That viruses may be propagated in cultivated cells was known
for about three decades but technical difficulties limited its
general usefulness in virus laboratories. This technical account
of the cultivation of poliovirus in cultures of nonneural tissue
was a momentous discovery for virologists which initiated an
era of spectacular advances in virus research. Not only was
this discovery directly responsible for the successful development of poliovirus vaccine, but it directed the attention and
efforts of virologists to the utilization of tissue culture techniques in virus research. Some of the immediate consequences
of the adoption of this system were (1) production of virus
and antigens for vaccines and serological tests, (2) isolation and
identification of many new viruses, (3) development of techniques for the quantitative measurement of virus infectivity,
and (4) establishment of standard strains of cells.*

An extraneural site for the multi-
plication of the virus of poliomyelitis has been considered by a number of
investigators (2, 5). The evidence that this may occur is almost entirely

---

[1] Aided by a grant from the National Foundation for Infantile Paralysis, Inc. Reprinted by permission of the author and publisher from Science, 1949, **109**: 85-87 (1949).

* Footnotes two and three have been deleted from the article.—ed.

indirect, although recent data indicate that Theiler's mouse encephalo-myelitis virus as well as various mouse pathogenic poliomyelitis-like viruses of uncertain origin may multiply in nonnervous tissue (1, 3). Direct attempts by Sabin and Olitsky (4) to demonstrate *in vitro* multiplication of a monkey-adapted strain of poliomyelitis virus (MV strain) in cultures composed of certain nonnervous tissues failed. They obtained, however, an increase in the agent in fragments of human embryonic brain.

The general recognition that the virus may be present in the intestinal tract of patients with poliomyelitis and of persons in contact with them emphasizes the desirability of further investigation of the possibility of extra-neural multiplication. Accordingly, experiments with tissue cultures were undertaken to determine whether the Lansing strain of poliomyelitis virus could be propagated in three types of human embryonic tissues. The results are summarized here in a preliminary manner.

The technique was essentially the same as that recently described for the cultivation of mumps virus (6). The cultures consisted of tissue fragments suspended in 3 cc of a mixture of balanced salt solution (3 parts) and ox serum ultrafiltrate (1 part). Tissues from embryos of $2\frac{1}{2}$ to $4\frac{1}{2}$ months as well as from a premature infant of 7 months' gestation were used. These were: the tissues of the arms and legs (without the large bones), the intestine, and the brain. Each set of cultures included 4 or more inoculated with virus, and usually a similar number of uninoculated controls. The primary inoculum consisted of 0.1 cc of a suspension of mouse brain infected with the Lansing strain of poliomyelitis virus.[4] The identity of the virus was verified by (a) the character of the disease it produced in white mice following intracerebral inoculation; and (b) its neutralization by specific antiserum.[5] Subcultures were inoculated with 0.1 cc of pooled *centrifuged* supernatant fluids removed from the previous set of cultures.

The procedure of cultivation differed from that usually followed by other workers in that the nutrient fluid was removed as completely as possible and replaced at periods ranging from 4 to 7 days. Subcultures to fresh tissue were prepared at relatively infrequent intervals, ranging from 8 to 20 days.

Two experiments have been carried out employing cultures composed chiefly of skin, muscle and connective tissue from the arms and legs. The findings in each have been essentially the same. In the first, a series of cultures has now been maintained for 67 days. During this interval, in addition to the original set, three successive subcultures have been made to fresh tissue and the fluids have been removed and replaced 10 times

[4] This strain was isolated by Dr. Charles Armstrong and obtained through the courtesy of Dr. S. D. Kramer.

[5] This serum was obtained through the courtesy of Dr. Isabel Morgan. It was prepared by hyperimmunization of rhesus monkeys with her strain of the Lansing virus.

(Table 1). Assuming that at each change of fluid a dilution of approximately 1:15 was effected and that at the initiation of each set of cultures the inoculum was diluted 30 times, it has been calculated that the 10% suspension of infected mouse brain used as the primary inoculum had been diluted approximately 10^{17} times in the fluids removed from the third subculture on the 16th day of cultivation. These fluids, however, on inoculation into mice and monkeys, produced typical paralysis. Accordingly, since the mouse LD_{50} of the original inoculum was 10^{-2}, it would appear that the increase in virus during the course of the experiment was at least of the order of 10^{15} times. During the 67-day period of cultivation a progressive decrease in mouse infectivity was recorded (Table 1). On the other hand, in the second experiment, mentioned above,

TABLE 1. *Multiplication of Lansing poliomyelitis virus in tissues obtained from the extremities of human embryos*

Culture set	No. of nutrient fluid changes prior to subculture		Day of incubation subculture done		Mouse LD_{50} of pooled fluids used to inoculate subcultures		Calculated dilution of original inoculum at time of subculture	
	Exp. 1	Exp. 2	Exp. 1	Exp. 2	Exp. 1	Exp. 2	Exp. 1	Exp. 2
Original*	3	4	20th	20th	$10^{-2.0}$	$10^{-1.57}$	10^{-5}	$10^{-6.2}$
1st subculture	2	2	19th	12th	$10^{-1.57}$	$10^{-1.71}$	$10^{-8.8}$	$10^{-10.0}$
2nd subculture	2	4	12th	20th	$10^{-0.63}$	$10^{-1.34}$	$10^{-12.6}$	$10^{-16.2}$
3rd subculture	3	..	16th	....	$10^{-0.16}$	.....	$10^{-17.7}$	.....

* The LD_{50} of the suspension of mouse brain used as the inoculum in the first experiment was 10^{-2}; that of the suspension employed in the second experiment was $10^{-1.01}$.

the calculated increase in virus during a 52-day period is now of the order of 10^{16} times and no decrease in mouse infectivity has so far been observed.

The agent propagated in the first experiment continued to exhibit the principal characteristics of the Lansing strain during the period of cultivation, as indicated by the following observations: (a) fluids from each set of cultures produced paralysis and death in mice after intracerebral inoculation; (b) the agent present in the fluids of the second set of subcultures was neutralized by antiserum specific for the Lansing strain; (c) following intracerebral inoculation, the fluids from the third set of subcultures produced flaccid paralysis within 7 and 10 days, respectively, in two rhesus monkeys. Microscopic examination of the spinal cords of these animals revealed lesions characteristic of poliomyelitis.

Cultures of intestinal tissue were prepared with fragments from the entire intestine of human embryos, except in one experiment in which jejunum of a premature infant was used. In the latter, the bacteria were eliminated in the majority of cultures by thorough washing of the tissue and by the inclusion in the original nutrient fluid of 100 units/cc of penicillin and of streptomycin.

In one experiment with embryonic intestine, which included two sub-cultures and 7 changes of nutrient fluid, the calculated dilution of the original inoculum was of the order of $10^{13.7}$ times. On the basis of the mouse LD_{50} of the original inoculum and that of the last supernatant fluid, it was calculated that the virus had increased about $10^{12.7}$ times. The identity of the agent thus cultivated in intestinal tissue has not yet been confirmed by neutralization tests or monkey inoculation, but it elicits a response in the mouse typical of the Lansing virus.

The cultures prepared with intestine of the premature infant have, so far, been maintained 17 days with 3 changes of nutrient fluid. Virus has been demonstrated, by mouse inoculation, in the fluids removed during the course of the experiment, including that of the 17th day. The calculated multiplication of the virus was approximately 10^3 times. This finding suggests that multiplication occurred in this tissue which, from the embryologic point of view, is more mature.

To compare the increase of virus in nervous tissue with that in tissue of the intestine and the extremities, cultures of embryonic brain were prepared. The multiplication of the virus in this medium has been comparable to that in the other types. Thus in one experiment carried out contemporaneously with the series of embryonic intestinal cultures mentioned above, the calculated multiplication of virus was of the order of 10^{12} times.

No evidence was obtained which indicated that an agent other than the Lansing strain of virus was propagated in any of the three types of tissue. Mouse infectivity tests for the presence of virus in the supernatant fluids of uninoculated control cultures were negative. Aerobic and anaerobic cultures of supernatant fluids yielded no growth of bacteria.

On microscopic examination of fragments of the three types of tissue, removed after about 30 days of cultivation, differences have been observed in cell morphology between those derived from inoculated and uninoculated cultures. Many of the fragments from uninoculated cultures contained cells which appeared to be viable at the time of fixation, as indicated by the normal staining properties of the nuclei and cytoplasm. In contrast, the nuclei of the majority of the cells in fragments from inoculated cultures showed marked loss of staining properties. Since the amount of material which has been studied is as yet relatively small, one cannot conclude that the changes observed in the inoculated cultures were caused by the virus.[6]

[6] We are indebted to Dr. Duncan Reid and members of the staff of the Boston Lying-in Hospital for providing the human embryonic tissues and to Dr. Alwin M. Pappenheimer for the preparation and examination of sections of tissue culture material.

It would seem, from the experiments described above, that the multiplication of the Lansing strain of poliomyelitis virus in the tissues derived from arm or leg, since these do not contain intact neurons, has occurred either in peripheral nerve processes or in cells not of nervous origin.

REFERENCES

1. Evans, C. A., and Chambers, V. C. Proc. Soc. Exp. Biol. Med. **68:** 436 (1948).

2. Howe, H. A., and Bodian, D. Neural mechanisms in poliomyelitis. Commonwealth Fund, New York: 89 (1942).

3. Rustigian, R., and Pappenheimer, A. M. J. Exp. Med. **89:** 69 (1949) .

4. Sabin, A. B., and Olitsky, P. K. Proc. Soc. Exp. Biol. Med. **34:** 357 (1936).

5. Van Rooyen, C. E., and Rhodes, A. J. Virus diseases of man, 2nd ed. Nelson, New York: 939 (1948).

6. Weller, T. H., and Enders, J. F. Proc. Soc. Exp. Biol. Med. **69:** 124 (1948).

1950

Structure within Polyhedra Associated with Insect Virus Diseases[1]

by Kenneth M. Smith

Plant Virus Research Unit, Agricultural Research Council,
Molteno Institute, Cambridge,

and Ralph W. G. Wyckoff

Laboratory of Physical Biology, Experimental Biology and
Medicine Institute, National Institutes of Health,
Bethesda 14, Maryland

*From electron microscopy examinations of tissues of the larvae
of two tiger moths,* Artica caja *and* A. villica, *the existence of
a distinct and major group of insect viruses was discovered.
The larvae were infected with a polyhedral disease of the cytoplasmic type in which the virus was spherical, in contrast to
the rod-shaped forms occurring in nuclear infections. Since
then, spherical viruses have been found in many other species
of lepidopterous larvae. Certain physical and chemical characteristics have been recognized to distinguish between the
polyhedra of nuclear and cytoplasmic infections. Studies on
the chemical composition of the spherical and the rod-shaped
virus particles have revealed, subsequently, that the former
contain ribonucleic acid (RNA) whereas the latter contain
deoxyribonucleic acid (DNA). These findings appear to suggest some fundamental differences in the chemical structure
and mechanism of replication between these two forms of insect viruses, although one exception has been noted, i.e., Tipula
iridescent, a cytoplasmic virus which contains DNA exclusively.*

[1] Reprinted by permission of the author and publisher from Nature. 166: 861-862
(1950).

For some time we have been examining with the electron microscope thin sections of caterpillars infected with their polyhedral diseases. In this way it is possible to follow the development of the disease, to see the crystal-like polyhedra as they are formed *in situ* and to observe the fine structure of their contents.

Bergold (1, 2) has obtained electron micrographs showing thin rods freed when polyhedra of the silkworm larva, *B. mori,* of the gypsy moth caterpillar, *P. dispar,* and of the nun moth caterpillar, *L. monacha,* are treated with dilute sodium carbonate. Presumably these are elementary bodies of virus. Similar rods have been obtained by Steinhaus and his co-workers (3, 4) from polyhedra of the alfalfa caterpillar, the western yellow-striped army worm and the California oak worm. Treatment of the polyhedra from some of, but not all, the species of caterpillars which we have studied reveals similar rods.

Such rods have been obtained from the scarlet tiger moth caterpillar, *P. dominula,* and the currant moth caterpillar, *A. grossulariata.* In both these cases, alkaline disintegration has revealed thick as well as the thin elementary rods within and issuing from the membranes that enveloped the polyhedra (Fig. 1). As in this figure, the thin rods are frequently small groups in parallel array. In a few places the thick rods, which always have approximately the same length as the thin rods, are themselves disintegrating to reveal thin ones within them.

Polyhedra from other caterpillars, some belonging to species closely related to the foregoing, do not seem to contain these rods. Thus when the polyhedra from the cream spot tiger (*Arctia villaca*), the garden tiger (*A. caja*) moth caterpillars and the caterpillars of *Rhypara purpurata* are treated with sodium carbonate, there remain hollow shells of the polyhedra pitted with a large number of holes of very uniform diameter (Fig. 2). On the substrate surrounding these disintegrated polyhedra there can sometimes be seen clusters of spherical bodies having about the same diameter as the holes (Fig. 3). These spheres, often flattened, occur singly and in short chains. Similar holes and spheres can be seen within the polyhedra in sectioned tissues of the caterpillar itself. Unlike the polyhedra that yield rods, these usually show no evidence of enveloping membranes.

In all the caterpillars discussed here, the polyhedra developed within nuclei which may become so distended as nearly to fill their cells. This is true whether or not the rod-like particles are found. Figure 4, from a section through a diseased currant moth caterpillar, is typical of what is seen at low magnification under the electron microscope. The crystal-like outlines of the polyhedra are very evident in these sections. Figure 5 shows several sectioned polyhedra from a cream spot tiger caterpillar. They exhibit the same pitting that is seen after alkali treatment. Some-

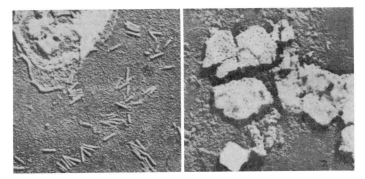

Fig. 1. Membrane and residual contents of an alkali-disintegrated polyhedral body from a diseased larva of *P. dominula*. The rod-shaped virus elementary bodies of uniform diameter are scattered over the substrate and can be seen within the membrane together with two of the thicker rods (near the bottom of the membrane) from which these virus particles come, as well as others in various stages of disintegration. Positive print. × 11,000.

Fig. 2. Pitted debris of polyhedra treated with sodium carbonate, from *A. villaca*. The holes have essentially uniform diameters of the same order of magnitude as flattened spheres often observed on the surrounding substrate. Positive print. × 8,500.

Fig. 3. Spherical particles, which may be elementary particles of virus, obtained by the alkaline disintegration of polyhedral bodies developed within a larva of virus-diseased A. caja. Positive print. × 8,500.

times there are protuberances in place of the holes. These facts, taken in connexion with what is seen in Figs. 2 and 3, suggest that the inclusions in these polyhedra are little spheres.

In no instance thus far have we found any indication of the spherical forms and pitted polyhedral matrix in species yielding rods, or *vice versa*. This suggests that the virus diseases of caterpillars that produce crystal-

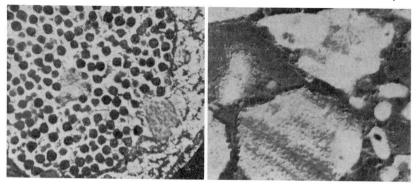

Fig. 4. Section showing part of a cell from a virus-diseased larva of *A. grossulariata* with almost all the nucleoplasm replaced by polyhedral bodies. Negative print. × 2,000.

Fig. 5. Section through parts of spherical polyhedra within a cell of a diseased larva of *A. villaca*. The spherical pits disseminated through these bodies are easily seen. Positive print. × 11,000.

like polyhedral inclusions may fall into at least two different groups. That exhibiting the spherical forms and typified by the disease of the cream spot tiger moth caterpillar has not previously been described.

We are continuing these combined studies of the virus polyhedra from a number of related species of caterpillars both in section and after disintegration. A more detailed report of the results already obtained will be published elsewhere.

REFERENCES

1. Bergold, G. 1947. Zeitschr. Naturforschg. **2b:** 122.

2. Bergold, G. 1948. Zeitschr. Naturforschg. **3b:** 25.

3. Hughes, K. M. 1950. J. Bact. **59:** 189.

4. Steinhaus, E. A. 1949. Bact. Rev. **3:** 203.

1952

Production of Plaques
in Monolayer Tissue Cultures
by Single Particles
of an Animal Virus[1]

by Renato Dulbecco

California Institute of Technology, Pasadena, California

The development of a practical method for producing plaques with animal viruses on monolayers of cell cultures was made available to researchers on animal viruses. The method, recounted here by Dulbecco, was comparable to that employed so successfully by workers on bacterial viruses. This achievement not only provided a quantitative technique for titration of animal viruses, marked by increased precision and sensitivity, but it made possible the study of the kinetics of viral infections, reproduction, and immunity at the cellular level. In addition, it was applicable to genetic studies of viruses, and this fact was quickly recognized and exploited by researchers.

Research on the growth characteristics and genetic properties of animal viruses has stood greatly in need of improved quantitative techniques, such as those used in the related field of bacteriophage studies.

The requirements for a quantitative virus technique are as follows: (1) The use of a uniform type of host cell; (2) an accurate assay technique; (3) the isolation of the progeny of a single virus particle; and (4) the separate isolation of each of the virus particles produced by a single infected cell. In bacterial virus work, production of plaques by single virus

---

[1] Reprinted by permission of the author and publisher from The Proc. Nat. Acad. Sci. **38**: 747-752 (1952).

particles on a uniform bacterial layer fulfills the first three requirements. The fourth requirement is easily met, in the case of bacteriophages.

In this article we shall show that plaques can similarly be produced by animal viruses and that their properties fulfill the first three requirements.

We have found that the virus of Western Equine Encephalomyelitis, adapted to chicken embryo,[2] will produce plaques when it is grown on a monolayer of cells obtainable from chicken embryos by a modification of a technique devised by Shannon, Earle and Walts.[3] We use the following procedure: Under aseptic conditions, five 9-day-old chicken embryos are collected, decapitated, washed in Earle's saline solution (ES)[4] and pressed through a stainless steel, 24-mesh, wire cloth (supplied by Ludlow-Saylor Wire Company, Los Angeles) which had been fitted at the bottom of a 50-ml. syringe. The resulting tissue pulp is collected in a 40-ml. centrifuge tube containing 15 ml. ES. After gravity sedimentation (10 minutes) the supernatant liquid containing cell debris and red blood cells is discarded and replaced with 15 ml. of a 0.5% solution of pure trypsin in ES. The tube is placed in a water bath at 37°C. for 10 minutes and then vigorously stirred by repeated pipetting with a 2-ml. automatic pipette. Owing to digestion of the connective fibers, a large fraction of the cells become free. The pieces of tissue which remain are eliminated by straining the suspension through the sieve unit described by Evans et al.[5] The cell suspension is then washed twice by centrifuging at 1000 r. p. m. for two minutes and resuspending the sediment in 15 ml. ES. The cell concentration in the final suspension is determined by counting in a hemocytometer.

An aliquot of the cell suspension containing 3×10^7 cells is introduced into a large Pyrex Carrel flask (80 mm. inside diameter) which had been acid cleaned by the procedure described by Earle.[6] The volume is brought up to 5 ml. with ES. There are added 5 ml. of horse serum and 1 ml. of 1:1 chicken embryo extract. The flask is hermetically closed with a rubber stopper. Approximately two such flasks can be prepared from one embryo.

The flasks are incubated in horizontal position at 37°C.

During the first few hours of incubation the cells settle out and stick to the bottom of the flask singly or in small clumps. They start to grow very soon and within 48 hours produce a continuous cell layer which covers the bottom of the flask. The layer is mostly one cell thick and is formed by rather uniform spindle cells and by a small number of macrophages. The spindle cells are similar in morphology and rate of growth to the fibroblasts obtained by culturing the connective tissue of

[2] Obtained from Dr. S. Lennette, California State Department of Public Health, Berkeley, Calif.

[3] Shannon, J. E., Earle, W. R., and Walts, H. K. J. Natl. Cancer Inst. In press.

[4] Earle, W. R. J. Nat. Cancer Inst. 4: 165-212 (1943).

[5] Evans, V. J., Earle, W. R., Sanford, K. K., and Shannon, J. E. Ibid. 11: 907-927 (1951).

[6] Earle, W. R. Ibid. 4: 131-133 (1943).

TABLE 1. *Relative number of plaques produced by western equine encephalo-myelitis virus exposed to specific antiserum and other substances before inoculation into the flasks*

Time of contact with the virus, min.	Treatment				
	Dist. water	ES	Normal horse serum 1:10 in ES	Horse serum heated at 56°C. 30 min., 1:10 in ES	Hyperimmune horse serum heated at 56°C. 30 min., 1:10 in ES
0	1	1	1	1	1
7	...	...	...	0.92	0.15
10	...	...	0.63	...	...
15	1.1	0.8	...	0.74	0.085
20	...	...	0.25	...	...
22	...	...	...	0.67	0.055
30	0.9	1	...	...	0.01

the chicken embryo; for this reason we called them fibroblasts. Other cell types carried with the inoculum must obviously be present in the culture, but they are outnumbered by the fast-growing fibroblasts. A more uniform cell population can be obtained by using as inoculum a cell suspension obtained from the cell layer of one of these flasks by means of the described trypsin technique.

The relatively uniform cell layer is infected with the virus in the following way. The nutrient fluid is removed from the flask and the cell layer is washed with 5 ml. ES, which is then discarded. A virus sample of 0.5 ml. is introduced into the flask and uniformly spread on the cell layer by rocking. The flask is incubated for 30 minutes at 37°C. to allow attachment of the virus to the cells, and the cell layer is then covered with a layer of 5 ml. of melted agar containing nutrient fluid similar to that used for growing the cell layer. After solidification of the agar, the flasks are incubated for three days at 37°C. At this time they show round necrotic areas of 2 to 4 mm. in diameter, visible to the eye as bright areas against a dark background (Fig. 1—*deleted–ed.*). These areas are easily recognized under low-power magnification because the cells have been transformed into a granular debris that scatters the light. That these areas, which we call plaques, are produced by virus activity is shown by the fact that they are absent when the virus is absent and their number increases with the concentration of the virus. Prior treatment of the virus with specific antiserum reduces the number of plaques produced (table 1).

Each of these plaques is produced by one virus particle. This can be shown by determining the effect of dilution on the number of plaques produced by a given virus sample. The theoretical relation between the number of plaques and the virus concentration depends on the minimum number of virus particles required to produce a lesion. A linear dependence of the number of plaques on virus concentration can be obtained only if each plaque is produced by one virus particle. The results of several experiments show that this dependence is in fact linear, and so prove that one particle is sufficient to produce one plaque (table 2).

TABLE 2. *Number of plaques obtained from stocks of western equine encephalomyelitis virus at different dilutions*

Experiments 1 and 2 were made with the same virus stock, experiments 3, 4 and 5 with a different stock. The virus consisted always of 20% extract of chicken embryo moribund after inoculation with the virus. Each flask was inoculated with 0.1 ml. of the diluted virus.

Number of the experiment	Dilution of the virus	Number of plaques on each flask
1	5×10^3	117; 180
	10^4	65; 87
2	10^4	59; 53
	3×10^4	28; 13; 18; 14; 19; 14; 18
3	10^3	79
	3×10^3	23
4	10^3	50
	4×10^3	12
	8×10^3	2
5	2×10^3	26
	6×10^3	10

What fraction of the virus particles contained in a sample is able to produce plaques is not known. We have determined the relation between the number of particles able to produce a plaque under our conditions and the number of particles able to infect the chicken embryo by the standard inoculation procedure on the chorioallantoic membrane.[7] Two batches of 15 eggs each, incubated for 10 days, were inoculated with an amount of virus able to produce, respectively, 0.7 and 0.35 plaques on the average. The egg were then incubated for 30 hours at 37°C., then scored for live and dead. The live ones were further incubated for 24 hours to check their vitality; all survived. From the fraction of live eggs in each batch the average number of infecting virus particles with which each egg was inoculated was determined by assuming a Poisson distribution of the particles per egg. This assumption is legitimate in view of the proof previously given in this article that infection of the cells is produced by one virus particle. The data of one such experiment, reported in table 3,

[7] Beveridge, W. I. B., and Burnet, F. M., The cultivation of viruses and rickettsiae in the chick embryo. His Majesty's Stationery Office, London: 14 (1946).

TABLE 3. *Comparison of the titer of a single stock of western equine encephalomyelitis virus by plaque count and egg titration*

The plaque count titer is derived from Exp. 1, table 2 and equals 7.5×10^6/ml. The data of the egg titration are given here. Each egg was inoculated with 0.1 ml. of the virus dilution.

Batch of eggs	Virus dilution	Surviving egg fraction	$-\text{Log } e$ surviving egg fraction	Titer per ml.
1	10^6	0.16	1.8	1.8×10^7
2	2×10^6	0.50	0.7	1.4×10^7

show that the titer was approximately twice the titer obtained by plaque count—a difference which is not significant because of the large standard error of egg titration. In another experiment the egg titration gave a titer somewhat lower than the plaque count.

We conclude from these experiments that there is a nearly one-to-one ratio between the number of plaques and the number of infective virus particles. This result on the one hand indicates that the plaque count is an efficient assay technique; on the other hand, it establishes a basic concept concerning animal virus action, namely, that infection of an embryo is produced by one virus particle.

The use of the plaque count as an assay technique has important practical advantages, as shown by the fact that the accuracy obtained with only one flask of this type is equal to that obtained with not less than one hundred chicken embryos in the currently used Reed and Muench technique.

We do not know whether many other viruses will exhibit this property of producing plaques under our conditions. So far, we have tried only one other virus, the Newcastle Disease virus,[8] and the results here were positive. The plaques formed by Newcastle Disease virus and those formed by Western Equine Encephalomyelitis virus are distinguishable under the microscope; the areas of cell destruction in the former are outlined by a halo of abnormally large cells or cell clumps of unknown nature, whereas in the latter there is seen only cell debris. The possibility of distinguishing the plaques produced by two different viruses on the same flask should be very valuable for the study of problems where two different viruses are involved, as in the phenomenon of interference.

SUMMARY

Plaque formation by single virus particles has been obtained with the virus of Western Equine Encephalomyelitis in a monolayer of chicken

[8] Strain B, obtained from F. B. Bang, Johns Hopkins Medical School, Baltimore, Md.

embryo fibroblasts grown *in vitro*. That a plaque is produced by a single virus particle is shown by the proportionality between number of plaques and virus concentration. The comparison between the number of plaques produced and the fraction of chicken embryos infected by the same virus sample indicates that nearly all virus particles able to infect the embryo produce a plaque; there is therefore a nearly 1:1 relation between infecting particles and plaques.

Plaques produced by this virus are distinguishable from the plaques produced by one other virus tested, the Newcastle Disease virus.

1952

Genetic Exchange in Salmonella[1]

by Norton D. Zinder and Joshua Lederberg

Department of Genetics, University of Wisconsin,
Madison, Wisconsin

*The description of a new mechanism for the transfer of genetic
characters from one bacterial strain to another which is carried
then through successive generations of the organism is recounted in this paper. The mechanism was termed "transduction" and involved bacteriophage particles as the vectors of
the genetic exchange. Transduction experiments proved an
invaluable aid in elucidating genetic mechanisms in bacteria.
In bacteriophage studies, it has given an insight into the
genetic nature of latent viruses. The applicability of transduction to lysogeny proffers a unique method for defining the relations between prophage and bacteria, and more specifically,
the size and orientation of the prophage on the bacterial
chromosome.*

Genetic investigations with many
different bacteria have revealed parallelisms and some contrasts with the
biology of higher forms. The successful application of selective enrichment techniques to the study of gene recombination in *Escherichia coli*
(Tatum and Lederberg, 1947; Lederberg *et al.,* 1951) suggested that a

[1] Department of Genetics, paper no. 479. This investigation was supported by research grants (E72) from the National Microbiological Institute of the National Institutes of Health, Public Health Service, from the Rockefeller Foundation and from
the Research Committee of the Graduate School from funds supplied by the Wisconsin
Alumni Research Foundation. This work has been submitted by the senior author to
the University of Wisconsin as a dissertation for the degree of Doctor of Philosophy.
His present address is: Rockefeller Institute for Medical Research, New York, New
York. Abridged and reprinted by permission of the author and publisher from the
Journal of Bacteriology. **64:** 679-699 (1952).

similar approach should be applied to other bacteria. This paper presents the results of such experiments with *Salmonella typhimurium* and other *Salmonella* serotypes. The mechanism of genetic exchange found in these experiments differs from sexual recombination in *E. coli* in many respects so as to warrant a new descriptive term, transduction.

MATERIALS AND METHODS

Most of the strains of *S. typhimurium* were provided by Lilleengen (1948) as representative of his 21 "phage types," LT-1 through LT-22. Most if not all strains of *S. typhimurium* are lysogenic (Boyd, 1950), and these have provided 12 lines of bacteriophage. Other cultures were obtained from F. Kauffmann, E. K. Borman, and P. R. Edwards. All cultures were maintained on nutrient agar slants.

Specific growth factor dependent mutants (auxotrophs) were obtained from ultraviolet irradiated cell suspensions subjected to the penicillin method for selective isolation (Davis, 1950a; Lederberg and Zinder, 1948). Similar mutants have been obtained in *Salmonella* by Plough *et al.* (1951) and Bacon *et al.* (1951). Other methods for the isolation and characterization of auxotrophic and fermentation mutants have been documented elsewhere (Lederberg, 1950; Lederberg and Lederberg, 1952). Streptomycin resistant mutants were selected by plating dense, unirradiated cell suspensions into agar containing 500 mg per L of dihydrostreptomycin.

"Complete" indicator medium (EMB) was made up from the same formula as for *E. coli* (Lederberg, 1950). The defined eosin methylene blue medium ("EML agar") contained in g per L: sodium lactate, 2.5; $(NH_4)_2SO_4$, 5; NaCl, 1; $MgSO_4$, 1; K_2HPO_4, 2; methylene blue hydrochloride, 0.05; eosin Y, 0.3; and agar, 15. Difco products, penassay broth, and nutrient agar, were employed as "complete" media.

Unless otherwise stated, all cultures were incubated at 37 C, and plates were scored after 24 and 48 hours.

EXPERIMENTAL RESULTS

DIRECT CROSSES: PLATINGS OF MIXED CULTURES

In *E. coli,* recombinants were detected selectively by plating various auxotrophs together on minimal agar. Both parents are suppressed on this medium and, barring various experimental errors, colony formation is confined to prototrophic recombinant cells. Such errors can be detected by appropriate controls but are best mitigated by the use of double nutritional mutants (diauxotrophs). These are obtained by the iterated isolation of mutants in previously established auxotroph lines.

One of Lilleengen's strains was refractory to our techniques of mutant isolation. Two-step mutants with mutually complementary nutritional requirements were prepared from each of the remaining twenty types. Of the two hundred possible pairwise combinations, including "selfed" crosses, one hundred were tested. Each combination was studied by mixing plating 10^9 washed cells of the two parents on a minimal agar plate. Fifteen mixture plates and five control plates for each parent by itself were inoculated in each test. Fifteen combinations yielded prototrophs in contrast to barren controls. Strain LA-22 was the most "fertile," especially with LA-2 (see table 1). This cross yielded about one prototroph

TABLE 1. *Mutant strains and symbols used*

No.	Mutations	Pertinent Symbol
LT-2	Type 2 prototrophic	Prot
SW-272	Methionineless, auxotrophie	Aux
SW-414 (LA-2)	SW-272 histidineless	
LT-22	Type 22 parent	
SW-240	Phenylalanine and tyrosineless	
SW-279 ⎫	SW-240 tryptophanless	
SW-307 ⎪	SW-279 galactose-negative	Gal—
SW-351 ⎪	SW-307 xylose-negative	Xyl—
SW-435 ⎬ LA-22	SW-351 streptomycin-resistant	S^r
SW-479 ⎪	SW-435 mannitol-negative	Mtl—
SW-443 ⎭	SW-435 maltose-negative	Mal—
LT-7	Type 7 parent	
SW-184	Prolineless	
SW-188	Methionineless	
SW-191	Leucineless	
SW-481	SW-184 galactose-negative	
SW-492	SW-188 galactose-negative	
SW-503	SW-191 galactose-negative	
SW-514	LT-7 streptomycin-resistant	
SW-515	SW-503 streptomycin-resistant	

per hundred thousand parental cells plated. Crosses in which LA-22 was not involved gave prototrophs so infrequently and sporadically as to be of doubtful significance. It has since become evident that LA-22 is genetically a single, stable mutant although it was derived in two steps and has a complex nutrition.

LT-22 is lysogenic for a virus (hereafter referred to as PLT-22) active on LT-2. This virus is capable of inducing lysogenicity in LT-2. Among the lysogenic derivatives of LA-2 three different interaction groups were found: the majority no longer interacted with LA-22 to give prototrophs; a few interacted with impaired efficiency; still fewer were not affected in this respect. These experiments indicated that genetic exchanges did occur and that latent bacteriophage played some role in the interaction.

INDIRECT CROSSES: PLATINGS OF CELLS AND FILTRATES

To test the possible role of filtrable factors in this interaction, a U-tube with an "ultra-fine" sintered pyrex filter partition was prepared according to Davis's (1950b) design. By alternating suction between the arms of the tube, two intact populations of growing bacteria could be made to share the same medium. The integrity of the filter was verified in control experiments by leaving one compartment uninoculated. Then 10^8 cells of each parent were inoculated into twenty ml of broth and placed in either arm of the tube. Ten ml were flushed from side to side every twenty minutes for four hours while the culture grew to saturation. The two populations were washed and plated upon minimal medium. Prototrophs appeared in the platings of LA-22 but not of LA-2. Sterile filtrates of LA-2 broth cultures did not elicit prototrophs from LA-22. However, filtrates from mixed cultures of LA-2 and LA-22 elicited about one prototroph per million LA-22 cells. Thus LA-2 produced a filtrable agent (FA), under stimulation from LA-22, that could elicit prototrophs from LA-22. Filtrates of LA-22 cultures, containing substantial amounts of phage (PLT-22) active on LA-2, also stimulated FA production from LA-2. The role of this phage will be discussed later.

To help the further expositon of our experiments, we shall use the term transduction for genetically unilateral transfer in contrast to the union of equivalent elements in fertilization. The working hypothesis that Salmonella FA is an agent of genetic transduction provides a useful frame of reference for our discussion.

ADSORPTION OF FA

The first step in transduction must be the adsorption of FA on competent cells. LA-22 was harvested from nutrient agar plates. Aliquots were suspended in one ml of an active filtrate for various intervals. The cells were sedimented and plated on minimal agar to determine the number of exchanges. After a heat shock at 56 C to destroy any unsedimented cells, the supernatants were assayed with LA-22 for unadsorbed FA. Moderate amounts of FA were completely adsorbed within the time necessary for centrifugation (15 minutes) and were recovered quantitatively in the precipitated cells.

All tested smooth strains of S. typhimurium adsorbed FA. Cells of the donor strain adsorbed as efficiently as the others, consistently with the success of intrastrain transfers. Disinfection by boiling or ultraviolet irradiation (to leave an extremely small viable fraction) did not affect adsorption. Rough cultures, selected by aging in broth (Page et al., 1951) did not adsorb. These results indicated that the site of adsorption is heat stable, is not affected by the death of the cell, and may be related to the somatic antigen.

* Figures 1 through 5 have been deleted from the article.—ed.

With the amounts previously used, *FA* assays were directly proportional to *FA* concentration. Cells of LA-22 were harvested from nutrient agar. Aliquots containing 10^{10} cells were sedimented in each of ten centrifuge tubes and the supernates discarded. Multiple aliquots of *FA* (one to ten ml) were added and 15 minutes at 37 C allowed for adsorption. Supernates and cells were collected and assayed on EML galactose. No concordant changes (i.e., galactose positive) were observed among the prototrophs. Figure 6 shows that a maximum number of transductions

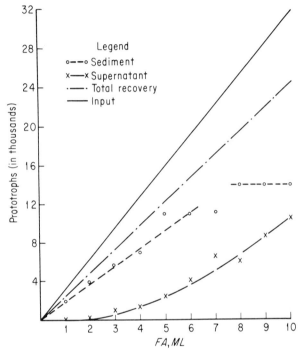

Fig. 6. Adsorption of *FA*. 10^{10} cells of LA-22 were exposed to *FA*(LT-2) for 15 to 30 minutes. Supernatants and sediments were collected after centrifugation and assayed, respectively, for residual *FA* and for transductions already initiated.

occurred with about eight ml of *FA*. The saturated sediments adsorb no more *FA* from larger aliquots. Except for a small systematic loss, probably mechanical, all units of *FA* are accounted for either in the supernatant or the sediment.

The interference in adsorption implied by saturation was demonstrated more explicitly in a blocking experiment. SW-188 (methionineless, M−) was exposed to an excess of *FA* from M− cells for fifteen minutes. *FA* from LT-7 (M+) was then added to the sedimented cells for an additional fifteen minutes before the cells were again sedimented. The M+ FA was not bound, nor was the SW-188 transduced. This verifies the blocking concept and indicates that the adsorption is irreversible after the fifteen minutes allowed for saturation.

Since adsorption of FA is so rapid it appears safe to assume that the large proportion of the individual bacteria are capable of adsorbing it. We can make an approximate minimum estimate of the number of adsorbable particles per ml of this filtrate by dividing the total number of bacteria by the number of ml required to saturate them (one particle per bacterium); $10^{10}/8$ or 1.3×10^9. A maximum number of particles per ml is set by the fact that the active filtrate showed no turbidity as might be expected with more than 10^{11} particles per ml.

So many unverified postulates are required that a detailed discussion of possible models for the kinetics of adsorption would be unprofitable here. It may be pointed out, however, that the low or zero frequency of double exchanges does not imply that one species of FA particle excludes another. If most of the bacteria are competent to be transduced, the frequency of a particular transduction will be the probability that any of the particles adsorbed will have a particular effect. Double transductions will occur in the same ratio to single exchanges as the absolute frequency of the latter, and this is too low (ca 10^{-5}) for double exchanges to be detected in our experiments. However, if transduction is limited to a small proportion of competent cells, dual transductions would not have independent probabilities, and further assumptions such as mutual exclusion would be required to account for the low frequency of observed dual events.

The following picture appears to be most consistent with the observations to date. An active filtrate contains a population of numerous species of granules, each corresponding to a genetic effect although some may be intrinsically inert. Each bacterium may absorb a limited number of particles, in the possible range from one to perhaps one hundred. Each adsorbed particle has a fixed, independent probability of exerting its particular transductive effect. The low frequency of single, and particularly of double transductions, is limited by the total number of particles that may be adsorbed as well, perhaps, as by the low probability that an adsorbed particle will complete its effect.

Serial Transduction

Dual transduction has never been observed in a single experiment. That this is due to the considerations described previously rather than some intrinsic limitation is shown by serial transfers. Once a cell has been transduced it can be grown out, reexposed to FA, and selected for other changes. SW-351 (Aux, Gal−, Xyl−) has been serially transduced from auxotrophy to prototrophy, from galactose negative to positive, and from xylose negative to positive. The order in which these transfers were accomplished made no difference. There was no loss of efficiency with the iterated transductions as compared to the single transduction of SW-351 for any of the characters.

The adsorption experiments had indicated a correlation of adsorptive ability and immunological specificity. Preliminary experiments with some dozen *Salmonella* serotypes confirmed and narrowed this correlation to the presence of somatic antigen XII. Broth cultures of the serotypes to be tested were sedimented and one ml of *FA* was added. Adsorption proceeded for fifteen minutes, and then the reaction tubes were heat shocked at 56°C for one hour to sterilize the cells. Preliminary experiments with known adsorbing cells had shown that *FA* once adsorbed was not eluted by this procedure. The mixtures were assayed on LA-22 for free *FA*. Some fifty different serotypes have been tested in this manner. Although some types with XII are inert, none of the types without XII adsorbed. This correlation is maintained with the *"Salmonella coli"* types. The XII carrying strains that adsorbed were: *S. paratyphi* B, *S. typhi-murium* (25 strains), *S. stanley, S. heidelberg, S. chester, S. san-diego, S. abortus-ovis, S. typhi* W, *S. typhi* V, *S. enteritidis, S. moscow, S. blegdam, S. east-bourne, S. sendai, S. abony, E. coli* 3, *E coli* 4, *S. kaapstad, S. salinatis, S. pullorum,* and *S. gallinarum.* The following XII types did not adsorb: *S. paratyphi* A and *S. abortus-bovis,* presumably owing to the absence of the XII$_2$ component. The nonadsorbing, non-XII types tested were: *S. typhi-murium* (rough variant), *S. cholerae-suis, S. newport, S. london, S. senftenberg, S. aberdeen, S. poona, S. worthington, S. hvittingfoss, S. kentucky, S. wichita, S. urbana, S. habana, S. altendorf, S. vejle, S. montevideo, E. coli* 1, *E. coli* 2, *E. coli* 5, *E. coli* K-12, *S. bonariensis, S. florida,* and *S. madelia.*

It is not known whether the adsorption of *FA* is sufficient to indicate susceptibility to genetic transfer, but preliminary data identify a possible receptor group, among which inter-type transductions may be possible.

S. typhi and *S. typhimurium* differ in a number of cultural and serological characters. The latter ferments both arabinose and rhamnose while the former does not ferment and is inhibited by either of these sugars. *S. typhi* Watson V was exposed to *FA* from *S. typhimurium* and inoculated into Durham fermentation tubes containing one per cent of either sugar in nutrient broth. After 24 hours a more luxuriant growth appeared in the *FA* treated cultures, and acid was produced by 48 hours. From these tubes cultures were isolated that differ from *S. typhi* only in their ability to ferment these sugars. The control cultures, without *FA,* show little evidence of growth and no evidence of fermentation. Although *S. typhimurium* produces gas from rhamnose and arabinose, these new forms remain typically anaerogenic. The experiment has also been conducted on agar. Treated cells were plated on EMB arabinose and EMB rhamnose. *S. typhi* occasionally mutates to a noninhibited form (Kristensen, 1948) which was represented by white papillae which were observed on both the experimental and control plates. However, the purple (fermenting) papillae were observed only on the experimental plates. Culturally they resembled the fermenting strains isolated after transduction in broth. These results have been repeated with two other strains of *S. typhi*. Using a streptomycin resistant mutant of *S. typhimurium* as the source of *FA*, it has been possible to transfer this character to *S. typhi*. Attempts to produce aerogenic fermentation of glucose by *S. typhi* by treatment with *FA* have all met with failure, possibly owing to insufficiently selective conditions to detect cells transduced for this character.

S. *typhi* is antigenically characterized IX, XII: *d*, —— (monophasic) while *S. typhimurium* is I, IV, V, XII: *i* — 1, 2, 3. *S. typhi* was exposed to *FA* from *S. typhimurium*, and transduction of the flagellar antigen was selected for. A tube based upon the mycological growth tube (Ryan *et al.*, 1943) was half filled with soft agar containing diluted anti-*d* serum (1/200 of serum titrating to 1/5,000). The cells were heavily inoculated at one side of the tube and watched for migration. In one experiment, two out of four experimental tubes showed migration while the three control tubes showed complete fixation of the inoculum. There was a sharp delineation between the migrating cells and the fixed inoculum. The former were fished from the uninoculated end of the tube and tested culturally and serologically. Both of the isolates culturally resembled *S. typhi*. One of them reacted with anti-*i* serum while the other did not react with either *S. typhi* or *S. typhimurium* flagellar antiserum and was diagnosed as a *j* phase *(Kauffmann, 1936)*. The analysis of these two strains was confirmed by Dr. P. R. Edwards. Transduction of the *i* antigen was obtained from twelve of thirty-one tested inocula of 10^8 *FA* saturated *S. typhi* cells. "*j*" phases have appeared occasionally in both experimental and control tubes. No *i* phases were *detected* in 50 control tests without *FA*. The complete antigenic analysis of the "hybrids" is IX, XII: *i*, ——. Unlike *S. typhimurium*, from which the *i* flagellar phase was derived, phasic variation has not been found in these "hybrids." Experiments are now in progress seeking transduction of other flagellar and somatic antigens.

THE TRANSDUCED CELL

Prototrophs produced by transduction [*FA* (LA-2) on LA-22] have been tested for their stability both in vegetative reproduction and further transduction. After isolation from the experimental plate they were purified by streaking. Five single colonies were grown in complete broth and plated. Two hundred colonies from each were picked and retested on minimal agar: all were prototrophic. The transduced culture was reexposed to *FA,* and another change was selected (galactose negative to positive). Of some 1,500 colonies tested by replica plating, all retained the initial transduction to prototrophy.

The transduced culture does not release *FA* during its growth nor is *FA* obtainable from it by any other means than those employed for the parent culture. Some difficulty has been encountered in this respect with the products of intrastrain transduction. They were all resistant carriers of the phage associated with active filtrates and some new phage was needed to evoke *FA* from them. Phage resistance also reduces the efficiency of iterated transduction, presumably because of impaired adsorption of *FA.*

Spontaneous reverse-mutations regain the ability to transduce their mutant parents as do transduced reversions. That is, when a cell goes from A— to A+ by either means, it can again produce A+ agent. Mutation in free *FA* has not yet been studied.

The Relationship between Bacteriophage and *FA*

Several recent convergent lines of evidence point to the identity of *FA* particles and bacteriophage. *FA* and phage have a common filtration end point; ninety-nine per cent of both are retained by a membrane of A.P.D. 120 mμ. They have a common specificity of adsorption on *Salmonella* serotypes, correlated with somatic antigen XII. In adsorption on *S. typhimurium* both reach saturation at the same point, and the phage to *FA* ratio remains constant. During the course of purification, *FA* and phage remain together. In short term experiments, *FA* and phage are released simultaneously from phage infected bacteria. Electron micrographs show a morphological similarity of particles of proper size.

That the phage particle can be only a passive carrier of the transductive genetic material is shown by the following experiments. From single phage particles grown on bacterial cells there are obtained high titered phage and a population of *FA* encompassing the entire genotype of the parental cells but capable of only one transduction per bacterial cell. Single phage particles, from this filtrate, can be grown on bacterial cells from the same original parent but of different genotype. The *FA* produced is comparable to the genotype of the secondary donor.

In the section on the evocation of *FA,* mention was made of the apparent regeneration of *FA* by transfer. This was explained as being due to the association of *FA* with phage which served to continuously stimulate its production. To test this, A—, B+, C+ cells were treated with penicillin. The filtrate was transferred with the same cells to yield *FA* (A—, B+, C+) and a phage which could be assayed on these same cells.

When added to A+, B−, C+ cells (from the same original parent), the *FA* obtained was A+, B−, C+. All of the B+ agent was adsorbed and lost, and agents paralleling the genotype of the B− cells obtained. *FA* had not propagated as such but rather was associated with the necessary stimulus for further production, the phage.

DISCUSSION

Genetic exchange in *S. typhimurium* is mediated by a bacterial product which we have called *FA* (filtrable agent). An individual active filtrate can transfer (transduce) many hereditary traits from one strain to another. Although the total activity of this filtrate encompasses the genotype of its parental culture, each transduction transmits only a single trait per bacterium. This contrasts with genetic exchange in *E. coli,* strain K-12, where there is unrestricted recombination of the several markers that differentiate two parental lines.

FA may be considered as genetic material which enters the fixed heredity of the transduced cell. We may ask whether this transfer is a simple super-addition or a substitutive exchange and replacement of the resident genetic factors. If streptomycin resistance is a recessive mutation, as inferred from studies of heterozygous diploids in *E. coli* (Lederberg, 1951b), the transduction of resistance disqualifies the simple addition mechanism.

Two aspects of *FA* must be carefully distinguished: the biological nature of the particles themselves and their genetic function. There is good reason to identify the particle with bacteriophage. Nevertheless, the phage particle would function as a passive carrier of the genetic material transduced from one bacterium to another. This material corresponds only to a fragment of the bacterial genotype. For example, when *FA* from a marked prototroph is plated with an auxotroph on minimal agar, the genotype of the presumed "donor nucleus" is not observed among the transduced prototrophs. The hypothesis of *FA* as a genetic complex rather than a unit might be maintained if the singular effects produced depended on a small chance of release of any particular activity from a complex particle or on some localized nonheritable happenstance in the cell that ordinarily left only one function sensitive to transduction. Still the originally singly transduced cell develops as an isolated clone. Since the clone is composed of some 10^7 bacteria, one might expect that a complex residuum of an *FA* particle, if viable, would transduce some one of the daughter cells for another character during the growth of the clone. However, each *FA* particle produces only a single transduced clone. This speaks for the simplicity of its constitution as well as of its genetic effect.

When LA-22 is transduced from auxotrophy (phenylalanineless and tyrosineless; tryptophanless) to prototrophy, we have an apparent dual change. If this mutant is plated on minimal agar supplemented with phenylalanine and tyrosine, it occasionally reverts to the first step auxo-trophic condition. However, when LA-22 is transduced on this medium, no more first step auxotrophs are found than can be explained by spontaneous reversion. The majority of the selected colonies are prototrophs. We have not been able to affect more than one trait in any other inter- or intrastrain transductions. It seems likely that the nutrition of LA-22 was determined by two successive mutations at the same genetic site. Davis' (1951) scheme for aromatic biosynthesis corroborates this notion. Although the mutant LA-22 can revert spontaneously to an intermediate allele, transduction brings about a substitution of the wild type gene for full synthesis.

The most plausible hypothesis for the *FA* granules is that they are a heterogeneous population of species each with its own competence—in other words, each carries a "single gene" or small chromosome fragment.

Regardless of the nature of the *FA* particles, some mechanism must be postulated for the introduction of the transduced genetic material to the fixed heredity of the recipient cell. Muller's (1947) analysis of type transformation in the pneumococcus is apropos here: ". . . there were, in effect, still viable bacterial chromosomes, or parts of chromosomes, floating free in the medium used. These might, in my opinion, have penetrated the capsuleless bacteria and in part taken root there, perhaps, after having undergone a kind of crossing-over with the chromosomes of the host."

In a preliminary report on the *Salmonella* recombination system (Lederberg *et al.*, 1951) it was suggested that *FA* might be related to bacterial L-forms (Klieneberger-Nobel, 1951). The occurrence of swollen "snakes," filtrable granules, and large bodies in response to certain agents is characteristic both of *FA* and L-forms. Except for the suggestion of viable filter passing granules we have not repeated the reported cycles. The visible agglutinable granules and the antiserum-induced swollen form are not necessary for *FA* activity. However, this failure to fit all of the elements to a simple scheme may be due to a system more complex than we are now aware.

The bacteriological literature has numerous reports of results which might be interpreted as transduction (see reviews by Luria, 1947, and Lederberg, 1948). These experiments have been criticized or neglected because of difficulties in their reproduction and quantitization but might now be reinvestigated in light of the findings presented. A citation of some of the more pertinent ones should suffice at this time. Wollman and Wollman (1925) reported the acquisition of *Salmonella* immunological specificity by *E. coli* via filter passing material. Similar material (which can be obtained by phage lysis) has been implicated in the change of penicillin resistant staphylococci and streptococci to relative penicillin sensitivity (Voureka, 1948; George and Pandalai, 1949). *Shigella para-*

dysenteriae (Weil and Binder, 1947) acquired new immunological specificity when treated with extracts of heterologous types. Boivin (1947) reported a similar change in *E. coli.* Unfortunately his strains have been lost and confirmation is impossible. Bruner and Edwards (1948) in a report of variation of somatic antigens of *Salmonella* grown in the presence of specific serum commented on the possibility that bacterial products dissolved in the serum were responsible for the changes.

These systems, provocative as they are, are insufficiently documented for detailed comparison with *Salmonella* transduction. The transformations in the pneumococcus (Avery *et al.,* 1944; McCarty, 1946) and *Hemophilus influenzae* (Alexander and Leidy, 1951) have been studied more completely.

The genetic "transformation" of the capsular character of the pneumococcus depends on a specific bacterial product (pneumococcus transforming principle, *PTP*). Originally interpreted as a directed mutation, it is now regarded as a variety of genetic exchange (Ephrussi-Taylor, 1950). Thus far transformations have been achieved for the full capsular character (Griffith, 1928), a series of intermediate capsular characters (Ephrussi-Taylor, 1951), M protein character (Austrian and MacLeod, 1949), and penicillin resistance (Hotchkiss, 1951). As in *Salmonella* each character is transformed independently. However, there are several differences between the two systems. *FA* must be evoked while the *PTP* is extractible from healthy cells. The resistance of *FA* to various chemical treatments has given only negative evidence of its chemical nature. The role of desoxyribonucleic acid in the *PTP* was verified by its inactivation by desoxyribonucleic acidase. Retention of activity by gradocol membranes has given comparable estimates for the size (about 0.1μ) of the *FA* particles affecting two different characters. On the other hand, while the particle size of the *PTP* has been variously estimated from an average centrifugal mass of 500,000 (Avery *et al.,* 1944) to an ionizing irradiation sensitive volume equivalent to a molecular weight of 18,000,000 with high asymmetry (Fluke *et al.,* 1951), it is considerably smaller than the *FA* particle. Pneumococci must be sensitized by a complex serum system for adsorption of *PTP*. The low but poorly determined frequency of transformations has been thought to be due to the low competence of the bacteria. In the absence of adsorption experiments a system similar to *Salmonella* has not been ruled out. Important information is still lacking in both systems and time may resolve these apparent differences.

The relationship of transduction in *Salmonella* to sexual recombination in *E. coli* is obscure. Transduction has not been found in crossable *E. coli* nor sexual recombination in *Salmonella*. These genera are extremely closely related taxonomically but seem to have entirely different modes of genetic exchange.

Sexual recombination was first demonstrated in *E. coli,* strain K-12. With the development of an efficient screening procedure, two to three per cent of *E. coli* isolates were proved to cross with strain K-12 (Lederberg, 1951a). The agent of recombination in *E. coli* is almost certainly the bacterial cell. The cells apparently mate, forming zygotes from which parental and recombinant cells may emerge following meiosis, in which linkage is a prominent feature (Lederberg, 1947). The combination of genomes within a single cell has been confirmed by the exceptional occurrence of nondisjunctions which continue to segregate both haploid and diploid complements (Zelle and Lederberg, 1951). Although lysogenicity plays a critical role in transduction in *Salmonella,* all combinations of lysogenic and nonlysogenic cultures of *E. coli* cross with equal facility (Lederberg, E. M., 1951).

Owing to the lack of recombination of unselected markers, transduction is a less useful tool than sexual recombination for certain types of genetic analysis. However, as *FA* may correspond to extracellular genetic material, such problems as gene reproduction, metabolism, and mutation may be more accessible to attack. Sexual systems usually provide for the reassortment of genetic material and give an important source of variation for the operation of natural selection in organic evolution. Both sexual recombination and transduction, because of their low frequency, allow only limited gene interchange in bacteria. Transductive exchange is limited both in frequency and extent.

It is too early to assess the role that transduction may have played in the development of the immunologically complex *Salmonella* species. White (1926) speculated that the many serotypes evolved by loss variation from a single strain possessing all of the many possible antigens. Bruner and Edwards (1948) obtained specific examples of loss variation with contemporary species. Transduction provides a mechanism for transfer of some of the variation developed spontaneously and independently between the "descending" lines. The genus *Salmonella* includes a group of serotypes which share a receptor for *S. typhimurium FA.* Other receptor groups have yet to be sought. Within such groups it should be possible to evolve in the laboratory other new serotypes comparable to the antigenic hybrid of *S. typhi* and *S. typhimurium.*

Several different bacterial genera have been intensively studied with regard to modes of genetic exchange. Each of the several known systems differs in details that enlarge our notions of bacterial reproduction and heredity.

ACKNOWLEDGMENTS

The authors are indebted to a number of workers cited in the text for providing cultures and other materials. They are especially obligated to

Dr. P. R. Edwards, Public Health Service Communicable Diseases Center, Chamblee, Georgia, for patiently providing innumerable cultures, sera, antigenic diagnoses, and counsel.

SUMMARY

When *Salmonella typhimurium* is grown in the presence of a variety of mildly deleterious agents, especially weakly lytic phages, it produces a filtrable agent (*FA*) capable of transferring hereditary traits from one strain to another.

Individual filtrates may transduce many different traits, but no more than one in a single bacterium. The activities of a filtrate parallel the characteristics of the donor cells. Nutritional, fermentative, drug resistance, and antigenic characters have been transduced. The new characters are stable after many generations of subcultures.

FA is resistant to such bacterial disinfectants as chloroform, toluene, and alcohol and to such enzymes as pancreatin, trypsin, ribonuclease, and desoxyribonuclease. The size of the *FA* particle, as determined by filtration through gradocol membranes, is about 0.1 micron. Adsorption of *FA* is rapid and, among various serotypes tested, is correlated with the presence of somatic antigen XII.

The maximum frequency of transduction for any one character has been 2×10^{-6}, a limit set by saturation during adsorption. Some intertype transfers have been observed. For example, the *i* flagellar antigen from *Salmonella typhimurium* has been transduced to *S. typhi* to give a new serotype: IX, XII; *i,* —. Genetic transduction in *Salmonella* is compared and contrasted with "type transformation" in *Hemophilus* and the pneumococcus and with sexual recombination in *Escherichia coli*.

REFERENCES

Alexander, Hattie E., and Leidy, Grace. 1951. Determination of inherited traits of *H. influenzae* by desoxyribonucleic acid fractions isolated from type-specific cells. J. Exp. Med. 93: 359.

Austrian, R., and MacLeod, C. M. 1949. Acquisition of M protein through transformation reactions. J. Exp. Med. **89**: 451-460.

Avery, O. T., MacLeod, C. M., and McCarty, M. 1944. Studies on the chemical nature of the substance inducing transformation of pneumococcal types. J. Exp. Med. **79**: 137-158.

Bacon, G. A., Burrows, W. W., and Yates, Margaret. 1951. The effects of biochemical mutation on the virulence of *Bacterium typhosum*: the loss of virulence of certain mutants. Brit. J. Exp. Path. 32: 85-96.

Bawden, F. C. 1950. Plant viruses and virus diseases. Chronica Botanica, Waltham, Mass.

Boivin, A. 1947. Directed mutation in colon bacilli, by an inducing principle of desoxyribonucleic acid: its meaning for the general biochemistry of heredity. Cold Spring Harbor Symp. Quant. Biol. **12**: 7-17.

Boyd, J. S. K. 1950. The symbiotic bacteriophages of *Salmonella typhimurium*. J. Path. Bact. **62**: 501-517.

Boyd, J. S. K. 1951. Observations on the relationship of symbiotic and lytic bacteriophage. J. Path. Bact. **63**: 445-457.

Bruner, D. W., and Edwards, P. R. 1948. Changes induced in the O antigens of *Salmonella*. J. Bact. **55**: 449.

Burnet, F., and McKie, Margot. 1929. Observations on a permanently lysogenic strain of *B. enteritidis* Gaertner. Australian J. Exp. Biol. Med. Sci. **6**: 276-284.

Davis, B. D. 1950a. Studies on nutritionally deficient bacterial mutants isolated by means of penicillin. Experientia. **6**: 41-50.

Davis, B. D. 1950b. Nonfiltrability of the agents of recombination in *Escherichia coli*. J. Bact. **60**: 507-508.

Davis, B. D. 1951. Aromatic biosynthesis. III. Role of p-aminobenzoic acid in the formation of vitamin B_{12}. J. Bact. **62**: 221-230.

Dienes, L., and Weinberger, H. J. 1951. The L forms of bacteria. Bact. Revs. **15**: 245-288.

Ephrussi-Taylor, Harriett. 1950. Heredity in pneumococci. Endeavor. **9**: 34-40.

Ephrussi-Taylor, Harriet. 1951. Genetic aspects of transformations of pneumococci. Cold Spring Harbor Symp. Quant. Biol. **16**: 445-456.

Fleming, A., Voureka, Amalia, Kramer, I. R. H., and Hughes, W. H. 1950. The morphology and motility of *Proteus vulgaris* and other organisms cultured in the presence of penicillin. J. Gen. Microbiol. **4**: 257-269.

Fluke, D. F., Drew, R. M., and Pollard, C. 1951. The effect of ionizing radiations on the transforming factor of pneumococci. Science. **114**: 480.

George, M., and Pandalai, K. M. 1949. Sensitization of penicillin resistant pathogens. Lancet. **256**: 955-957.

Griffith, F. 1928. The significance of pneumococcal types. J. Hyg. **27**: 113-159.

Hotchkiss, R. D. 1951. The transfer of penicillin resistance in pneumococci by the desoxyribonucleate derived from resistant cultures. Cold Spring Harbor Symp. Quant. Biol. **16**: 457-462.

Kauffmann, F. 1936. Ueber die diphasische Natur der Typhusbacillen. Zeitschr. Hyg. Infcctkr. **119**: 104-118.

Klieneberger-Nobel, Emma. 1951. Filterable forms of bacteria. Bact. Revs. **15**: 77-103.

Kristensen, M. 1948. Mutative bacterial fermentation. Acta Path. Microbiol. Scand. **25**: 244-248.

Lederberg, Esther M. 1951. Lysogenicity in *E. coli* K-12. Genetics. **36**: 560.

Lederberg, J. 1947. Gene recombination and linked segregations in *Escherichia coli*. Genetics. **32**: 505-525.

Lederberg, J. 1948. Problems in microbial genetics. Heredity. 2: 145-198.

Lederberg, J. 1950. Isolation and characterization of biochemical mutants of bacteria. Methods in Medical Research. 3: 5-22.

Lederberg, J. 1951a. Prevalence of *Escherichia coli* strains exhibiting genetic recombination. Science. 14: 68-69.

Lederberg, J. 1951b. Streptomycin resistance: a genetically recessive mutation. J. Bact. 61: 549-550.

Lederberg, J., and Lederberg, Esther M. Replica plating and indirect selection of bacterial mutants. J. Bact. 63: 399-406.

Lederberg, J. and Zinder, N. 1948. Concentration of biochemical mutants of bacteria with penicillin. J. Am. Chem. Soc. 70: 4267.

Lederberg, J., Lederberg, Esther, Zinder, N. D., and Lively, Ethelyn R. 1951. Recombination analysis of bacterial heredity. Cold Spring Harbor Symp. Quant. Biol. 16: 413-443.

Lilleengen, K. 1948. Typing *Salmonella typhimurium* by means of bacteriophage. Acta Path. Microbiol. Scand. Suppl. 77.

Luria, S. E. 1947. Recent advances in bacterial genetics. Bact. Revs. 11: 1-40.

McCarty, M. 1946. Chemical nature and biological specificity of the substance inducing transformations of pneumococcal types. Bact. Revs. 10: 63-71.

Muller, H. J. 1947. The gene. Proc. Roy. Soc. London. B. 134: 1-37.

Page, L. A., Goodlow, R. J., and Braun, W. 1951. The effects of threonine on population changes and virulence of *Salmonella typhimurium*. J. Bact. 62: 639-647.

Plough, H. H., Miller, Helen Y., and Berry, Marion E. 1951. Alternative amino acid requirements in auxotrophic mutants of *Salmonella typhimurium*. Proc. Nat. Acad. Sci. 37: 640-644.

Ryan, F., Beadle, G., and Tatum, E. 1943. The tube method of measurement of growth rate of *Neurospora*. Am. J. Bot. 30: 784-799.

Tatum, E. L., and Lederberg, J. 1947. Gene recombination in the bacterium *Escherichia coli*. J. Bact. 53: 673-684.

Tulasne, R. 1951. Les formes L des bactéries. Revue Immunol. 15: 223-251.

Voureka, Amalia. 1948. Sensitization of penicillin resistant bacteria. Lancet. 254: 62-65.

Weil, A. J., and Binder, M. 1947. Experimental type transformation of *Shigella paradysenteriae* (Flexner). Proc. Soc. Exptl. Biol., N.Y. 66: 349-352.

White, P. B. 1926. Further studies of the *Salmonella* group. Med. Res. Council (Britain). Spec. Rept. Ser. No. 103.

Wollman, E., and Wollman, E. 1925. Sur la transmission parahéréditaire de caractères chez les bacterues. Compt. Rend. Soc. Biol., Paris. 93: 1568-1569.

Zelle, M. R., and Lederberg, J. 1951. Single cell isolations of diploid heterozygous *Escherichia coli*. J. Bact. 61: 351-355.

1952

Independent Functions
of Viral Protein and Nucleic Acid
in Growth of Bacteriophage[1]

by A. D. Hershey and Martha Chase

From the Department of Genetics, Carnegie Institution of
Washington, Cold Spring Harbor, Long Island

*That deoxyribonucleic acid (DNA) may be the carrier of
genetic information was not readily recognized, despite its
presence in chromosomes, until Avery, MacLeod, and Mc-
Carthy in 1944 defined its status in bacterial transformation
studies. By employing radioactive labelled bacteriophage, Hershey and Chase clearly demonstrated that the nucleic acid
of the bacteriophage particle is released from its protein moiety
to enter the cell on infection while the protein coat remains
at the cell surface. These findings suggested that DNA transmitted all the genetic information that directed virus reproduction. Within a few years after the appearance of this report,
convincing evidence was amassed with plant and animal
viruses to establish conclusively the genetic role of viral nucleic acid.*

The work of Doermann (1948), Doer-
mann and Dissosway (1949), and Anderson and Doermann (1952) has
shown that bacteriophages T2, T3, and T4 multiply in the bacterial cell

[1] This investigation was supported in part by a research grant from the National
Microbiological Institute of the National Institutes of Health, Public Health Service.
Radioactive isotopes were supplied by the Oak Ridge National Laboratory on alloca-
tion from the Isotopes Division, United States Atomic Energy Commission. Abridged
and reprinted by permission of the author and publisher from The J. Gen. Physiol.
36(1): 39-56 (1952).

in a non-infective form. The same is true of the phage carried by certain lysogenic bacteria (Lwoff and Gutmann, 1950). Little else is known about the vegetative phase of these viruses. The experiments reported in this paper show that one of the first steps in the growth of T2 is the release from its protein coat of the nucleic acid of the virus particle, after which the bulk of the sulfur-containing protein has no further function.

LIBERATION OF DNA FROM PHAGE PARTICLES
BY ADSORPTION TO BACTERIAL FRAGMENTS

The sensitization of phage DNA to specific depolymerase by adsorption to bacteria might mean that adsorption is followed by the ejection of the phage DNA from its protective coat. The following experiment shows that this is in fact what happens when phage attaches to fragmented bacterial cells.

Bacterial debris was prepared by infecting cells in adsorption medium with four particles of T2 per bacterium, and transferring the cells to salt-poor broth at 37°C. The culture was aerated for 60 minutes, $M/50$ HCN was added, and incubation continued for 30 minutes longer. At this time the yield of extracellular phage was 400 particles per bacterium, which remained unadsorbed because of the low concentration of electrolytes. The debris from the lysed cells was washed by centrifugation at 1700 G, and resuspended in adsorption medium at a concentration equivalent to 3×10^9 lysed cells per ml. It consisted largely of collapsed and fragmented cell membranes. The adsorption of radioactive phage to this material is described in Table IV. The following facts should be noted.

1. The unadsorbed fraction contained only 5 per cent of the original phage particles in infective form, and only 13 per cent of the total sulfur. (Much of this sulfur must be the material that is not adsorbable to whole bacteria.)

2. About 80 per cent of the phage was inactivated. Most of the sulfur of this phage, as well as most of the surviving phage, was found in the sediment fraction.

3. The supernatant fraction contained 40 per cent of the total phage DNA (in a form labile to DNase) in addition to the DNA of the unadsorbed surviving phage. The labile DNA amounted to about half of the DNA of the inactivated phage particles, whose sulfur sedimented with the bacterial debris.

4. Most of the sedimentable DNA could be accounted for either as surviving phage, or as DNA labile to DNase, the latter amounting to about half the DNA of the inactivated particles.

Experiments of this kind are unsatisfactory in one respect: one cannot tell whether the liberated DNA represents all the DNA of some of the inactivated particles, or only part of it.

TABLE IV.* *Release of DNA from phage adsorbed to bacterial debris*

	Phage labeled with	
	S^{35}	P^{32}
Sediment fraction		
Surviving phage.............................	16	22
Total isotope................................	87	55
Acid-soluble isotope.........................	0	2
Acid-soluble after DNase.....................	2	29
Supernatant fraction		
Surviving phage.............................	5	5
Total isotope................................	13	45
Acid-soluble isotope.........................	0.8	0.5
Acid-soluble after DNase.....................	0.8	39

* Tables I through III have been deleted from the article.—ed.
S^{35} and P^{32} labeled T2 were mixed with identical samples of bacterial debris in adsorption medium and warmed for 30 minutes at 37°C. The mixtures were then centrifuged for 15 minutes at 2200 G, and the sediment and supernatant fractions were analyzed separately. The results are expressed as per cent of input phage or isotope.

Similar results were obtained when bacteria (strain B) were lysed by large amounts of UV-killed phage T2 or T4 and then tested with P^{32}-labeled T2 and T4. The chief point of interest in this experiment is that bacterial debris saturated with UV-killed T2 adsorbs T4 better than T2, and debris saturated with T4 adsorbs T2 better than T4. As in the preceding experiment, some of the adsorbed phage was not inactivated and some of the DNA of the inactivated phage was not released from the debris.

These experiments show that some of the cell receptors for T2 are different from some of the cell receptors for T4, and that phage attaching to these specific receptors is inactivated by the same mechanism as phage attaching to unselected receptors. This mechanism is evidently an active one, and not merely the blocking of sites of attachment to bacteria.

REMOVAL OF PHAGE COATS FROM INFECTED BACTERIA

Anderson (1951) has obtained electron micrographs indicating that phage T2 attaches to bacteria by its tail. If this precarious attachment is preserved during the progress of the infection, and if the conclusions reached above are correct, it ought to be a simple matter to break the empty phage membranes off the infected bacteria, leaving the phage DNA inside the cells.

The following experiments show that this is readily accomplished by strong shearing forces applied to suspensions of infected cells, and further that infected cells from which 80 per cent of the sulfur of the parent virus has been removed remain capable of yielding phage progeny.

Broth-grown bacteria were infected with S^{35}- or P^{32}-labeled phage in adsorption medium, the unadsorbed material was removed by centrifugation, and the cells were resuspended in water containing per liter 1 mM $MgSO_4$, 0.1 mM $CaCl_2$, and 0.1 gm. gelatin. This suspension was spun in a Waring blender (semimicro size) at 10,000 R.P.M. The suspension was cooled briefly in ice water at the end of each 60 second running period. Samples were removed at intervals, titrated (through antiphage serum) to measure the number of bacteria capable of yielding phage, and centrifuged to measure the proportion of isotope released from the cells.

The results of one experiment with each isotope are shown in Fig. 1. The data for S^{35} and survival of infected bacteria come from the same

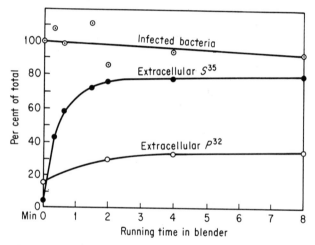

Fig. 1. Removal of S^{35} and P^{32} from bacteria infected with radioactive phage, and survival of the infected bacteria, during agitation in a Waring blender.

experiment, in which the ratio of added phage to bacteria was 0.28, and the concentrations of bacteria were 2.5×10^8 per ml. infected, and 9.7×10^8 per ml. total, by direct titration. The experiment with P^{32}-labeled phage was very similar. In connection with these results, it should be recalled that Anderson (1949) found that adsorption of phage to bacteria could be prevented by rapid stirring of the suspension.

At higher ratios of infection, considerable amounts of phage sulfur elute from the cells spontaneously under the conditions of these experiments, though the elution of P^{32} and the survival of infected cells are not affected by multiplicity of infection (Table V). This shows that there is a cooperative action among phage particles in producing alterations of

TABLE V. *Effect of multiplicity of infection on elusion of phage membranes from infected bacteria*

Running time in blendor	Multiplicity of infection	P^{32}-labeled phage		S^{35}-labeled phage	
		Isotope eluted	Infected bacteria surviving	Isotope eluted	Infected bacteria surviving
min.		*per cent*	*per cent*	*per cent*	*per cent*
0	0.6	10	120	16	101
2.5	0.6	21	82	81	78
0	6.0	13	89	46	90
2.5	6.0	24	86	82	85

The infected bacteria were suspended at 10^9 cells per ml. in water containing per liter 1 mM $MgSO_4$, 0.1 mM $CaCl_2$, and 0.1 gm. gelatin. Samples were withdrawn for assay of extracellular isotope and infected bacteria before and after agitating the suspension. In either case the cells spent about 15 minutes at room temperature in the eluting fluid.

the bacterial membrane which weaken the attachment of the phage. The cellular changes detected in this way may be related to those responsible for the release of bacterial components from infected bacteria (Prater, 1951; Price, 1952).

A variant of the preceding experiments was designed to test bacteria at a later stage in the growth of phage. For this purpose infected cells were aerated in broth for 5 or 15 minutes, fixed by the addition of 0.5 per cent (*v/v*) commercial formalin, centrifuged, resuspended in 0.1 per cent formalin in water, and subsequently handled as described above. The results were very similar to those already presented, except that the release of P^{32} from the cells was slightly less, and titrations of infected cells could not be made.

The S^{35}-labeled material detached from infected cells in the manner described possesses the following properties. It is sedimented at 12,000 *G*, though less completely than intact phage particles. It is completely precipitated by antiphage serum in the presence of whole phage carrier. 40 to 50 per cent of it readsorbs to sensitive bacteria, almost independently of bacterial concentration between 2×10^8 and 10^9 cells per ml., in 5 minutes at 37°C. The adsorption is not very specific: 10 to 25 per cent adsorbs to phage-resistant bacteria under the same conditions. The adsorption requires salt, and for this reason the efficient removal of S^{35} from infected bacteria can be accomplished only in a fluid poor in electrolytes.

The results of these experiments may be summarized as follows:—

1. 75 to 80 per cent of the phage sulfur can be stripped from infected cells by violent agitation of the suspension. At high multiplicity of infection, nearly 50 per cent elutes spontaneously. The properties of the S^{35}-labeled material show that it consists of more or less intact phage

membranes, most of which have lost the ability to attach specifically to bacteria.

2. The release of sulfur is accompanied by the release of only 21 to 35 per cent of the phage phosphorus, half of which is given up without any mechanical agitation.

3. The treatment does not cause any appreciable inactivation of intracellular phage.

4. These facts show that the bulk of the phage sulfur remains at the cell surface during infection, and takes no part in the multiplication of intracellular phage. The bulk of the phage DNA, on the other hand, enters the cell soon after adsorption of phage to bacteria.

TRANSFER OF SULFUR AND PHOSPHORUS FROM PARENTAL PHAGE TO PROGENY

We have concluded above that the bulk of the sulfur-containing protein of the resting phage particle takes no part in the multiplication of phage, and in fact does not enter the cell. It follows that little or no sulfur should be transferred from parental phage to progeny. The experiments described below show that this expectation is correct, and that the maximal transfer is of the order 1 per cent.

Bacteria were grown in glycerol-lactate medium overnight and subcultured in the same medium for 2 hours at 37°C. with aeration, the size of seeding being adjusted nephelometrically to yield 2×10^8 cells per ml. in the subculture. These bacteria were sedimented, resuspended in adsorption medium at a concentration of 10^9 cells per ml., and infected with S^{35}-labeled phage T2. After 5 minutes at 37°C., the suspension was diluted with 2 volumes of water and resedimented to remove unadsorbed phage (5 to 10 per cent by titer) and S^{35} (about 15 per cent). The cells were next suspended in glycerol-lactate medium at a concentration of 2×10^8 per ml. and aerated at 37°C. Growth of phage was terminated at the desired time by adding in rapid succession 0.02 mM HCN and 2×10^{11} UV-killed phage per ml. of culture. The cyanide stops the maturation of intracellular phage (Doermann, 1948), and the UV-killed phage minimizes losses of phage progeny by adsorption to bacterial debris, and promotes the lysis of bacteria (Maaløe and Watson, 1951). As mentioned in another connection, and also noted in these experiments, the lysing phage must be closely related to the phage undergoing multiplication (e.g., T2H, its h mutant, or T2L, but not T4 or T6, in this instance) in order to prevent inactivation of progeny by adsorption to bacterial debris.

To obtain what we shall call the maximal yield of phage, the lysing phage was added 25 minutes after placing the infected cells in the culture medium, and the cyanide was added at the end of the 2nd hour. Under these conditions, lysis of infected cells occurs rather slowly.

Aeration was interrupted when the cyanide was added, and the cultures were left overnight at 37°C. The lysates were then fractionated by centrifugation into an initial low speed sediment (2500 G for 20 minutes), a high speed supernatant (12,000 G for 30 minutes), a second low speed sediment obtained by recentrifuging in adsorption medium the resuspended high speed sediment, and the clarified high speed sediment.

The distribution of S^{35} and phage among fractions obtained from three cultures of this kind is shown in Table VI. The results are typical (except for the excessively good recoveries of phage and S^{35}) of lysates in broth as well as lysates in glycerol-lactate medium.

TABLE VI. *Per cent distributions of phage and S^{35} among centrifugally separated fractions of lysates after infection with S^{35}-labeled T2*

Fraction	Lysis at $t = 0$ S^{35}	Lysis at $t = 10$ S^{35}	Maximal yield	
			S^{35}	Phage
1st low speed sediment.............	79	81	82	19
2nd low speed sediment...........	2.4	2.1	2.8	14
High speed sediment..............	8.6	6.9	7.1	61
High speed supernatant...........	10	10	7.5	7.0
Recovery.......................	100	100	96	100

Infection with S^{35}-labeled T2, 0.8 particles per bacterium. Lysing phase UV-killed k mutant of T2. Phage yields per infected bacterium: <0.1 after lysis at $t = 0$; 0.12 at $t = 10$; maximal yield 29. Recovery of S^{35} means per cent of adsorbed input recovered in the four fractions; recovery of phage means per cent of total phage yield (by plaque count before fractionation) recovered by titration of fractions.

The striking result of this experiment is that the distribution of S^{35} among the fractions is the same for early lysates that do not contain phage progeny, and later ones that do. This suggests that little or no S^{35} is contained in the mature phage progeny. Further fractionation by adsorption to bacteria confirms this suggestion.

Adsorption mixtures prepared for this purpose contained about 5 × 10^9 heat-killed bacteria (70°C. for 10 minutes) from 18 hour broth cultures, and about 10^{11} phage (UV-killed lysing phage plus test phage), per ml. of adsorption medium. After warming to 37°C. for 5 minutes, the mixtures were diluted with 2 volumes of water, and centrifuged. Assays were made from supernatants and from unwashed resuspended sediments.

The results of tests of adsorption of S^{35} and phage to bacteria (H) adsorbing both T2 progeny and h-mutant lysing phage, to bacteria (B/2) adsorbing lysing phage only, and to bacteria (B/2h) adsorbing neither, are shown in Table VII, together with parallel tests of authentic S^{35}-labeled phage.

TABLE VII. *Adsorption tests with uniformly S³⁵-labeled phage and with products of their growth in non-radioactive medium*

	Per cent adsorbed				
	Uniformly labeled S^{35} phage		Products of lysis at $t = 10$	Phage progeny (Maximal yield)	
	+UV-k	No UV-k			
Adsorbing bacteria	S^{35}	S^{35}	S^{35}	S^{35}	Phage
Sensitive (H).............	84	86	79	78	96
Resistant (B/2)..........	15	11	46	49	10
Resistant (B/2h).........	13	12	29	28	8

The uniformly labeled phage and the products of their growth are respectively the seed phage and the high speed sediment fractions from the experiment shown in Table VI.

The uniformly labeled phage is tested at a low ratio of phage to bacteria: +UV-h means with added UV-killed h mutant in equal concentration to that present in the other test materials.

The adsorption of phage is measured by plaque counts of supernatants, and also sediments in the case of the resistant bacteria, in the usual way.

The adsorption tests show that the S^{35} present in the seed phage is adsorbed with the specificity of the phage, but that S^{35} present in lysates of bacteria infected with this phage shows a more complicated behavior. It is strongly adsorbed to bacteria adsorbing both progeny and lysing phage. It is weakly adsorbed to bacteria adsorbing neither. It is moderately well adsorbed to bacteria adsorbing lysing phage but not phage progeny. The latter test shows that the S^{35} is not contained in the phage progeny, and explains the fact that the S^{35} in early lysates not containing progeny behaves in the same way.

The specificity of the adsorption of S^{35}-labeled material contaminating the phage progeny is evidently due to the lysing phage, which is also adsorbed much more strongly to strain H than to B/2, as shown both by the visible reduction in Tyndall scattering (due to the lysing phage) in the supernatants of the test mixtures, and by independent measurements. This conclusion is further confirmed by the following facts.

1. If bacteria are infected with S^{35} phage, and then lysed near the midpoint of the latent period with cyanide alone (in salt-poor broth, to prevent readsorption of S^{35} to bacterial debris), the high speed sediment fraction contains S^{35} that is adsorbed weakly and non-specifically to bacteria.

2. If the lysing phage and the S^{35}-labeled infecting phage are the same (T2), or if the culture in salt-poor broth is allowed to lyse spontaneously (so that the yield of progeny is large), the S^{35} in the high speed sediment fraction is adsorbed with the specificity of the phage progeny

(except for a weak non-specific adsorption). This is illustrated in Table VII by the adsorption to H and B/2h.

It should be noted that a phage progeny grown from S^{35}-labeled phage and containing a larger or smaller amount of contaminating radio-activity could not be distinguished by any known method from authentic S^{35}-labeled phage, except that a small amount of the contaminant could be removed by absorption to bacteria resistant to the phage. In addition to the properties already mentioned, the contaminating S^{35} is completely precipitated with the phage by antiserum, and cannot be appreciably separated from the phage by further fractional sedimentation, at either high or low concentrations of electrolyte. On the other hand, the chemical contamination from this source would be very small in favorable circumstances, because the progeny of a single phage particle are numerous and the contaminant is evidently derived from the parents.

The properties of the S^{35}-labeled contaminant show that it consists of the remains of the coats of the parental phage particles, presumably identical with the material that can be removed from unlysed cells in the Waring blender. The fact that it undergoes little chemical change is not surprising since it probably never enters the infected cell.

The properties described explain a mistaken preliminary report (Hershey *et al.,* 1951) of the transfer of S^{35} from parental to progeny phage.

It should be added that experiments identical to those shown in Tables VI and VII, but starting from phage labeled with P^{32}, show that phosphorus is tranferred from parental to progeny phage to the extent of 30 per cent at yields of about 30 phage per infected bacterium, and that the P^{32} in prematurely lysed cultures is almost entirely non-sedimentable, becoming, in fact, acid-soluble on aging.

Similar measures of the transfer of P^{32} have been published by Putnam and Kozloff (1950) and others. Watson and Maaløe (1952) summarize this work, and report equal transfer (nearly 50 per cent) of phosphorus and adenine.

A PROGENY OF S^{35}-LABELED PHAGE NEARLY FREE FROM THE PARENTAL LABEL

The following experiment shows clearly that obligatory transfer of parental sulfur to offspring phage is less than 1 per cent, and probably considerably less. In this experiment, the phage yield from infected bacteria from which the S^{35}-labeled phage coats had been stripped in the Waring blender was assayed directly for S^{35}.

Sensitive bacteria grown in broth were infected with five particles of S^{35}-labeled phage per bacterium, the high ratio of infection being necessary for purposes of assay. The infected bacteria were freed from un-adsorbed phage and suspended in water containing per liter 1 mM

$MgSO_4$, 0.1 mM $CaCl_2$, and 0.1 gm. gelatin. A sample of this suspension was agitated for 2.5 minutes in the Waring blender, and centrifuged to remove the extracellular S^{35}. A second sample not run in the blendor was centrifuged at the same time. The cells from both samples were resuspended in warm salt-poor broth at a concentration of 10^8 bacteria per ml., and aerated for 80 minutes. The cultures were then lysed by the addition of 0.02 mM HCN, 2×10^{11} UV-killed T2, and 6 mg. NaCl per ml. of culture. The addition of salt at this point causes S^{35} that would otherwise be eluted (Hershey *et al.*, 1951) to remain attached to the bacterial debris. The lysates were fractionated and assayed as described previously.

The data show that stripping reduces more or less proportionately the S^{35}-content of all fractions. In particular, the S^{35}-content of the fraction containing most of the phage progeny is reduced from nearly 10 per cent to less than 1 per cent of the initially adsorbed isotope. This experiment shows that the bulk of the S^{35} appearing in all lysate fractions is derived from the remains of the coats of the parental phage particles.

DISCUSSION

We have shown that when a particle of bacteriophage T2 attaches to a bacterial cell, most of the phage DNA enters the cell, and a residue containing at least 80 per cent of the sulfur-containing protein of the phage remains at the cell surface. This residue consists of the material forming the protective membrane of the resting phage particle, and it plays no further role in infection after the attachment of phage to bacterium.

These facts leave in question the possible function of the 20 per cent of sulfur-containing protein that may or may not enter the cell. We find that little or none of it is incorporated into the progeny of the infecting particle, and that at least part of it consists of additional material resembling the residue that can be shown to remain extracellular. Phosphorus and adenine (Watson and Maaløe, 1952) derived from the DNA of the infecting particle, on the other hand, are transferred to the phage progeny to a considerable and equal extent. We infer that sulfur-containing protein has no function in phage multiplication, and that DNA has some function.

It must be recalled that the following questions remain unanswered. (1) Does any sulfur-free phage material other than DNA enter the cell? (2) If so, is it transferred to the phage progeny? (3) Is the transfer of phosphorus (or hypothetical other substance) to progeny direct—that is, does it remain at all times in a form specifically identifiable as phage substance—or indirect?

Our experiments show clearly that a physical separation of the phage T2 into genetic and non-genetic parts is possible. A corresponding functional separation is seen in the partial independence of phenotype and genotype in the same phage (Novick and Szilard, 1951; Hershey *et al.*, 1951). The chemical identification of the genetic part must wait, however, until some of the questions asked above have been answered.

Two facts of significance for the immunologic method of attack on problems of viral growth should be emphasized here. First, the principal antigen of the infecting particles of phage T2 persists unchanged in infected cells. Second, it remains attached to the bacterial debris resulting from lysis of the cells. These possibilities seem to have been overlooked in a study by Rountree (1951) of viral antigens during the growth of phage T5.

SUMMARY

1. Osmotic shock disrupts particles of phage T2 into material containing nearly all the phage sulfur in a form precipitable by antiphage serum, and capable of specific adsorption to bacteria. It releases into solution nearly all the phage DNA in a form not precipitable by antiserum and not adsorbable to bacteria. The sulfur-containing protein of the phage particle evidently makes up a membrane that protects the phage DNA from DNase, comprises the sole or principal antigenic material, and is responsible for attachment of the virus to bacteria.

2. Adsorption of T2 to heat-killed bacteria, and heating or alternate freezing and thawing of infected cells, sensitize the DNA of the adsorbed phage to DNase. These treatments have little or no sensitizing effect on unadsorbed phage. Neither heating nor freezing and thawing releases the phage DNA from infected cells, although other cell constituents can be extracted by these methods. These facts suggest that the phage DNA forms part of an organized intracellular structure throughout the period of phage growth.

3. Adsorption of phage T2 to bacterial debris causes part of the phage DNA to appear in solution, leaving the phage sulfur attached to the debris. Another part of the phage DNA, corresponding roughly to the remaining half of the DNA of the inactivated phage, remains attached to the debris but can be separated from it by DNase. Phage T4 behaves similarly, although the two phages can be shown to attach to different combining sites. The inactivation of phage by bacterial debris is evidently accompanied by the rupture of the viral membrane.

4. Suspensions of infected cells agitated in a Waring blender release 75 per cent of the phage sulfur and only 15 per cent of the phage phosphorus to the solution as a result of the applied shearing force. The cells remain capable of yielding phage progeny.

5. The facts stated show that most of the phage sulfur remains at the cell surface and most of the phage DNA enters the cell on infection. Whether sulfur-free material other than DNA enters the cell has not been

determined. The properties of the sulfur-containing residue identify it as essentially unchanged membranes of the phage particles. All types of evidence show that the passage of phage DNA into the cell occurs in non-nutrient medium under conditions in which other known steps in viral growth do not occur.

6. The phage progeny yielded by bacteria infected with phage labeled with radioactive sulfur contain less than 1 per cent of the parental radioactivity. The progeny of phage particles labeled with radioactive phosphorus contain 30 per cent or more of the parental phosphorus.

7. Phage inactivated by dilute formaldehyde is capable of adsorbing to bacteria, but does not release its DNA to the cell. This shows that the interaction between phage and bacterium resulting in release of the phage DNA from its protective membrane depends on labile components of the phage particle. By contrast, the components of the bacterium essential to this interaction are remarkably stable. The nature of the interaction is otherwise unknown.

8. The sulfur-containing protein of resting phage particles is confined to a protective coat that is responsible for the adsorption to bacteria, and functions as an instrument for the injection of the phage DNA into the cell. This protein probably has no function in the growth of intracellular phage. The DNA has some function. Further chemical inferences should not be drawn from the experiments presented.

REFERENCES

Anderson, T. F. 1949. The reactions of bacterial viruses with their host cells, Bot. Rev. 15: 464.

Anderson, T. F. 1951. Tr. New York Acad. Sc. 13: 130.

Anderson, T. F., and Doermann, A. H. 1952. J. Gen. Physiol. 35: 657.

Benzer, S. 1952. J. Bact. 63: 59.

Doermann, A. H. 1948. Carnegie Institution of Washington Yearbook, No. 47: 176.

Doermann, A. H., and Dissosway, C. 1949. Carnegie Institution of Washington Yearbook, No. 48: 170.

Dulbecco, R. 1952. J. Bact. 63: 209.

Herriott, R. M. 1951. J. Bact. 61: 752.

Hershey, A. D. 1946. Genetics. 31: 620.

Hershey, A. D., Roesel, C., Chase, M., and Forman, S. 1951. Carnegie Institution of Washington Yearbook, No. 50: 195.

Lwoff, A., and Gutmann, A. 1950. Ann. Inst. Pasteur. 78: 711.

Maaløe, O., and Watson, J. D. 1951. Proc. Nat. Acad. Sci. 37: 507.

Novick, A., and Szilard, L. 1951. Science. 113: 34.

Prater, C. D. 1951. Thesis, University of Pennsylvania.

Price, W. H. 1952. J. Gen. Physiol. **35**: 409.

Putnam, F. W., and Kozloff, L. 1950. J. Biol. Chem. **182**: 243.

Rountree, P. M. 1951. Brit. J. Exp. Path. **32**: 341.

Watson, J. D., and Maaløe, O. 1952. Acta Path. Microbiol. Scand. In press.

1952

Direct Evidence for the Multiplication
of Aster-Yellows Virus
in Its Insect Vector[1]

by Karl Maramorosch

Suggestive evidence for the multiplication of virus in both arthropod and plant hosts came from observations on the delay in the infectivity power of the leafhopper in transmitting aster-yellows virus to healthy plants.[2] Subsequently, it was demonstrated by transovarial passage that plant viruses propagate in the insect vector (See Fukushi's paper). Additional proof of virus multiplication was made possible by the discovery that some plant viruses may be transferred directly from insect to insect by inoculation of infective material.[3] In the paper presented here, Maramorosch succeeded in the serial transmission of aster-yellows virus from leafhopper to leafhopper using the insect injection technique. The dilution of virus inoculum that was attained, after ten passages in series, was 10^{-40}. These experiments provided conclusive proof of the multiplication of a plant virus in its insect vector. In a similar manner, wound tumor virus was transmitted from insect to insect through seven serial passages and a dilution of 10^{-18} was attained without decrease in virus concentration in insects.[4] The cumulative evidence from studies in this area of virology established the existence of a unique group of viruses and helped to deemphasize the lines of demarcation that were formed among major categories of viruses.

The existence of viruses that multiply, both in plants and insects, and the recent finding that a plant and animal virus

---

[1] Reprinted by permission of the author and publisher from Phytopathology. **42:** (2), 59-64 (1952). Figures 1-4 omitted.

[2] Kunkel. Am. J. Bot. 13: 646 (1926).
[3] Storey. Proc. Roy. Soc. B. 113: 463 (1933).
[4] Black and Brakke. Phytopathology. 42: 269 (1952).

share a common antigen capable of fixing complement,[5] invite
some intriguing speculations on the origin of viruses.

Although transovarial passages (5,
6, 10, 11) of two plant viruses through the eggs of their vectors provided
evidence of virus multiplication in these vectors, the evidence was considered inadequate by some workers (1). This stimulated a return to the
problem. It seemed that the question of whether or not any given plant
virus multiplied in its insect vector could easily be settled if the virus
were carried in serial passages from insect to insect, with the inoculum
adequately diluted at each passage. Such a test was made for the animal
virus of equine encephalomyelitis by Merrill and TenBroeck (25), but no
similar evidence was available for any plant virus. The discovery by Black
(3) that aster-yellows virus could be transmitted by needle inoculations to
its insect vector, the aster leafhopper *Macrosteles divisus* Uhler, made it
possible to obtain such evidence for aster-yellows virus in its carrier insect.
A preliminary report of work on the problem has already been presented
(20). This paper describes in detail ten consecutive passages through the
leafhopper in experiments started in March 1950, and carried out over a
period of 13 months.

MATERIALS

All experiments were carried out under controlled conditions of
temperature, light, humidity, and wind velocity. Figure 1 represents a
diagram of one of the temperature control chambers used. The inside
dimensions were 65 × 75 × 75 cm. A removable ceiling made of 0.020-in.
(0.5-mm.) transparent cellulose acetate was found to reduce the light intensity by only 2 per cent and at the same time to insulate the working
part of the box sufficiently. Six holes, 0.5 cm. in diameter, were made in
the celluloid to avoid excessive water vapor condensation on the ceiling.
Two inner walls were perforated by 13 rows of holes, 0.5 cm. in diameter,
4 cm. apart. These holes served primarily for air flow, but were also used
for the insertion of metal blocks which supported the platform at desired
levels. Behind one of the perforated walls a heater of high-resistance wire
was placed and covered by a metal box with a blower. The speed of this
blower was regulated by a rheostat. The air flow was directed through the
space below the proper inside box and back into it through the opposite
wall, as indicated in the diagram. It proved desirable to cover the holes
below the platform by pieces of cardboard. A gas bulb type thermostat
(Minneapolis Honeywell) was placed behind the wall opposite to the

[5] Streissle and Maramorosch. Science. **140:** 996 (1963).

heater. The boxes were kept in an air-conditioned room at 10°C. and the inside temperature maintained at $25° \pm 0.5°C$. Cool air from the room entered each box through holes in the outer walls and mixed continuously with the warm air inside. Fluorescent lamps were chosen as the source of light because of their low temperature, in spite of some disadvantages like low intensity and excessive weight of electric resistance (ballast) equipment, which could be partially or completely overcome. Each box was lighted by 19 fluorescent tubes, mounted on a panel as close together as their widths made practical. The ballasts were placed outside the room so that their heat was not dissipated in the refrigerated area. By means of separate switches, each fluorescent tube could be connected with either one or two ballasts. By the use of double ballasts for single lights, the intensity was increased by approximately 60 per cent. With new tubes at a distance of 44 cm. (19 in.) from the plastic ceiling, the maximum intensity of light was 4000 foot-candles, whereas with single ballasts at the same distance it was 2500 foot-candles. The ballast arrangements were suggested by Went's description of the Earhart Plant Research Laboratory in Pasadena (31). The lights were turned on for 16 hr. a day by a standard automatic electric clock.

China asters (*Callistephus chinensis* Nees), used as test plants, were grown from commercial seed in flats and transplanted to 2½-in. pots.

A stock colony of virus-free *Macrosteles divisus* Uhler was kept in an insectary (Fig. 2) on rye plants, which are immune from aster yellows.

A specially constructed microsyringe, calibrated to 1/8000 cc., described by McMaster and Hageboom (24), permitted an accurate measurement of the volume of inoculum introduced into each insect. Ordinary (metal hypodermic needles of 23 to 26 gauge and Pyrex micropipettes cemented to them with a paste of litharge and glycerine were used (21) (Fig. 3). When a colony of insects was employed, the insects were macerated in a commercially available TenBroeck tissue grinder (29). Single insects were ground in a similar micromortar of small dimensions (8).

METHODS

The viruliferous insects, which served as virus source, were obtained by feeding 100 virus-free leafhoppers from stock cultures containing approximately equal numbers of males and females on diseased aster plants for 2 weeks at 25°C. When tested individually for 2 days on asters, 83 of them proved infective. The 100 insects, weighing approximately 140 mgm., were crushed in the tissue grinder and 999.860 cc. of neutral buffered saline added at the time of maceration, to make approximately a 1:7000 dilution of the insect pulp. In subsequent passages the weight of the survivors was taken as the basis for making a 1:1000 dilution. Single insects weigh at least 10 times as much as the inoculum used for their injection (1.2 to 1.4 mg., as compared to the weight of 1/8000 cc. = 0.12 mg., approximately). Therefore the actual dilution of the original inoculum in each consecutive passage increased by a factor of 10^{-4}.

The diluted pulp was centrifuged at 3000 r.p.m. for 10 min. at 0°C. and the supernatant fluid was used for injections. The injections were performed under a fluorescent light and a magnifying glass in a coldroom at 0°C., which immobilized the insects. An attempt was made to insert the needle between the third and fourth segment of the abdomen, thus introducing the measured amount of 1/8000 cc. into the abdominal cavity. This procedure was a modification of leafhopper inoculations developed by Storey (27) and Black (3). The essential difference consisted of the introduction of a very small but accurately measured volume of inoculum. Figure 3 shows an insect during injection. The insects were pushed off the needle by means of an insect pin sealed in a glass rod; they were then slowly warmed to room temperature. Subsequently they were caged on rye plants (*Secale cereale* L.), and placed in chambers at 25°C. Females were employed for the injections because they were somewhat larger and therefore more easily injected. The size of the leafhoppers is illustrated in Figure 4. Injected insects were transferred every 10 days to fresh rye plants and after 30 days the survivors were tested individually for 48 hr. on young aster plants. They were then macerated, diluted, and used for the next passage. The aster plants were kept under observation in a greenhouse for 6 weeks after the removal of the insects. Noninjected control insects from the same stock culture were caged on aster plants and transferred on the same days as the injected leafhoppers.

EXPERIMENTS AND RESULTS

SERIAL PASSAGE

The results of infectivity tests of the first six passages were not known at the time of maceration of the survivors. These passages are summarized in Table 1, A. One hundred viruliferous insects were used as a source of virus in the first transfer. The leafhopper pulp (140 mg.) was diluted 1:7000, so that the dilution of the virus in the insect juices actually was greater than stated. Parts of these diluted juices were injected into 200 virus free leafhoppers which were maintained for the succeeding 30 days on rye plants at 25°C. The 36 insects that survived were tested individually for 48 hr. on young aster plants. After 3 weeks this test showed that eight hoppers were infective. In the meantime the 36 insects were used as a source of virus for the next passage. Three hundred insects were injected; 16 survived 30 days and were used for the third passage. Three of them were later found to have been infective. In the third passage, 150 insects were injected and only two survived. These two survivors were macerated and, in an attempt to reduce the high mortality rate, penicillin was added and the supernatant filtered through a coarse

TABLE 1. *Serial passage of aster-yellows virus through the aster leafhopper*

Passage[a]	No. of injected insects	Days after injection on:		Survivors[c]	Calculated dilution
		Rye	Asters[b]		
A.					
1	200	30	2	36 (8)	$10^{-3.8}$
2	300	30	2	16 (3)	10^{-8}
3	150	30	2	2 (0)	10^{-12}
4	300	30	2	34 (5)	10^{-16}
5	100	30	2	5 (0)	10^{-20}
6	200	30	2	22 (5)	10^{-24}
B.					
7	100	6	54*	8 (2)	10^{-28}
8	240	40	25**	12 (4)	10^{-32}
9	50	19	13*	16 (6)	10^{-36}
10	50	30	20	4 (1)	10^{-40}

[a] The diluted insect juice in the fourth passage was filtered through sintered glass. Penicillin was added in the fourth, fifth, sixth, and seventh passages.

[b] Individual insects were transferred to individual aster plants: *three times weekly; **every 5 days.

[c] Number of infective survivors in parentheses. In series A, all 100 control insects for each passage survived, and in series B all 20 control insects for each passage survived.

glass filter. Of 300 injected insects in this passage, 34 survived and five proved infective. Thus the virus was not lost in the third passage in spite of the negative infectivity test. Penicillin was also added in the next three passages. In the fifth passage five insects survived but none of these proved infective; in the sixth passage, five of 22 survivors transmitted the virus.

The following four passages (Table 1, B) were made with some modifications of the previously used method. The 22 survivors of the sixth passage, were macerated with the addition of penicillin, and 100 virus-free insects were injected. Eight survived a period of 60 days and two of them were infective. The eight survivors served as a source for the injection of 240 insects, of which 12 survived 65 days and four were infective. The insects of these two passages were not kept on rye continuously, but after a 6-day and a 19-day period, respectively, they were caged on asters and transferred three times weekly. Only the four infective survivors of the eighth passage were used for the inoculum of the ninth group. The injected insects were transferred three times weekly to fresh asters. After 32 days, 16 of the 50 injected leafhoppers survived and four of them proved infective. The tenth and last passage, with 50 injected leafhoppers, was kept 30 days on rye, then tested on aster plants, and of four survivors one proved to be infective. The estimated dilution used to inoculate the insects of the tenth passage in the series, if no multiplication had occurred, would be at least 10^{-40}, but aster-yellows virus in insect juices has been found infective at dilutions of 10^{-3} but not 10^{-4} or higher.

In experiments which will be discussed in more detail elsewhere (23), the concentration of virus in the first and ninth passages was measured by the use of a new method. The tests showed no decrease in virus concentration of the inoculum used in the ninth passage over that used in the first, and provided further direct evidence for multiplication of aster-yellows virus in the insect host.

Transfers of Virus from "Noninfective" Viruliferous Insects

It was found, in two instances, that virus was carried over to the next group of insects although infectivity tests of the source insects proved negative. This occurred in the third and fifth passages. It is possible that some insects that did not transmit virus during the 48-hr. test feeding period were nevertheless infective, or that the incubation period of the virus in some insects was not completed by the time of their maceration. An attempt was therefore made to find whether or not very long incubation periods may account for the negative infectivity tests. The insects of the seventh passage were kept for 54 days on test plants, and not, as in the first six passages, for but 2 days. They were transferred to fresh plants three times weekly. The survivors were macerated individually and diluted to 10^{-3} and groups of 30 insects injected with each dilution. Insects No. 5 and No. 30 were infective in the seventh passage. The virus from No. 30 passed to two injected insects, whereas none of the insects injected with juice of No. 5 became infective. But the noninfective No. 21 of the seventh passage also contained enough virus to render two insects of the eighth passage infective. This may mean that in insect No. 21 the incubation period of the virus was not completed in the long span of 60 days which had elapsed since it was injected. This appears likely because in insect No. 5 of the seventh group the required incubation period was shown to be 52 days. It should be mentioned that in other tests of insects that acquired the virus by feeding, the average incubation period at 25°C. was 12 days. It was shown by Black (4) that aster-yellows virus can be recovered and transferred from viruliferous insects a number of days before the incubation is completed.[6]

Control Experiments

The control insects, amounting to 100 for each of the first six passages, came from the same stock as the injected ones and all proved virus-free. During winter months, when the last four passages were made, and outside

[6] Transfer from such insects can be described as "blind." This term is used in experimental transmission of animal viruses for the method whereby transfer to a healthy animal is made from an inoculated one at a time when no signs of infection can be noted.

contamination was unlikely to occur, the number of control insects was reduced to 20 for each passage. This was considered as a sufficient number because the stock of leafhoppers lived and bred entirely on rye plants, and the possibility of contamination of the stock culture in the insectary was therefore practically eliminated. In the seventh, eighth, and ninth passages insects were transferred to aster plants three times weekly by means of "leaf cages" (22). Individual hoppers were confined to single cages that were fastened to leaves. From five to ten control plants were inoculated at each transfer and all remained healthy.

To confirm the immunity of rye from aster-yellows, established long ago by Kunkel in early experiments with the disease (12), 50 viruliferous females were caged on rye and kept on it until some nymphs of the next generation reached the third instar stage. The 100 largest nymphs were caged individually on asters at 25°C. for 4 weeks. None of them transmitted aster yellows.

In a preliminary test it was found that at 25°C. approximately 47 per cent of insects acquired aster-yellows virus in a one-day infection feeding. It seemed desirable to define more accurately the length of time during which insects could be kept, without acquiring the virus, on inoculated test plants in which the incubation period was not completed. Forty aster plants were inoculated by means of infective insects, five feeding on each plant. Together with these infective adult insects, single virus-free nymphs were caged on the plants. After 24 hr. the infective adults and the test nymphs were removed, the adults discarded, and the nymphs caged on rye. Forty virus-free female leafhoppers were caged on the plants for 24 hr., then removed to rye and replaced by another group of 40 virus-free females. This was repeated until, on the 9th day, the first plant in the group showed symptoms of disease. The 40 insects which were removed on each day and kept at 25°C. on rye for 21 following days, were then tested on asters for one week. Of 312 survivors, one picked up virus on the 7th day, that is, 2 days before the first disease symptoms were observed. On the 8th day an additional nine insects acquired aster-yellows virus. Of the 40 inoculated plants all but three eventually became diseased. Ninety control insects, tested on asters, proved virus-free. The test showed that at 25°C. under the conditions of the experiment none of the tested insects were able to acquire the virus during the first 6 days of the incubation period of the virus in the plant. Therefore it was also concluded that the 2-day test feeding after each of the first six passages, as well as the transfers on asters in the later passages which were made every 2 to 5 days, could not have accounted for any increase of the virus in the tested insects.

MORTALITY OF INJECTED INSECTS

The high mortality of injected insects during the second and subsequent transfers presented a serious problem to the continuation of the serial passage experiment. It actually may have accounted for Black's failure to succeed with similar experiments in 1939-1942.[7] It was known from earlier tests by Black that the mortality could be decreased by filtration, but filtration also reduced the amount of virus in the inoculum.[8] Aster-yellows virus is presumably large and can be filtered only with difficulty. A preliminary test was made to find whether or not the mortality was due to an increase in pathogenicity of the virus towards the vector. This hypothesis could not be excluded in view of the fact that the serial passage eliminated the alternating plant host entirely from the life cycle of the virus. Ordinarily, when the virus alternates between plant and insect vector, no deleterious effect on the vector can be observed, although it would be difficult to detect any small disturbances or even small differences in the percentage that died. An alternative hypothesis could explain the increased mortality as due to bacterial and fungus contamination in injected insects. Undoubtedly many injected insects die of septicemia, and the mechanical injury even without infection may be responsible for some deaths.

An attempt was made to compare the mortality rate of insects injected with virus-containing and virus-free insect juices. Fifty virus-free females were injected with a 1:100 dilution of juices from infective leafhoppers, and another group of 50 virus-free females of the same age injected with a 1:100 dilution of juices from virus-free hoppers. Both groups of injected insects were transferred five times during 30 days to fresh rye plants and kept continuously at 25°C. under identical controlled conditions. The death rate in the two groups was almost exactly the same. On the 31st day the 10 and 12 survivors, respectively, of the viruliferous and virus-free leafhoppers were macerated and diluted 1.100, and two groups of 50 virus-free females were injected with the dilutions. The injections were carried out with a single needle, the virus-free dilution being injected first. Utmost care was exercised to prevent excessive wounding. The 1/8000 cc. of inoculum was measured in the same way as in the serial passages. A pronounced decrease in the survival of the virus-carrying insects was observed during the first 3 days following injection (from 50 to 24, as compared to 50/42 in the virus-free group), and after 9 days the number decreased to 13, as compared to 32 in the second group. But on the 23rd day the number of survivors in both groups reached the same level (12 and 13, respectively). Noninjected insects decreased very slightly in number, due to death, and of 50 control insects in the two tests survivors numbered 40 and 37, respectively, by the 30th day of the experiments.

DILUTION END-POINT

It seemed desirable to find the dilution end-point of aster-yellows virus from insect juice in view of the fact that evidence for multiplication

[7] Personal communication.

[8] Personal communication.

was derived from the calculated "dilution" in the serial passage. From earlier experiments by Black (4) it was known that a dilution of 10^{-3}, but not 10^{-4}, will render injected insects infective.

Several tests were made and a more detailed account will be given elsewhere in a study of virus concentration as related to the length of incubation periods in inoculated insects. Only one of the experiments will be briefly mentioned. Groups of 30, 45, 50, and 40 insects, respectively, were injected with dilutions of 10^{-1}, 10^{-2}, 10^{-3}, and 10^{-4} of juices from virus-containing leafhoppers. The injected insects were transferred on every day to individual fresh aster plants in colonies of not more than three, for 48 days, and afterwards three times weekly until the 64th day, when the last insect died. Transmission was obtained in the groups injected with 10^{-1}, 10^{-2}, and 10^{-3} dilutions. No transmission occurred with a 10^{-4} dilution. In two other tests negative results with 10^{-4} dilutions and transmission with 10^{-3} also confirmed Black's finding.

The positive infectivity test in the first transfer of the serial passage experiment occurred within 32 days, as shown by the eight insects that were rendered infective (Table 1). It seems very likely that the dilution of the inoculum used, $10^{-3.8}$, was near the dilution end-point. It is still possible, however, that occasionally an insect would become infective following an injection of a somewhat higher dilution.

DISCUSSION

Earlier evidence indicated that several viruses multiply in both plants and insects. Experimental evidence was presented for the multiplication of rice stunt (10, 11), aster-yellows (4, 13, 15, 19), club-leaf (5, 6), and wound-tumor virus (7, 18). These viruses have three characteristic features in common: the high specificity of vectors, the retention of the virus, and the incubation period. These features had led long ago to the assumption that such plant viruses might possibly multiply in their vectors. The opposite view was expressed in the past 15 years by a few workers (1, 2, 9, 26, 28, 30).

The aster-yellows virus was carried in 10 serial passages in the aster leafhopper. If the virus had been diluted without multiplication, the final dilution used to inoculate the tenth group of the series would have been 10^{-40}. This, of course, is inconceivable for a number of reasons. The virus of aster-yellows derived from viruliferous insects was shown to have a dilution end-point below 10^{-4}. No virus is known to have a dilution end-point[9] above 10^{-10}. In a recent paper Black pointed out that a mass of

[9] The highest dilution end-points of 10^{-10}, of viruses derived from tissues, without concentration, were found for Russian Far East Encephalitis, Venezuelan Equine Encephalitis, Western Equine Encephalitis, and Eastern Equine Encephalitis (Olitsky, Peter K., personal communication), also for St. Louis Encephalitis (16) and yellow fever (17). Tobacco-mosaic virus in tobacco plant juices has a dilution endpoint of 10^{-7} (Kunkel, L. O., personal communication).

hydrogen weighing the same as a female leafhopper (1.7 mgm.) contains only about 5.1×10^{20} molecules (6). Therefore, the serial passage provided adequate direct evidence for multiplication of the aster-yellows virus in the aster leafhopper. Further evidence was provided when the concentrations of virus in the first and ninth transfers were compared and it was found that no decrease occurred in the virus concentration during the nine passages.

It should be pointed out that leafhoppers are sucking insects and do not take up living plant cells. Since viruses multiply only inside of living cells, the multiplication must have occurred in cells of the insect.

A few of the implications of plant virus multiplication in insects have recently been pointed out by Black (6). The virus of aster-yellows can no longer be considered as solely a plant virus. It is really both a plant and an animal virus and may therefore serve as a connecting link between the two groups. This will have to be considered in any future classification of viruses, heretofore separated into animal, plant, and bacterial groups. It allows also some speculation as to the origin of the yellow group of plant viruses. They could have originated as insect or animal viruses. Some of them have the capacity of passing through the egg of the vector to the progeny and are thus maintained indefinitely in insects without the necessity of alternating plant hosts (6, 11). An adaptation permitting them to multiply in plants may possibly have come about as a further step in evolution, and the passage through the egg may then have been gradually lost.

The ability of some viruses to multiply in such diversified hosts as plants and animals suggests strongly that they are living organisms. The early hypothesis of a precursor responsible for virus multiplication, which even in recent years received some support, can hardly account for aster-yellows multiplication. It seems unlikely that a large molecule-precursor would occur in two hosts that are so unrelated.

The high specificity of yellows viruses in relation to their insect vectors can easily be explained on the basis of multiplication. The specificity also supports the hypothesis of the origin of these viruses in insects. The aster-yellows virus is certainly better adapted to its vector, in which it causes no visible harm, than to plant hosts in which it invariably causes disease symptoms and sometimes death.

The possible harmful influence of the virus on the vector after it was passed from insect to insect has been pointed out. Although preliminary results had first suggested such deleterious effect, closer analysis does not permit such a conclusion at present.

The "blind" passage of virus was most likely due to a very long incubation period in some injected insects. On the other hand, it is possible that some injected insects harbored virus but never became infective because the virus did not reach the saliva. It is hoped that further investigations will elucidate this possibility.

The finding that the incubation period varied markedly in the vector, in relation to the dose, may indicate an essential difference between the mechanism of infection of plants and animals. Wounding may be a necessary condition for the infection of plants but not of animals.

The basic study of yellows viruses promises to be of importance to animal workers as well as plant workers.

SUMMARY

The virus of aster yellows was carried in the vector *Macrosteles divisus* through 10 serial passages. The transfer from insect to insect was made by means of injections, of measured volumes of 1/8000 cc. per insect, into the abdominal cavity. The insect pulp was diluted with neutral buffered saline to 10^{-3} of the weight of the surviving leafhoppers. In the first six passages each group of injected hoppers was kept for 30 days, following injection, on rye plants immune from aster yellows, then tested 48 hr. on aster plants and used for the next transfer. In the later passages insects were tested on asters and transferred three times weekly to a fresh set of plants for periods up to 60 days. Direct evidence was provided for the multiplication of the virus in the insect vector, as some insects of all but the third and fifth groups were found infective. The estimated dilution used to inoculate the tenth group of the series, if no multiplication had occurred, would have been 10^{-40}, but the dilution endpoint of the virus from macerated insects was found to be below 10^{-4}. A comparison of virus concentration in the inoculum of the first and ninth passages showed no decrease in concentration. It is concluded that the aster-yellows virus, multiplying in both its plant and insect hosts, can be considered an animal as well as a plant virus.

THE LABORATORIES OF THE ROCKEFELLER INSTITUTE FOR
    MEDICAL RESEARCH
    NEW YORK, NEW YORK

LITERATURE CITED

1. Bawden, F. C. 1950. Plant viruses and virus diseases. 3rd ed., revised. 335 pp. Chronica Botanica, Waltham, Mass.

2. Bennett, C. W., and Wallace, Hugh E. 1938. Relation of the curly top virus to the vector, Eutettix tenellus. J. Agr. Res. [U.S.] 56: 31-52.

3. Black, L. M. 1940. Mechanical transmission of aster-yellows virus to leafhoppers. (Abstr.) Phytopathology. 30: 2.

4. Black, L. M. 1941. Further evidence for multiplication of the aster-yellows virus in the aster leafhopper. Phytopathology. 31: 120-135.

5. Black, L. M. 1949. Multiplication of clover club-leaf virus (Aureogenus clavifolium) in its vector. (Abstr.) Phytopathology. 39: 2.

6. Black, L. M. 1950. A plant virus that multiplies in its insect vector. Nature, **166**: 852-853.

7. Black, L. M., and Brakke, M. K. Serial passage of the wound-tumor virus through its leafhopper vector. (Manuscript in preparation.)

8. Bugher, John C. 1940. A micromortar especially adapted to virus studies in insects. Proc. Soc. Exp. Biol. and Med. **43**: 422-424.

9. Freitag, J. H. 1936. Negative evidence on multiplication of curly top virus in the beet leafhopper, Eutettix tenellus. Hilgardia. **10**: 305-342.

10. Fukushi, T. 1935. Multiplication of virus in its vector. Proc. Imp. Acad. Japan **11**: 301-303.

11. Fukushi, T. 1939. Retention of virus by its vectors through several generations. Proc. Imp. Acad. Japan **15**: 142-145.

12. Kunkel, L. O. 1926. Studies on aster yellows. Am. J. Bot. **13**: 646-705.

13. Kunkel, L. O. 1937. Effect of heat on ability of Cicadula sexnotata (Fall.) to transmit aster yellows. Am. J. Bot. **24**: 312-327.

14. Kunkel, L. O. 1938. Insects in relation to diseases of fruit trees and small fruits. J. Econ. Entom. **31**: 20-22.

15. Kunkel, L. O. 1941. Heat cure of aster yellows in periwinkles. Am. J. Bot. **28**: 761-769.

16. Lennette, Edwin H., and Koprowski, Hilary. 1944. Neutralization tests with certain neurotropic viruses. J. Immunol. **49**: 375-385.

17. Lennette, Edwin H., and Koprowski, Hilary. 1944. Influence of age on the susceptibility of mice to infection with certain neurotropic viruses. J. Immunol. **49**: 175-191.

18. Maramorosch, Karl. 1950. Influence of temperature on incubation and transmission of the wound-tumor virus. Phytopathology. **40**: 1071-1093.

19. Maramorosch, Karl. 1950. Effect of dosage on length of incubation period of aster-yellows virus in its vector. Proc. Soc. Exp. Biol. and Med. **75**: 744.

20. Maramorosch, Karl. 1951. Serial passage of aster-yellows virus through the aster leafhopper. (Abstr.) Phytopathology. **41**: 25.

21. Maramorosch, Karl. 1951. A simple needle for micro-injections. Nature. **167**: 734.

22. Maramorosch, Karl. 1951. Handy insect-vector cage. J. N.Y. Entomol. Soc. **59**: 49-50.

23. Maramorosch, Karl. New evidence for multiplication of aster-yellows virus in its vector. Nature (in press).

24. McMaster, P. D., and Hagebom, G. H. 1942. Formal Progress Report No. 683. Off. Sci. Res. and Dev.

25. Merrill, Malcolm H., and Tenbroeck, Carl. 1934. Multiplication of equine encephalomyelitis virus in mosquitoes. Proc. Soc. Exp. Biol. and Med. **32**: 421-423.

26. Smith, Kenneth M. 1949. Viruses and virus diseases. I. Jour. Roy. Hort. Soc. **74**: 482-491.

27. Storey, H. H. 1933. Investigations of the mechanism of the transmission of plant viruses by insect vectors. I. Proc. Roy. Soc. London. **B. 113:** 463-485.

28. Storey, H. H. 1939. Transmission of plant viruses. Bot. Rev. **5:** 240-272.

29. TenBroeck, Carl. 1931. A simple grinder for soft tissues. Science. **74:** 98-99.

30. Watson, M. A., and Roberts, F. M. 1939. A comparative study of the transmission of Hyoscyamus virus 3, potato virus Y and cucumber virus 1 by the vectors Myzus persicae (Sulz), M. circumflexus (Buckton), and Macrosiphum gei (Koch). Proc. Roy. Soc. London. **B. 127:** 543-576.

31. Went, F. W. 1950. The Earhart Plant Research Laboratory. Chronica Botanica. **12:** 89-108.

1955

Crystallization of Purified MEF-1 Poliomyelitis Virus Particles[1]

by F. L. Schaffer and C. E. Schwerdt

Virus Laboratory, University of California, Berkeley

The crystallization of the first animal virus described in this paper was accomplished twenty years after the similar achievement by Stanley with the virus of tobacco mosaic. In general, the lapse of time that occurred between these two significant events may be attributed to (1) the need of a system that would provide an abundant supply of animal viruses free of contaminating, nonviral particles, and (2) a technique for quantitative assay of virus. Both of these requirements were admirably fulfilled with the popularization of cell cultivation (tissue culture) a few years previously. A second animal virus, Coxsackie, was prepared in crystalline form shortly thereafter.[2]

The crystallization of animal viruses emphasizes certain basic similarities with plant viruses, but more important, it furnishes material for detailed investigation of the physical and chemical properties of viruses. Studies of this nature are a prerequisite to knowledge of virus structure and to the understanding of virus replication.

Highly purified preparations of poliomyelitis virus, strain MEF-1, have been shown by analytical ultracentrifugation to contain only one homogeneous component.[3] Electron

[1] Aided by a grant from the National Foundation for Infantile Paralysis. This paper was presented before a meeting of the National Academy of Sciences at Pasadena, California, on November 3, 1955 (see *Science.* **122**: 879 (1955)). Reprinted by permission of the author and publisher from Proc. Nat. Acad. Sci. **41**: 1020-1023 (1955).

[2] Mattern and DuBuy. Science. **123**: 1037 (1956).

[3] Schwerdt, C. E., and Schaffer, F. L. Ann. N.Y. Acad. Sci. **61**: 740 (1955).

microscopic and other studies have revealed this component to consist of spherical particles approximately 27 mμ in diameter which are readily aligned in two-dimensional, close-packed arrays and with which infectivity is associated.[4] The present report is concerned with the preparation and the description of properties of three-dimensional crystals, readily visible in the light microscope, which were obtained from a highly purified and concentrated preparation of such virus particles. Although several plant viruses have been crystallized [5] since the initial crystallization of tobacco mosaic virus by Stanley in 1935,[6] this is believed to be the first report of the crystallization of a virus affecting man or animals.

CRYSTALLIZATION

The source of virus was the fluid harvested from monkey kidney tissue cultures infected with strain MEF-1 poliomyelitis virus and provided by the Connaught Laboratories, Toronto. The initial purification procedure, which has been previously outlined,[3] included methanol precipitation, butanol extraction, ultracentrifugation, nuclease digestion, and electrophoretic fractionation. Further purification of the preparation was achieved by sedimentation through a sucrose density gradient in a swinging cup rotor (Spinco SW-39), as described by Brakke for plant viruses.[7] In this way approximately 1.2 mg. of nucleoprotein material was obtained as a single sedimenting band in 0.73 ml. of 0.14 M NaCl containing approximately 30 per cent sucrose. This represented the virus concentrated from 15 liters of infected monkey kidney tissue culture fluid. The preparation was diluted to 2.0 ml. with 0.14 M NaCl and was sedimented by ultracentrifugation in an average centrifugal field 100,000 $\times$ g for 2.5 hours. The clear, gel-like pellet was covered with 0.3 ml. of unbuffered 0.14 M NaCl at pH 5.9 and gently rocked overnight at 4°C. After this treatment the pellet appeared white and opaque, and upon suspension discrete crystals were seen.

After removing a small fraction of the suspended crystals for further observation, the mother-liquor was removed from the remaining crystals. The latter were washed twice with isotonic saline and the washings pooled with the mother-liquor. The crystals were readily dissolved by warming to room temperature in 0.14 M NaCl adjusted to pH 8.5 with dilute NaOH.

The virus was recrystallized as follows: An aliquot of the dissolved crystals was diluted with a small volume of 0.14 M NaCl buffered with 0.001 M phosphate at pH 7.6, and the virus was then sedimented in a sealed capsule[8] in the swinging cup rotor of the ultracentrifuge. After

[4] Schwerdt, C. E., Williams, R. C., Stanley, W. M., Schaffer, F. L., and McClain, M. E. Proc. Soc. Exp. Biol. Med. **86:** 310 (1954).

[5] Bawden, F. C. Plant viruses and virus diseases: 200. Chronica Botanica (1950).

[6] Stanley, W. M. Science. **81:** 644 (1935); Phytopathology. **26:** 305 (1936).

[7] Brakke, M. K. Arch. Biochem. Biophys. **45:** 275 (1953).

[8] Backus, R. C., and Williams, R. C. Science. **117:** 221 (1953).

removal of the supernatant fluid, the pellet was suspended in a small volume of isotonic saline buffered with 0.01 M phosphate at pH 5.9 and allowed to stand at 4°C. Small crystals were seen by microscopic examination. After low-speed centrifugation, the mother-liquor was removed from the recrystallized material, which was washed with pH 5.9 saline. The washings were pooled with the mother-liquor. These crystals again were easily dissolved in isotonic saline buffered at pH 7.8 with 0.01 M phosphate.

PROPERTIES OF THE CRYSTALS

A series of photomicrographs of the crystals taken in ultraviolet light at various wave lengths is shown in Figure 1. The rapid decrease in transmission between 295 and 280 mμ is consistent with the nucleoprotein nature of the virus particles and their ultraviolet absorption spectrum in suspension.[3] The photomicrograph in visible light shown in Figure 2 gives some idea of the shape of the crystals. They appear to be tetragonal prisms with pyramids at both ends. The larger specimens measure approximately 30 μ in length.

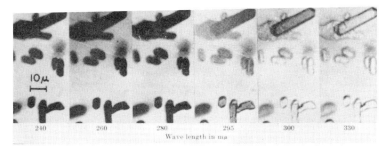

Fig. 1. Crystals of MEF-1 poliomyelitis virus particles photomicrographed at various wave lengths in the ultraviolet.

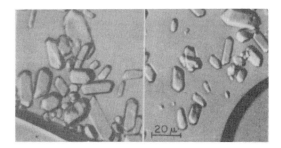

Fig. 2. Crystals of MEF-1 poliomyelitis virus particles photomicrographed in visible light.

Evidence that the crystals contained the virus particles was provided by the essentially constant specific infectivity measurements of solutions of washed crystals, of mother-liquors, and of the two fractions of purified and concentrated virus from which the crystals were derived. Infectivity measurements were made by plaque assay on monkey kidney cultures by a modification[9] of the technique of Dulbecco and Vogt.[10] Specific infectivities were expressed as the number of plaque-forming units (PFU) per unit mass of nucleoprotein. The latter was measured by optical density at 260 mμ in a Beckman spectrophotometer and in some instances by direct chemical analysis for nitrogen. By means of analytical electron microscopy, an estimate was also made of the ratio of countable physical particles to PFU.[11] Since there was no electron microscopic evidence of material other than the 27-mμ particles in the dissolved crystals, it was possible to estimate the mass of a single physical particle from the experimental data. The results of various experiments are summarized in Table 1.

TABLE 1. *Specific infectivities* of various purified and crystalline fractions of MEF-1 virus*

Fractions	Relative sequence of fractionation	PFU/MI per unit OD†	PFU per grant‡	27-mμ particles per PFU	Estimated grams‡ per particle
Electrophoretic	1	2.2×10^9	1.6×10^{13}	3,000	2.1×10^{-17}
Density gradient	2	3.1×10^9	. . .	. . .	. . .
Crystalline virus	3	3.3×10^9	2.2×10^{13}	2,250	2.0×10^{-17}
Mother-liquor from 1st crystallization	4	3.2×10^9	2.3×10^{13}	1,300	3.3×10^{-17}
Recrystallized virus	5	3.5×10^9	. . .	850	. . .
Mother-liquor from recrystallization	6	3.4×10^9	. . .	1,200	. . .

* Infectivity measured by plaque assay (see Fogh and Lund, *Proc. Soc. Exptl. Biol. Med.* [in press], and Dulbecco and Vogt, *J. Exptl. Med.*, 99, 167, 1954) and expressed as plaque-forming units (PFU).

† $OD_{260m\mu}^{1\ cm.}$ = optical density measured at 200-mμ wave length for a solution 1 cm. thick.

‡ Nitrogen $\times$ 6.25.

DISCUSSION

The constant specific infectivity values listed in the third and fourth columns of Table 1 for the density gradient, crystalline, and mother-liquor fractions attest to the comparable degrees of purity of these fractions. In the fifth column, the reciprocal specific infectivities expressed as physical particles per PFU are more variable. This probably

[9] Fogh, J., and Lund, R. Proc. Soc. Exp. Biol. Med. **90**: 80 (1955).

[10] Dulbecco, R., and Vogt, M. J. Exp. Med. **99**: 167 (1954).

[11] Bachrach, H. L., and Schwerdt, C. E. J. Immunol. **72**: 30 (1954).

can be accounted for by a variable loss of physical particles by adsorption and disintegration experienced in the preparation, dilution, and spraying of extremely small samples of highly purified virus for quantitative electron microscopy.

Physical and chemical data obtained earlier on highly purified though not crystalline MEF-1 virus provided sufficient information to estimate by Stokes's low a virus-particle mass of $1\text{-}1.5 \times 10^{-17}$ gm.[3] The mass of the particles is also calculable from the nucleoprotein and physical-particle concentrations of the purified virus preparations determined by direct chemical analysis and analytical electron microscopy, respectively. If the physical-particle count is low, owing to losses discussed above, the value of the mass per particle (sixth column) will be high. The difference between the particle mass estimated from Stokes's law and the 2.0×10^{-17} gm. obtained for the particles from crystalline virus can probably be attributed, therefore, to low electron microscope counts. The above data, supported by ultracentrifugal and electron microscopic evidence for homogeneity, lead to the conclusion that the crystals were composed of the $27\text{-}m\mu$ particles.

It is probable that a large percentage of the particles in the crystalline state are inactive due to prolonged storage of the virus. That fraction which is inactive is difficult to determine because of our uncertain knowledge of the efficiency of the plaque-assay technique.[9] It is possible, however, that essentially all the physical particles were at one time mature, viable virus and that biological inactivation resulted in no physical and chemical alteration detectable by presently available tests. This idea is compatible with the ability of the particles to crystallize, since it has been generally observed that no denatured protein will crystallize.[12]

Preliminary experiments in our laboratory with purified Saukett poliomyelitis virus indicate that it can also be crystallized under conditions successfully applied to the MEF-1 virus. It does not seem unreasonable, therefore, to expect all three types of human poliomyelitis as well as other animal viruses of small size to be capable of crystallization under proper conditions. This crystallization of a virus affecting man and animal emphasizes anew certain basic similarities between animal and plant viruses.

SUMMARY

The crystallization of human poliomyelitis virus particles from a highly purified and concentrated preparation has been reported for the first time. The appearance of the crystals and the evidence that the crystals are composed of characteristic virus particles, 27 $m\mu$ in diameter, are presented and discussed.

[12] Neurath, H., and Bailey, K. The proteins: 29. Academic Press, New York (1953).

The authors are indebted to Drs. Russell L. Steere and Robert C. Backus for the visible and ultraviolet photomicrographs, respectively, of the virus crystals, and to Miss Joan Sprecher and Miss Helen Fisher for their excellent technical assistance.

1955

Reconstitution of Active Tobacco Mosaic Virus from its Inactive Protein and Nucleic Acid Components[1]

H. Fraenkel-Conrat and Robley C. Williams

A dramatic and heuristic accomplishment—the reconstitution of a virus from the combination of its native nucleic acid and protein subunits into the characteristic morphological rods of tobacco mosaic virus replete with the property of infectivity. This achievement was an important and provocative stimulus to the study of virus replication at the molecular level. Once again, the virus of tobacco mosaic served as the avant-garde of progress in virological research.

The reconstitution experiments preceded the discovery that naked nucleic acid derived from tobacco mosaic virus is infectious. As a consequence, it was believed that the reconstitution reaction was solely an expression of the activity of infectious nucleic acid. The original results were substantiated with the findings that the combination of nucleic acid of relatively high infectivity (0.5% found in standard tobacco mosaic virus) with virus protein formed virus rods which were fully infective.[2] That the infectivity of ribonucleic acid of tobacco mosaic virus can be increased by the reconstitution reaction has been confirmed by others.[3]

A natural extension of the reconstitution reaction was published in two later communications by Fraenkel-Conrat and in

[1] Reprinted by permission of the author and the publisher from The Proceedings of the National Academy of Science, Washington. 41: 690-698 (1955).

Aided by a grant from the National Foundation for Infantile Paralysis and research grant No. C-2245 from the National Cancer Institute of the National Institutes of Health, Public Health Service.

[2] Fraenkel-Conrat, N.Y. Acad. Sci. Spec. Publs. 5: 217 (1957).

[3] Siegel, *et al.* Virology. 3: 554 (1956); Commoner, *et al.* Nature. 178: 767 (1956); Bawden. N.Y. Acad. Sci. Spec. Publs. 5: 249 (1957).

collaboration with B. Singer.[4] By mixing nucleic acid and protein derived from different strains of tobacco mosaic virus they showed that the chemical composition of the progeny were generally similar to those of the strain supplying the nucleic acid. The findings strongly suggested that nucleic acid is the sole genetic determinant of the virus particle.

Much recent evidence from chemical, physiochemical, electron microscopical, and X-ray studies has resulted in a definite concept of the structure of the tobacco mosaic virus (TMV) particle.[5-9] It appears that about 2,800 protein subunits of a molecular weight near 18,000 are arranged in a helical manner to form a rod with a hollow core. The nucleic acid is believed to occur as strands in the core. Electron micrographs which support this concept have been obtained of the virus at various stages of disaggregation.[7-9] A protein isolated from infected plants has been found to reaggregate—first to short pieces of the presumed helix lying on end and resembling disks with central holes and then to much longer, but inactive, rods of the diameter of the virus yet free from nucleic acid.[10] It has now been possible to achieve the co-aggregation of inactive virus protein subunits and inactive virus nucleic acid to give nucleoprotein rods which appear to be infective.

PREPARATION OF PROTEIN AND NUCLEIC ACID COMPONENTS

TMV was dialyzed against pH 10-10.5 glycine buffer (0.01 M) or pH 10.5 carbonate-bicarbonate (0.1 M) at 3°C. for 48-72 hours. Undegraded virus was separated by cold ultracentrifugation, and the supernatant was brought to 0.4 saturation with ammonium sulfate. The protein alone precipitates (optical density$_{260 m\mu}$/optical density$_{280 m\mu} = R = 0.65$), leaving only nucleic acid ($R = 2.0$) in the supernatant; if this separation is not

[4] J. Amer. Chem. Soc. **78:** 882 (1957); Biochim. Biophys. Acta. **24:** 540 (1957).

[5] Harris, J. I., and Knight, C. A. Nature. **170:** 613 (1952); and J. Biol. Chem. **214:** 231 (1955); Schramm, G. Zeitschr. Naturforschg. 2b. **112:** 249 (1947); Watson, J. D. Biochim. Biophys. Acta. **13:** 10 (1954); Franklin, R. Nature. **175:** 379 (1955).

[6] Fraenkel-Conrat, H., and Singer, B. J. Am. Chem. Soc. **76:** 180 (1954).

[7] Schramm, G., Schumacher, G., and Zillig, W. Nature. **175:** 549 (1955).

[8] Rice, R. V., Kaesberg, P., and Stahmann, M. A. Biochim. Biophys. Acta. **11:** 337 (1953).

[9] Hart, R. G. These Proceedings. **41:** 261 (1955).

[10] Takahashi, W. N., and Ishii, M. Nature. **169:** 419 (1952); Delwiche, C. C., Newmark, P., Takahashi, W. N., and Ng, M. J. Biochim Biophys. Acta. **16:** 127 (1955); Commoner, B., Yamada, M., Rodenberg, S. D., Wang, F. Y., and Basler, E., Jr. Science. **118:** 529 (1953).

clean, longer alkali treatment is necessary. The protein moiety is precipitated twice more with 0.25-0.35 saturated ammonium sulfate, dialyzed, brought to pH 7.0-8.0 with NaOH, and finally again freed from
heavy particles, such as undergraded
virus, by ultracentrifugation. The protein gives a water-clear solution at pH
7; the masked —SH group is still present. The spectrum resembles that of a
mixture of trytophan, tyrosine, cysteine,
and phenylalanine, simultating the composition of the protein, although the
minimum (at 250 mμ) is not quite as low
(max./min. = 2.4 versus 2.9) (Fig. 1); P
analyses (0.01-0.03 per cent) indicate removal of about 95-98 per cent of the
nucleic acid. Evidence for the absence of
detectable virus particles will be discussed below.

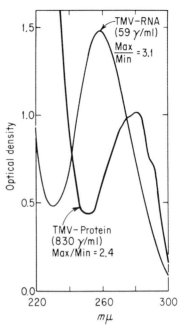

Fig. 1. Ultraviolet absorption
spectrum of purified virus protein and nucleic acid.

The nucleic acid fractions from such
alkali-degraded TMV are not as effective
for reconstitution as that obtained by the
detergent method.[2] A virus solution (1
per cent) containing 1 per cent sodium
dodecyl sulfate is adjusted to pH 8.5 and
held at 40° for 16-20 hours. Following
this treatment, ammonium sulfate is
added to 0.35 saturation, and the protein
precipitate is separated by centrifugation. When the supernate is refrigerated, from 60 to 90 per cent of the nucleic acid precipitates ($R = 2.0$) and
is centrifuged off the next day; it is further purified by repeated resolution
in ice water and precipitation with two volumes of cold ethanol and a few
drops of 3 M pH 5 acetate. The nucleic acid solution is finally subjected
to cold ultracentrifugation to remove any traces of virus. The virtual
absence of protein is indicated by a minimum in O.D. near 230 mμ
(max./min. = 3.0) (Fig. 1).

In a few preliminary ultracentrifuge experiments, kindly performed
by Dr. Howard K. Schachman, the nucleic acid preparations exhibited
one principal boundary with a sedimentation coefficient of about 8 S,
resembling the preparation of Cohen and Stanley.[11] The protein, in pH 9
borate (0.01 M) or in 0.01 M NaCl at that pH, exhibited largely a single
boundary with a sedimentation coefficient of 4.5 S. At lower pH values
larger components, presumably due to aggregation, were observed.

[11] Cohen, S. S., and Stanley, W. M. J. Biol. Chem. 142: 863 (1942).

method

RECONSTITUTION OF ACTIVE VIRUS

For reconstitution of the virus, 1 ml. of approximately 1 per cent protein solution is mixed with 0.1 ml. of a 1 per cent nucleic acid solution. Opalescence appears after addition of a suitable buffer; 0.01 ml. of pH 6 acetate (3 M) has given the best results, but phosphate (pH 6.3 and 7.0) and pH 6 ammonium acetate have also been used successfully. The samples are held at 3° for at least 24 hours. They may then be directly diluted and assayed. More often they were ultracentrifuged, the pellets redissolved in water, traces of insoluble material separated by centrifugation, and aliquots of the opalescent supernatants diluted for spectrophotometry. Most of the protein and 40-60 per cent of the nucleic acid [12] were in the pellet, and the spectrum was that expected for a nucleoprotein such as TMV (max./min. = about 1.17). On the basis of the O.D. of TMV (0.27 at 260 mμ for an 0.01 per cent solution), approximate concentrations were calculated, and the sample was diluted to a range of 100 to 10 μg/ml. for assay. For pellets composed of protein only (absorption maximum at 280 mμ), calculations were based on the O.D. of the virus proteins (0.13 for an 0.01 per cent solution at that wave length). Assays were performed on groups of 8-12 plants (*Nicotiana glutinosa*), distributing each of an equal number of samples (including at least one standard and often a solvent blank) over 10 equivalent half-leaves. It was indeed quite surprising to find that the reconstituted nucleoprotein preparations produced local lesions (from 2 to 30 per half-leaf), when tested at 10-100 μg/ml., which were indistinguishable in appearance from those of TMV at 0.1 μg/ml. In contrast, no activity was observed when the protein or nucleic acid alone was tested up to 1,800 and 52 μg/ml., respectively.[13] When 0.005 per cent TMV was held for several hours in 5 per cent protein or 0.5 per cent nucleic acid, it was found fully active upon dilution and assay. This strongly suggests that the noninfectivity of the two components cannot be attributed to inhibition phenomena (Table 1).

When each of the two components was diluted for assay to 0.2 and 0.02 mg./ml., respectively, prior to mixing, no activity was generated.

---

[12] When less than 6 per cent of nucleic acid is added to the protein, almost all is incorporated in the pellet, but lower infectivity is the result. Protein alone also forms pellets upon ultra-centrifugation at pH 6.

[13] The usual assay method yielded usually 0.0, but at times up to 0.4, lesions per half-leaf when phosphate alone was applied. This result is probably due to accidental contamination by active material applied to other sites of the plant. Therefore, separate plants were used when the absence of active virus was in question. Standard TMW was applied to one bottom leaf and the unknowns to all others. This gave consistently 0.0 lesions with the components used in virus reconstitution, except when the nucleic acid was applied at 200 μg./ml., twenty times the amount present at the highest assay level of the reconstituted virus (0.3 lesions per half-leaf).

TABLE 1. *Activity of three preparations of reconstituted virus and of TMV at different assay levels; absence of inhibitors from components*

Material tested	μg./ml.	Assays Lesions/half-leaf*		
Reconstituted virus:				
25,000-rpm pellet	100	27	54	31
				120†
	30	18	—	—
	25	—	35	—
	10	9	7	14†
40,000-rpm. pellet	100	2	23	—
TMV stock preparation	0.25	27		
		15		
	0.1	9(6.1-12.1)‡		
	0.02	5		
TMV-protein added at 1000:1	0.1	10		
TMV-RNA added at 100:1	0.1	5		
		13		

* Each figure is the average of 10 equivalent half-leaves. The 3 columns in top half of table refer to separate preparations.

† This is one of the preparations which appeared to increase in activity during storage.

‡ Average and range of 9 assays (10 half-leaves each) of one TMV preparation over 3 months.

Also, when the complete reaction mixture (5-10 mg./ml.) was diluted to 0.1 mg./ml. one minute after addition of the buffer which triggers the aggregation, no activity was obtained. About one hour at room temperature appears to be required for the formation of any active rods. These experiments represent convincing control data; they also seem to prove that we are dealing with a definite chemical reaction and to exclude most other interpretations. The observation that the nucleic acid gradually loses most of its activity during several weeks of storage at $3°$ (in aqueous solution, pH 5) also serves as a control experiment, indicating the crucial nature of its physical state. Treatment of the nucleic acid (600 μg.) with ribonuclease (0.2 μg) in 10^{-4} M magnesium sulfate rendered it unable to combine with the protein to produce active rods; also, substitution of other nucleic acids (DNA from thymus and RNA from turnip yellow mosaic virus)[14] yielded almost nucleic acid-free pellets which were inactive (Table 2).

A few preliminary experiments on the properties of the reconstituted virus indicated somewhat greater liability to alkali (pH 9) than that of TMV. Ribonuclease (0.2 μg for 5 mg.) also appeared to decrease the activity. A fractionation of the nucleoprotein material by centrifugation at 25,000 rpm. for 30 minutes yielded a pellet of considerably higher

[14] Kindly supplied by Dr. S. S. Cohen and Dr. V. Cosentino.

TABLE 2. *Effect of reaction conditions on regeneration of virus activity*

Reaction conditions*	Assays	
	µg./ml.	Lesions/half-leaf
Protein (1 per cent) + RNA (0.1 per cent):		
1 minute, pH 6	100	0.6
24 hours	100	10.2, 13.1†
96 hours	100	13.0
Protein (0.01 per cent) + RNA (0.001 per cent):		
24 hours, pH 6	100	0.6, 0.2†
96 hours	100	0.1, 0.2†
Protein + RNase-digested RNA	100	0.0
Protein + TYMV-RNA	100	0.3
Protein‡	500; 625; 1800	0.0; 0.0; 0.0
RNA‡	30; 52; 230	0.0; 0.0; 0.3

* Protein and RNA stand for the preparations isolated from TMV by the methods described in the text. TYMV-RNA is the ribonucleic acid isolated from turnip yellow mosaic virus. RNase is ribonuclease.

† Reassayed dilute solution after one week.

‡ Different preparations, assayed about 10 times, generally on separate plants (see n. 13); in the customary half-leaf assay method, up to 0.5 lesions were occasionally obtained with the same preparations.

infectivity than the residual half of the material, pelleted at 40,000 rpm. (1 hour). Material so purified seemed to increase in activity upon storage in 0.3-0.5 per cent solution at 3°. It also appeared to become more resistant to alkali and to ribonuclease.

ELECTRON MICROSCOPIC STUDIES

Electron microscopy was used qualitatively to study the shapes and sizes of the components involved in the formation of the virus rods and quantitatively[15] to assess the degree of homogeneity of the suspensions as well as to obtain counts and length distributions of the reconstituted rods. In the protein, the only visible particles, aggregates presumably of the original 4.5 S material, appeared as disks about 5-15 mµ thick and with central holes. The diameter of the disk was 15 mµ and that of the central hole about 4 mµ (Fig. 2). The appearance of these perforated disks is identical with that of partially polymerized X-protein.[9] In the nucleic acid solution only occasional poorly defined fibrils could be detected. The reconstituted rods appeared to be identical in shape and size with intact TMV, except for a greater randomness of length (Fig. 3).

Preparations of the purified protein and nucleic acid were examined for any electron microscopic evidence of contamination with intact TMV. In a specific instance the protein was sprayed upon the specimen screens at a concentration of 0.1 per cent and the RNA at 0.007 per cent. These are tenfold and sevenfold greater concentrations of the two components than the highest levels used in the assays of the reconstituted virus (100

[15] Williams, R. C., Backus, R. C., and Steere, R. L. J. Am. Chem. Soc. 73: 2062 (1951).

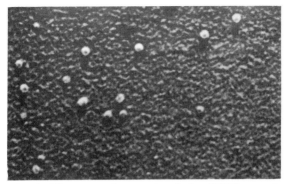

Fig. 2. Electron micrograph of the TMV protein used in the reconstitution experiments. The particles are characteristically disk-shaped, with central holes. × 120,000.

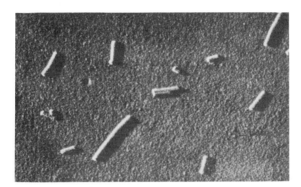

Fig. 3. Particles of the reconstituted tobacco mosaic virus. Their morphology is identical with that of normal TMV, except for a greater proportion of short particles. The longest rod in this field is about 300 mμ long. × 60,000.

μg./ml.). The protein preparation showed no rods of a length even as great as 100 mμ in six droplet patterns each of which had a volume of approximately 3×10^{-9} ml. The RNA material also showed no rods in six droplets of approximately this average volume. From these figures it can be calculated that the constituent protein and RNA solutions contribute fewer than 5×10^7 typical TMV particles per milliliter to the reconstituted virus in the highest concentration assayed. Additional counts made on the standard TMV used as an infectivity control showed that approximately 7×10^8 particles per milliliter, of typical length, are required to produce the 10 lesions per leaf customarily obtained. Inasmuch as several preparations of the reconstituted virus gave about twice that number of lesions at the 100 μg./ml. level, we can conclude that the starting materials failed by at least a factor of 30 to contain enough contaminating TMV particles to account for the final infectivity. This conclusion rests upon the supposition that the specific infectivity of any TMV particles that might remain as contaminants in the protein and RNA preparations is the same as that possessed by the untreated control TMV.

Counts and length distributions were secured for the particles of both TMV and the most active reconstituted virus, the 25,000-rpm. pellet described above, in order to ascertain the relative biological efficiency of the two materials in terms of numbers of particles per milliliter per lesions per leaf. The results of the counts and length distributions are given in

TABLE 3. *Electron microscope counts of particles of TMV and reconstituted virus at assay concentration*

Preparation	Assay Concentration (μg./ml.)	Lesions/ Half- Leaf	Total Particles/ML.	Particles/ML. of Length 290-310 mμ	Particles/ML./ 10 Lesions
Control TMV	0.1	10	1.6×10^9	7.0×10^8	7×10^8
Reconstituted virus (25,000 rpm.)	10	10	2.2×10^{11}	2.0×10^{10}	2×10^{10}

Table 3. From this table it appears that about one-tenth of the total particles in the reconstituted virus, representing about one-third of the total mass, were of length *ca.* 300 mμ, the length of the monomer of normal TMV. These particles were therefore only about 3 per cent as infective as the particles of similar length in the control TMV. It thus appears that polymerization of the protein by nucleic acid to form ~300-mμ rods is fairly frequent but that only a fraction of the rods is reconstituted with the structural faithfulness necessary for infectivity.

The length distribution of the rods of this pelleted material exhibited a reasonably random character for lengths less than about 260 mμ, but a highly uniform length between 290 and 310 mμ for the 10 per cent of the rods falling in this range. Only 3 per cent of the particles were of lengths greater than 310 mμ. This is in contrast to aggregates of X-protein, which show a complete randomness of distribution of lengths.

To ascertain whether the nucleic acid was localized in the center of the newly formed virus rods, Dr. R. Hart applied his technique of detergent treatment, followed by electron microscopical analysis.[9] He found the reconstituted rods appreciably more labile to SDS than was standard TMV, but after SDS treatment for 10 seconds many rods were partially degraded and showed a central strand of material protruding from the ends, as does standard TMV after 60 seconds of reaction (Fig. 4). These strands disappeared when ribonuclease was added.

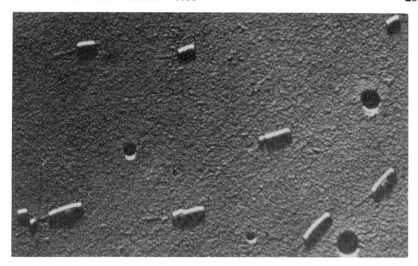

Fig. 4. Particles of reconstituted TMV treated briefly with hot detergent. Rods are seen with strands of nucleic acid projecting from their ends. This appearance is identical with that found for normal TMV more severely treated. × 55,000.

SUMMARY

The preparation from TMV of protein and RNA fractions which tend to recombine at about pH 6 to form a nucleoprotein carrying virus activity (0.1-1 per cent of that of TMV) is described.

An electron microscopic search revealed no TMV rods in either of the two component solutions at a concentration level thirty fold to three hundred fold greater than those at which the reconstituted virus was assayed. In the latter, on the other hand, up to about one-third of the material consisted of rods of the typical diameter and length of TMV, many, if not all, containing a nucleic acid core.

The concentration, time, and pH dependence of virus regeneration is that of a typical chemical reaction. Freshly prepared RNA is required for appreciable reaction; degraded RNA, or nucleic acids from other sources, are inactive.

No inhibition was observed if known small amounts of TMV were added to concentrated solutions of each of the components and subsequently diluted and assayed.

The evidence thus seems reasonably complete that, under the conditions described, TMV nucleic acid enters into combination with TMV protein subunits and favors aggregation to rods, some of which are of sufficient length and structural integration to carry infectivity.

The capable assistance of Mrs. B. Singer and Mr. J. Toby is gratefully acknowledged.

1956

Infectivity of Ribonucleic Acid from Tobacco Mosaic Virus[1]

by A. Gierer and G. Schramm

Max-Planck-Institut für Virusforschung, Tübingen

The thesis that nucleic acid may be the carrier of viral genetic information was advanced by Hershey and Chase in 1952 on the basis of work with bacteriophages. That nucleic acids of plant and animal viruses, devoid of their protein coat, were infectious and give rise to complete virus particles, helped strengthen this belief. The initial evidence of the infectivity of isolated ribonucleic acid (RNA) derived from tobacco mosaic virus was presented by Gierer and Schramm. A similar disclosure was reported almost simultaneously by Fraenkel-Conrat.[2] Within a year of the successful isolation of infectious RNA from a plant virus, infectious RNA preparations were obtained from several animal viruses, i.e., Mengo, West Nile, and Eastern equine encephalomyelitis.[3]

These findings, viewed together, strongly implicated nucleic acid as the transmittal agent of viral genetic information. Nucleic acid carries the code that directs the cell to synthesize not only the viral nucleic acid but viral protein, both of which are foreign to its nature. Attention was sharply focused on the mechanisms involved in the synthesis of viral nucleic acid, its role in directing protein synthesis, and its function in heredity.

An additional and distinguishing feature of Gierer and Schramm's report was the description of a new and simple method (phenol extraction) for isolating infectious RNA from plant viruses which proved applicable also with animal viruses containing RNA.

---

[1] Reprinted by permission of the author and publisher from Nature. **177:** 702-703 (1956).

[2] J. Am. Chem. Soc. **78:** 882 (1956).

[3] Colter, *et al.* Nature. **179:** 859 (1957); Virology. **4:** 522 (1957).

In their experiments with bacteriophages, Hershey and Chase[4] have shown that only the nucleic acid component plays a part in the intracellular multiplication. There are also indications that in simple viruses containing ribonucleic acid the nucleic acid plays a dominant part in the infection. Thus, experiments with tobacco mosaic virus have shown that the protein can be changed chemically without affecting the activity and the genetic properties;[5] recently, it was even found[6] that part of the protein can be removed from tobacco mosaic virus without destroying the activity.

We have now obtained evidence that after complete removal of the protein, the ribonucleic acid itself is still infectious.

The protein was extracted from tobacco mosaic virus with phenol by a procedure elaborated by Schuster, Schramm and Zillig (to be published). After a short treatment at low temperatures, a preparation of ribonucleic acid is obtained which has a high molecular weight during the first few hours but depolymerizes in the course of time. Its physical properties will be described elsewhere.

A solution of 10 per cent tobacco mosaic virus in 0.02 M phosphate buffer of pH 7.3 is shaken for 8 min. at 5°C. with an equal amount of watersaturated phenol. The aqueous phase which contains the ribonucleic acid is separated by centrifugation, and the process of extraction with phenol is repeated at least twice for 2 min. The phenol is then extracted by ether from the aqueous phase. The whole procedure is carried out at 5°C. and takes about 50 min.; it is followed immediately by testing the infectivity.

For that purpose, five to ten plants of *Nicotiana glutinosa* with five leaves each were inoculated with a diluted solution of the ribonucleic acid, and an equal number of plants with a standard solution of tobacco mosaic virus. The number of local lesions produced by ribonucleic acid and tobacco mosaic virus are compared in Table 1. It is found that 10 μgm. of ribonucleic acid produces about the same number of lesions as does 0.2 μgm. tobacco mosaic virus. The infectivity of the ribonucleic acid preparation is thus about 2 per cent of that of the native virus.

The following experiments, the results of which are collected in Table 2, have been carried out to show that the infection is due to the nucleic acid rather than to contamination of the ribonucleic acid with native virus.

(a) In the ribonucleic acid solution protein was not detectable by chemical methods (Schuster, Schramm and Zillig, unpublished work);

[4] Hershey, A. D., and Chase, M. J. Gen. Physiol. **36:** 39 (1952).

[5] Schramm, G., and Müller, H. Hoppe Seylers Z. physiol. Chem. **266:** 43 (1940); **274:** 267 (1942). Miller, G. L., and Stanley, W. M. J. Biol. Chem. **141:** 905 (1941); **146:** 331 (1942). Harris, J. I., and Knight, C. A. J. Biol. Chem. **214:** 215 (1955).

[6] Schramm, G., Schumaker, G., and Zillig, W. Nature. **175:** 549 (1955).

TABLE 1. *Comparison of the infectivity of ribonucleic acid and tobacco mosaic virus in 1.0 M phosphate buffer*

pH	Ribonucleic acid		Tobacco mosaic virus	
	μgm./ml.	lesions	μgm./ml.	lesions
6.1	10	153	⎰0.09	95
			⎱0.8	445
7.3	10	815	0.27	1,048
7.3	1	524	0.05	795
7.5	10	998	0.27	685

thus the amount must be less than 0.4 per cent of the ribonucleic acid content. By serological methods (complement fixation) it was shown that the ribonucleic acid contains less than 0.02 per cent of native tobacco mosaic virus protein.

TABLE 2. *Comparison of ribonucleic acid (10 μgm./ml.) and tobacco mosaic virus (0.27 μgm./ml) in 0.1 M phosphate buffer or pH 7.3*

(Infectivity expressed as lesions per 30 leaves)

	Ribonucleic acid	Tobacco mosaic virus
Normal	488	629
With normal serum	180	117
With antiserum	145	0
With ribonuclease	0	473
After ultracentrifugation	367	31
After 48 hr. at 20°C.	2	130

(b) Treatment of both the ribonucleic acid and tobacco mosaic virus with normal rabbit serum (concentration 3×10^{-3}, applied for 10 min. at 4°C.) somewhat reduces the infectivity. There is no significant further reduction if the ribonucleic is treated with the same amount of tobacco mosaic virus antiserum, whereas with antiserum the infectivity of the virus itself is almost completely destroyed.

(c) Incubation of the stock solutions of ribonucleic acid (0.3 per cent) and tobacco mosaic virus (0.06 per cent) with 2 μgm. per ml. of ribonuclease at 4°C. for 10 min. reduces the activity of the ribonucleic acid to 0, whereas that of the virus remains almost unaffected.

(d) The sedimentation constant of the ribonucleic acid is 12-18 S, compared with 180 S for tobacco mosaic virus. We have centrifuged the stock solution of ribonucleic acid for 30 min. at 50,000 rev. per min. and found the supernatant liquid to be only a little less active than the original solution. If the solution of the virus is treated in the same manner, the activity of the supernatant liquid is very low.

(*e*) The ribonucleic acid is known to be unstable; and, as would be expected, its infectivity is much reduced after 48 hr. at 20°C., whereas that of the virus is much less affected.

These experiments show that protein, if present at all, is only there in very small amounts and does not resemble closely the native protein of tobacco mosaic virus. We are thus led to conclude that the infectivity is due to the nucleic acid itself.

The infectivity of the ribonucleic acid preparation is about 0.1 per cent of that of the same amount of ribonucleic acid contained in native tobacco mosaic virus. Whether this relatively low value is due to a large inactive fraction of the ribonucleic acid preparation, or to low efficiency of the mechanism of infection, has still to be determined.

Studies on the combination of the ribonucleic acid with proteins are being carried out and may elucidate the connexion between our findings and the reactivation experiments of Fraenkel-Conrat and Williams,[7] of Lippincott and Commoner,[8] and of Hart.[9]

We are much indebted to Prof. H. Friedrich-Freksa for helpful discussions, to Mr. R. Engler and Dr. H. Schuster for their co-operation, and to Miss A. Kleih for assistance.

A detailed account of this work will be published in the *Zeitschrift für Narturforschung*.

[7] Fraenkel-Conrat, H., and Williams, R. C. Proc. Nat. Acad. Sci. **41**: 690 (1955).

[8] Lippincot, J. A., and Commoner, R., Biochim. Biophys. Acta. **19**: 198 (1956).

[9] Hart, R. G. Nature. **177**: 130 (1956).

1957

Virus Interference. I. The Interferon

by A. Isaacs and J. Lindenmann[1]

National Institute for Medical Research, London

The publication of more than 100 experimental studies on interferon, within the short span of 5 years since the appearance of this paper, is testimonial to the importance of its discovery. The role of interferon on the understanding of acute and chronic virus infections and its relation to host resistance has been the subject of intense investigation from both a fundamental and practical consideration. Simply defined, interferon is a protein that is produced from the interaction of virus and cells and has the property of interfering with the multiplication of viruses. Because of its broad antiviral spectrum, poor antigenicity, and lack of toxicity, it has received serious consideration as an antiviral therapeutic agent. Beneficial results have been reported from its use in humans to depress the smallpox vaccination reaction and in the treatment of vaccinal keratitis.[2]

SUMMARY

During a study of the interference produced by heat inactivated influenza virus with the growth of live virus in fragments of chick chorio-allantoic membrane it was found that following incubation of heated virus with membrane a new factor was released. This factor, recognized by its ability to induce interference in fresh pieces of chorio-allantoic membrane, was called interferon. Follow-

[1] In receipt of a fellowship from the Swiss Academy of Medical Sciences. Abridged and reprinted by permission of the author and publisher from Proceedings of the Royal Society of London, Series B. 147: 258-267 (1957).

[2] Lancet. 1: 873-875, 875-879 (1962).

ing a lag phase interferon was first detected in the membranes after 3 h incubation and thereafter it was released into the surrounding fluid.

INTRODUCTION

One of the most useful situations for studying interference among animal viruses has been the interference produced by inactivated influenza viruses with the growth of live influenza virus in the chorio-allantoic membrane of the chick embryo. In this system, a number of variables have been measured, e.g. the effects of varying the dose of interfering and challenge virus or the time interval between the two inoculations, the effects of different methods of virus inactivation and the use of different virus strains (see review by Henle 1950). As a result of studies by different workers, it is generally agreed that interference cannot be explained by blockage of cell surface receptors. Fazekas de St Groth, Isaacs & Edney (1952) found that interference by influenza virus inactivated at 56°C. took some hours until it was fully established, but it was difficult to decide by experiments in the intact chick embryo whether this time was required for the inactivated virus to be absorbed by the cells or for some further reactions to occur. We have studied this point with pieces of chorio-allantoic membrane suspended in buffered salt solution *in vitro* (Fulton & Armitage 1951; Tyrrell & Tamm 1955) a method which allows observation of fluid and cells separately and manipulations which are not possible in the chick embryo. As a result, a number of new features of the interference reaction have emerged and these are described in this and the following paper.

METHODS

INTERFERING VIRUS

The Melbourne (1935) strain of influenza virus A was used as freshly harvested allantoic fluid. It was mixed with a 2% sodium citrate solution in normal saline and borate buffer, pH 8.5, in the ratio of 6 parts virus, 2 parts citrate-saline and 1 part borate buffer, and heated at 56°C. for 1 h. This treatment abolishes the infectivity and enzyme activity of the virus while retaining its interfering activity (Isaacs & Edney 1950a). In the present experiments, it was shown by inoculating eggs allantoically that heating had inactivated the virus; this test was included in most, but not in all of the present experiments. The heated virus is referred to as heated MEL.

BUFFER

The buffer used to suspend and wash the pieces of chorio-allantoic membrane was that described by Earle (see Parker 1950).

Chorio-allantoic Membrane

Pieces of chorio-allantoic membrane were removed from 10- or 11-day fertile hen's eggs by a technique similar to that described by Tamm, Folkers & Horsfall (1953). Six or seven pieces were taken from each egg and membranes were pooled from a group of eggs and randomized. In order to find the weight of a piece of membrane, ten pieces were selected at random, drained on filter paper and weighed. The average weight of a piece of membrane was found to be 20 mg.

Interference and Challenge

An interference experiment was carried out in the following way: Six pieces of membrane were placed in $6 \times \frac{5}{8}$ in. test-tubes, and to each was added 1 ml. of test material. Six other tubes were similarly incubated with 1 ml. buffer. In each case 100 units of penicillin were added per ml. fluid. The tubes were stoppered and placed in a roller drum at 37°C. (8 rev/h). After 24 h incubation the membranes were removed, washed in two changes of buffer and put in fresh tubes along with 1 ml. buffer in which MEL virus at a final dilution of 10^{-3} was incorporated. The MEL virus came from a stock of capillary tubes kept at −70°C. and a single stock of virus lasted through almost all the experiments. The tubes were placed in the roller drum for a further 48 h at 37°C. after which the fluids were titrated individually for their haemagglutinin content.

Haemagglutinin Titrations

Two-fold dilutions (0.25 ml.) of test virus were made in normal saline using automatic pipettes and plastic plates. To each dilution 0.25 ml. of a 0.5% suspension of chick red-blood cells was added, and the cells allowed to settle. That pattern which showed partial agglutination was taken as the end-point, and it was read by interpolation if necessary. One agglutinating dose (a.d.) is defined as the amount of virus present at the partial agglutination end-point. The readings in the tables are given as $\log_2$, i.e. tube number of a series of two-fold dilutions. Thus if the end-point of agglutination occurs at a 1/2 dilution the reading is taken as $\log_2 = 1$. If the end-point of agglutination occurs at a 1/4 dilution the reading is taken as $\log_2 = 2$. A 1/1 dilution end-point has a $\log_2 = 0$ and material which did not agglutinate red cells at a 1/1 dilution was given an arbitrary score of −1.

Assessment of Results

A group of sixty titrations of control materials carried out in a single experiment was analyzed statistically. The logarithms of the haemagglutinin titres of individual fluids were found to occur in an approximately normal distribution. It was necessary, therefore, to measure geometric mean haemagglutinin titres when comparing two groups of materials. The mean ($\log_2$) titre of the sixty titrations was 6.78 and the variance 0.412 (standard deviation 0.642). If we took samples of six from this population we should expect that 99% of the sample means would fall in the range 6.78 ± 0.67. Therefore, if the means of two samples, drawn at random, differ by more than 0.67 $\log_2$ it is likely that they are drawn from different populations. In practice, we have assumed that if an experimental group of six tubes showed a geometric mean titre of one $\log_2$ unit less than a group of six controls tested at the same time this indicates a slight but significant degree of interference; a difference of two $\log_2$ units was taken as showing definite interference.

One difficulty was that groups of controls tested on different days showed highly significant differences in titre. This finding appears to be due to the variable sensitivity of the red cells from different fowls to influenza viral haemagglutinin. In order to overcome this difficulty a control group was included in each experiment, and to facilitate comparison between different experiments the results for an experimental group are shown in the table as the proportion (expressed as a percentage) of the geometric mean haemagglutinin titre of the corresponding controls. Thus a difference of one $\log_2$ unit between experimental and control groups corresponds to a 50% yield, a difference of two $\log_2$ units to a 25% yield, etc. Small arithmetic differences in the percentage yield have therefore a much greater significance at low than at high percentage yields.

RESULTS

RESIDUAL INTERFERING ACTIVITY

These experiments have indicated that the interfering virus is rapidly taken up by the cells, although interference in the cells takes some time to be established. One would expect, too, that in these experiments little interfering activity would remain in the fluid after 24 h contact between heated MEL and the membrane, since any unabsorbed virus would lose interfering potency as a result of inactivation at 37°C. and combination with inhibitor. It was surprising, therefore, to find that after 24 h incubation considerable interfering activity remained in the surrounding fluid. This can be seen from the experiment illustrated in table 4. In this experiment, different amounts of heated MEL were incubated with pieces of membrane for 24 h at 37°C. Membranes and fluids were then separated and the membranes were washed and challenged with MEL virus to assess the degree of *initial* interference. The amount of *residual* interference in the fluids was measured by adding fresh pieces of membrane to the fluids, incubating 24 h at 37°C and challenging with MEL virus in the same way. Clearly the degree of residual interfering activity is only slightly less than the amount of initial interfering activity.

TABLE 4.* *Comparison between initial interfering activity of heated MEL and residual interfering activity after incubation with chorioallantoic membrane for 24 h*

Interfering activity measured	Dose (a.d.) of heated MEL initially present	Geometric mean HA titre ($\log_2$)	% of control titre
initial	1120	<0	<1.3
initial	373	0.8	2.3
initial	124	1.9	4
initial	41	3.9	20
residual	1120	0.75	1.6
residual	373	3.6	12
residual	124	4.7	25
residual	41	5.7	50

* Tables 1 through 3 have been deleted from the article.—Ed.

In an effort to explain the results of the last experiment the possibility was considered that fresh interfering activity was produced by the membrane. This possibility was confirmed by the following experiment. Heated MEL virus was incubated with pieces of membrane for 2 h at 37°C. The membranes were then thoroughly washed and incubated in fresh buffer at 37°C. It was found that after some hours' incubation at 37°C. fresh interfering activity could be detected in the incubating fluid. Some of the properties of this newly released interfering agent are described in the accompanying paper, but we can anticipate meanwhile by saying that the newly released interfering agent is a non-haemagglutinating macromolecular particle which has many different properties from those of heated influenza virus. To distinguish it from the heated influenza virus we have called the newly released interfering agent "interferon." It was also found that the membranes which were liberating "interferon" showed a diminished production of MEL virus on challenge, i.e. establishment of interference was accompanied by liberation of interferon.

TIME OF APPEARANCE OF INTERFERON IN THE MEMBRANE
AND RELEASE INTO THE SURROUNDING FLUID

We next studied the appearance of interferon in the membranes and its liberation into the surrounding medium at different time-intervals after inoculating heated MEL virus. The experiment which is illustrated in figure 1 was carried out in the following way:

Pieces of chorio-allantoic membrane were mixed with a large dose of heated MEL (4000 agglutinating doses/membrane piece) and incubated in the roller drum for 3 h at 37°C. The membranes were then removed, washed thoroughly in buffer, resuspended in fresh test-tubes with 1 ml. of buffer/membrane piece and reincubated at 37°C. The end of this time was taken as zero hour and at various time intervals thereafter groups of tubes were removed, and the fluids and membranes tested separately for interferon activity. The membranes were pooled in groups of six, ground in a Ten Broeck grinder, suspended in 6 ml. buffer, lightly centrifuged and the supernatant fluid tested by adding six fresh pieces of membrane. (In a control experiment it had been shown that after lightly centrifuging a membrane extract in this way all the interfering activity was present in the supernatant fluid.) The further test of interfering activity of fluids and membrane extracts was carried out by incubating test fluids with fresh pieces of membrane for 18 to 24 h at 37°C., washing the membranes and challenging with MEL virus. The yields of haemagglutinin were compared with those of control membranes incubated in buffer. In the experiment illustrated in figure 1, the samples harvested at 0 and 6 h had

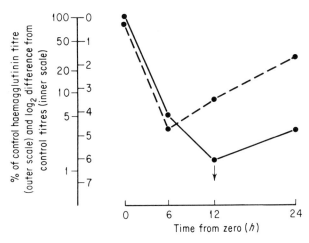

Fig. 1. Presence of interferon in membranes and fluids: —— fluids, - - - membrane extracts.

a different control group from the samples harvested at 12 and 24 h, and in each case the results in the experimental group were compared with their corresponding controls. The fluids and membrane extracts tested at 0 h showed no interfering activity, although the membranes had absorbed large amounts of heated MEL virus, and would themselves probably have been resistant to challenge as shown by control experiments. At 6 h there was a high degree of interferon activity in the membrane extracts and slightly less in the fluids. The greatest interfering activity in the fluids was found at 12 h, a finding which was confirmed in a sec-

ond experiment, and by this time the activity in the membrane extracts
had declined slightly. At 24 h there was little remaining activity in the
membrane extracts and most of the interferon had been liberated into
the medium.

This type of experiment was repeated with a number of variations. In
one experiment an initial period of 2 h contact between heated MEL
and membranes was allowed, and samples were taken at 0, 3, 6, 9 and
12 h. In this case, significant interfering activity was found in membranes
and fluids at 3 h, but the potency of both was less than at 6 h. The only
difference from the results shown in figure 1 was that in this experiment
the zero samples of both membranes and fluids showed slight but significant interfering activity. This finding may have been due to small
amounts of heated MEL remaining loosely attached to the membrane;
since the same finding was noted when the heated MEL and membranes
were left in contact for 24 h at 2°C. Under these conditions, Ishida
& Ackermann (1956) have shown that influenza virus becomes loosely and
reversibly attached to the chorio-allantoic membrane, irreversible attachment requiring incubation at 37°C. Preliminary incubation of heated
MEL and membranes at 2°C. followed by washing the membranes did
not give satisfactory results and there was a low production of interferons.

In another experiment, the *differential* release of interferons into the
fluid was studied. Heated MEL and membranes were kept 2 h in contact
at 37°C. and the membranes were then washed and incubated in buffer.
At two-hourly intervals thereafter the membranes were removed, washed
and incubated in fresh buffer; all the manipulations were carried out with
warm reagents and at 37°C. The yields of interferon during the different
time intervals were then measured and the results are shown in table 5.

TABLE 5. *Differential yield of interferons*
at intervals after inoculating heated MEL

Differential sample	Geometric mean HA titre ($\log_2$)	% of control titre
0-2 h	6.7	81
2-4 h	5.3	29
4-6 h	5.2	27
6-8 h	5.7	36
8-10 h	5.8	40
control	6.9	100
10-24 h	7.0	81
control	7.2	100

The maximal liberation of interferon occurred between the second
and sixth hours. The yield of interferon was much smaller at each

interval, largely due to the fact that the total yield was divided among so many samples. (In the accompanying paper it is shown that interferon prepared as described here has little interfering activity at a dilution of 1 in 10.) In this experiment little interferon was liberated after 10 h, but in another experiment slight activity was found in a 10 to 24 h sample.

RELATIONSHIP BETWEEN INTERFERING ACTIVITY OF THE VIRUS AND INTERFERON PRODUCTION

The amount of interferon produced depends on the amount of heated MEL used, as indicated by the results shown in table 4. The following experiment showed that interferon production is also dependent on the possession of interfering activity by the heated MEL. It is based on the fact that MEL virus heated for 1 h at 56°C. had strong interfering activity, whereas the same virus heated for 1 h at 60°C. had no significant interfering activity (Isaacs & Edney 1950a).

Aliquots of a preparation of MEL virus in citrate-borate buffer were heated for 1 h at 56 and 60°C. and incubated with pieces of membrane for 2 h at 37°C. The membranes were then washed and incubated in buffer for a further 20 h at 37°C. Thereafter, the membranes were removed and tested for their ability to support the multiplication of MEL virus, while the fluids were tested for their interferon content. The results are shown in table 6.

TABLE 6. *Relationship of interfering activity and interferon production by MEL heated at 56 and 60C.*

MEL heated at	Material tested	Geometric mean HA titre ($\log_2$)	% of control titre
56°C. for 1 h	membranes for interference	0.88	1.1
60°C. for 1 h	membranes for interference	6.4	53
56°C. for 1 h	interferons liberated	2.6	4
60°C. for 1 h	interferons liberated	7.1	100

The virus which had been heated at 56°C. induced significant interference in the membranes which also liberated interferon. The virus which had been heated at 60°C. caused a barely detectable degree of interference and no interferon was liberated.

ATTEMPTED PASSAGE OF INTERFERON IN SERIES

The results obtained have not made it clear whether interferon is part of the heated MEL virus which is liberated by the membrane, or whether it is newly synthesized in the membrane. In either event it was interesting to test the possibility that interferon might be able to replicate in series.

In order to test this, advantage was taken of the fact that interferon exerts its activity if it is left in contact with the membranes for 4 h at 37°C., and the membranes are then washed and incubated in buffer for a further 20 h at 37°C. before challenge. Under these conditions no new interferon activity could be detected in ground membranes or in the medium after a single passage or after two serial passages. Controls showed that the interferon grown in eggs or tissue cultures did not produce live virus.

DISCUSSION

In earlier studies on virus interference attempts were sometimes made to explain the phenomenon as due to an inert blocking action of the interfering virus preventing the challenge virus from entering the cells. This view has been contested by those who could find no evidence that the interfering virus prevented uptake of challenge virus, and in the present studies it was found that in order to establish interference more than 4 h incubation at 37°C. was required. Tyrrell & Tamm (1955) found that incubation at 37°C. was necessary for the establishment of interference in a similar system, but using virus "inactivated" at 22 or 37°C. However, it is known that virus incubated at 22 or 37°C. retains some infectivity and is able to undergo a modified cycle of virus multiplication resulting in the production of virus resembling incomplete virus (Henle 1953; Horsfall 1954). In contrast, virus heated at 56°C. for 1 h has hitherto shown no evidence of infectivity, or of the ability to produce virus haemagglutinin or soluble antigens (Isaacs & Fulton 1953). The present results suggest, nevertheless, that interference shows some of the characters we might expect of an abortive attempt at a single cycle of virus multiplication. A second finding which supports this idea (in addition to the fact that interference requires some metabolic activity on the part of the membrane) is that the interfering action of heated MEL is inactivated during incubation at 37°C. to approximately the same extent as is the infectivity of unheated virus. But the best support for the idea arises if we consider the interferon provisionally as an abortive product of virus multiplication. This suggestion is made mainly as a guide to further experimentation until the interferon is better characterized chemically and serologically.

The analogies between interferon and virus production are as follows: Little or no interferon activity could be detected in membranes or fluids shortly after inoculating heated MEL; this is analogous to the so-called "eclipse period," when only a small fraction of the inoculated influenza virus can be recovered from infected cells (Hoyle 1948; Henle 1949). Secondly, the times at which interferon activity can be detected in membranes and fluids correspond very well with those at which new virus antigens appear after inoculating live influenza virus. The fact that interferon is able to inhibit influenza virus growth, but is unable to replicate in series, suggests similarities to the single cycle of viral haemag-glutinin production caused by infection with incomplete virus (Burnet, Lind & Stevens 1955; Paucker & Henle 1955).

The experiment which showed that virus heated at 60°C. for 1 h had no interfering action and did not lead to the production of interferon, suggests a close relationship between the two phenomena. However, there is insufficient evidence to postulate yet that the influenza viral interfer-ence phenomenon is due directly to interferon production. It is also not yet known whether interferon is simply liberated from the heated MEL or is newly synthesized in the membrane. In favour of its being newly synthesized is an observation that in order to obtain good yields of inter-feron, adequate oxygenation of the membrane is necessary.

REFERENCES

Burnet, F. M., Lind, P. E., and Stevens, K. M. 1955. Aust. J. Exp. Biol. Med. Sci. **33**: 127.

Fazekas, de St Groth, S., Isaacs, A., and Edney, M. 1952. Nature, Lond. **170**: 573.

Fulton, F., and Armitage, P. 1951. J. Hyg., Camb. **49**: 247.

Henle, W. 1949. J. Exp. Med. **90**: 1.

Henle, W. 1950. J. Immunol. **64**: 203.

Henle, W. 1953. Cold Spring Harbor Symp. Quant. Biol. **18**: 35.

Horsfall, F. L., Jr. 1954. J. Exp. Med. **100**: 135.

Hoyle, L. 1948. Brit. J. Exp. Path. **29**: 390.

Isaacs, A., and Edney, M. 1950a. Aust. J. Exp. Biol. Med. Sci. **28**: 219.

Isaacs, A., and Edney, M. 1950b. Aust. J. Exp. Biol. Med. Sci. **28**: 231.

Isaacs, A., and Fulton, F. 1953. J. Gen. Microbiol. **9**: 132.

Ishida, N., and Ackermann, W. W. 1956. J. Exp. Med. **104**: 501.

Parker, R. C. 1950. Methods of tissue culture. London and Toronto, Cassell and Co.

Paucker, K., and Henle, W. 1955. J. Exp. Med. **101**: 493.

Schlesinger, R. W., and Karr, H. V. 1956. J. Exp. Med. **103**: 309.

Tamm, I., Folkers, K., and Horsfall, F. L., Jr. 1953. J. Exp. Med. **98**: 229.

Tyrrell, D. A. J., and Tamm, I. 1955. J. Immunol. **75**: 43.

1959

A Single-Stranded Deoxyribonucleic Acid from Bacteriophage φX174 [1]

by Robert L. Sinsheimer

Division of Biology, California Institute of Technology,
Pasadena, California

A deeper cognition of the complexity of cellular function and viral replication at the molecular level was provided with the discovery of genetic material from the minute E. coli bacteriophage φX174 which was not of the conventional hydrogen-bonded, two-stranded structure of the Watson-Crick variety. This virus, possibly representing a whole new class of bacterial viruses, contained a single-stranded form of deoxyribonucleic acid (DNA). Bacteriophage S-13, also believed to contain single-stranded DNA,[2] is closely related to bacteriophage φX174.[3] Furthermore, genetic recombination has recently been demonstrated between the two bacteriophages.[4]

The size of bacteriophage φX174 is in the range of RNA-containing plant and animal viruses, and its novel form of DNA behaves like RNA (microsomal or viral) which is believed to be single-stranded. Subsequent studies on single-stranded DNA have shown that it carries all the genetic information needed for the synthesis of complete virus particles and, furthermore, that free nucleic acid of the bacteriophage is capable of infecting bacterial protoplasts. Some experimental

[1] This research has been supported by grants from the U.S. Public Health Service, the American Cancer Society, and the California Division of the American Cancer Society. Reprinted by permission of the author and publisher from the Journal of Molecular Biology. 1: 43-45 (1959).

[2] Tessman. Virology. 9: 375 (1959).

[3] Zahler. J. Bacteriology. 73: 310 (1958).

[4] Tessman and Shleser. Virology. 19: 239 (1963).

information has been accumulated to answer the intriguing question as to how this single-stranded DNA material replicates. Sinsheimer and associates[5] have obtained evidence that φX174 DNA, soon after entering a susceptible bacterium, is converted to a structure called "replicative form" which then increases approximately 50-fold. Various properties of replicative form suggest that it is a two-stranded form of complementary DNA which is derived from a transformation of parental DNA. At a later stage, the replicative form serves as a precursor or template for the synthesis of progeny containing single-stranded DNA. Recently, Hayashi, et al.[6] reported on the isolation and properties of replicative form and confirmed its resemblance to double-stranded DNA.

The complexity of viral replication at the molecular level, exemplified by the studies with single-stranded DNA of bacteriophage φX174, is further compounded by reports of double-stranded RNA found in wound tumor (plant) virus by Black and Markham[7] and in reovirus (animal) by Tamm and Gomatos.[8]

SUMMARY

The deoxyribonucleic acid (DNA) of bacteriophage φX174 can be extracted by phenolic denaturation of the virus protein. The DNA thus obtained has a molecular weight of 1.7×10^6, indicating that there is one molecule per virus particle.

This φX DNA does not have a complementary nucleotide composition. The ultraviolet absorption of this DNA is strongly dependent upon temperature in the range 20° to 60°C, and upon NaCl concentration in the range 10^{-3} to 10^0 M. This DNA reacts with formaldehyde at 37°C and is precipitated by plumbous ions. This evidence is interpreted to mean that the purine and pyrimidine rings are not involved in a tightly hydrogen-bonded complementary structure.

Light scattering studies indicate that this DNA is highly flexible and that its configuration is strongly dependent upon the ionic strength of the solution. Upon treatment with pancreatic deoxyribonuclease, the weight-average molecular weight decreases in accordance with the function expected for a single-stranded molecule.

It is concluded that the DNA of bacteriophage φX174 is single-stranded.

[5] J. Mol. Biol. 4: 142 (1962).
[6] Science. 140: 1313 (1963).
[7] Netherlands J. Plant Path. 1963 In press.
[8] Proc. Nat. Acad. Sci. 49: 707 (1963).

INTRODUCTION

In a previous paper (Sinsheimer, 1959) describing the properties of bacteriophage ϕX174, evidence was presented that the deoxyribonucleic acid (DNA) of this virus appeared to be unusual, in that the amino groups of the purine and pyrimidine rings were accessible to reaction with formaldehyde, and that the atomic efficiency of inactivation of the virus by disintegration of ^{32}P atoms, incorporated into the viral DNA, was 1.0 (Tessman, 1959). In the present paper chemical and physical studies of the DNA extracted from this virus are presented. The evidence obtained indicates that each ϕX174 particle contains one molecule of a single-stranded DNA.

MATERIALS AND METHODS

Bacteriophage ϕX174 was prepared and purified as previously described.

PREPARATION OF ϕX DNA

To a cold suspension of ϕX174 containing 10 to 15 mg/ml. in borate buffer[7a] is added an equal volume of cold phenol [8a] (Gierer & Schramm, 1956) previously equilibrated with borate buffer by shaking. The resultant emulsion is shaken for 5 min in the cold room and then spun at 1800 g for 5 min to separate the phases. The aqueous phase is removed, added to an equal volume of cold phenol, and the process repeated two more times. The final aqueous layer which contains the DNA is removed and allowed to stand.

To improve the yield of DNA a volume of borate buffer, equal to one-half the initial volume of ϕX suspension, is added to the phenol phase from the first extraction, shaken and spun as above. The aqueous layer is removed and then used to extract in turn the DNA from the phenol layers of the second and third extractions. The final aqueous layer is pooled with the DNA solution obtained in the first series of extractions, and the combined solutions are shaken with an equal volume of cold ether. After shaking the emulsion is allowed to stand in a separatory funnel for 1 hr to allow the phases to separate. The clear aqueous layer is drawn off. The turbid ether layer is then extracted with a few ml. of borate, which, after separation of the phases, is added to the DNA solution. Two more ether extractions are employed to remove most of the residual phenol.

At this stage the DNA content of the extract accounts for 65 to 70% of the DNA in the initial suspension of virus.

The DNA is now dialyzed against two changes of 1.3 M-potassium

[7a] Borate buffer is a solution of sodium tetraborate, saturated at 4°C.

[8a] Mallinckrodt liquified phenol, AR "intended for chromatographic purposes," is used.

phosphate buffer, pH 7.5 (Kirby, 1957). There is no loss of ultraviolet absorbing material upon dialysis. To complete the removal of residual denatured protein, the DNA is extracted from the salt solution by shaking with one-half volume of either 2-methoxyethanol or N,N-dimethyl-formamide (Porter, 1955). After vigorous shaking the two phases are separated by centrifugation at 1800 g for 8 min. The upper organic layer contains all the DNA. A thin film of denatured material appears at the interface of the two phases.

The DNA solution is then dialyzed against three changes of 0.2 M-sodium chloride plus 0.001 M-phosphate buffer, pH 7.5. 20 to 30% of the ϕX DNA dialyses from the organic phase through the membrane into the first two changes.[9]

METHODS OF PURINE AND PYRIMIDINE ANALYSIS

Degradation to purines and pyrimidines was carried out with either 12 N-HClO$_4$ at 100°C (Marshak & Vogel, 1951) or with glass distilled 6 N-HCl at 100°C (Hershey, Dixon & Chase, 1953). With either method, the purines and pyrimidines recovered accounted for over 90% of the phosphorus of the DNA preparation. Phosphorus analyses were made by a modification of the method of Allen (1940). Purines and pyrimidines were separated by descending chromatography in the isopropanol-water-HCl solvent of Wyatt (1951) using S. and S. 597 paper. In two instances this separation was checked, with good agreement, by a paper electrophoretic separation of the same digest, using 20 volts/cm at pH 3.2, 0.1 M-tris formate buffer, and Whatman no. 3 paper (Nutter & Sinsheimer, 1959). In all cases the purines and pyrimidines were eluted from the ultraviolet absorbing spots in 0.1 N-HCl and the quantities determined by measurement of the ultraviolet absorption, after subtraction of the absorption of appropriate blanks. The extinction coefficients employed were: adenine, $A_M = 13,100$ at 260 mμ (Beaven, Holiday & Johnson, 1955); guanine, $A_M = 11,400$ at 248 mμ (ibid.); thymine, $A_M = 7,890$ at 264.5 mμ (Shugar & Fox, 1952); and cytosine, $A_M = 10,400$ at 275 mμ (ibid.).

Degradation to nucleotides was accomplished by successive use of pancreatic deoxyribonuclease (DNase) (Worthington Biochemical Company) and venom phosphodiesterase (Koerner & Sinsheimer, 1957). Ion exchange fractionation of the nucleotides with 98% recovery of the ultraviolet ab-

[9] This DNA can be recovered by evaporation of the pooled dialysate and solution in 0·2 M-NaCl plus 6 M-urea plus 0·001 M-versene, pH 7·0, followed by dialysis versus 0·2 M-NaCl. This DNA which has passed through the membrane has the same physical properties and composition as the DNA which remains within. It was at first thought that the escape of the ϕX DNA was a consequence of attack upon the membrane by methoxyethanol but the same result was observed with N,N-dimethyformamide and subsequent studies have indicated that the membranes are not permanently changed. Apparently ϕX DNA, in a largely organic medium, assumes a configuration in which it can slowly pass through the cellophane membrane.

sorption was carried out as previously described (Sinsheimer & Koerner, 1951). Extinction coefficients for the nucleotides have been previously presented (Sinsheimer, 1954).

All spectra were obtained on a Beckman DK2 spectrophotometer.

LIGHT SCATTERING

All light scattering measurements were made in a Brice-Phoenix light scattering photometer, model 1000 D, made by Phoenix Precision Instruments, Inc. ϕX DNA solutions were cleaned of dust by filtration through type AA Millipore filters.

RESULTS

COMPOSITION OF ϕX DNA

The results of several analyses of the purine and pyrimidine composition of two preparations of ϕX DNA are presented in Table 1. The

TABLE 1. *Purine and pyrimidine composition of ϕX DNA*

Preparation	Mode of degradation	Molar ratios			
		Adenine	Thymine	Guanine	Cytosine
A	6 N-HCl Hydrolysis	1.00	1.31	1.06	0.82
B	6 N-HCl Hydrolysis	1.00	1.31	1.06	0.82
B	12 N-HClO$_4$ Hydrolysis	1.00	1.06	0.99	0.76
B	Enzymatic digestion to nucleotides	1.00	1.33	0.98	0.75

nucleotide analysis achieved by enzymatic degradation is considered to be the most reliable. It is clear that the molar equalities of adenine and thymine and of guanine and cytosine observed in nearly all other DNA (Chargaff, 1955) are not observed. This DNA thus cannot have the complementary structure formulated by Watson & Crick (1953a). The only regularity that can be observed is that thymine/adenine = guanine/cytosine, but the significance of this is not immediately evident.

It appears that the methods of acid hydrolysis which have proven reasonably satisfactory for conventional forms of DNA are not entirely satisfactory for this DNA. A tendency to loss of thymine in HClO$_4$ hydrolysis (Wyatt, 1952) is exaggerated, as in the loss of adenine (Hershey, Dixon & Chase, 1953) in HCl hydrolysis.

HYDROGEN BONDING IN ϕX DNA

The extracted DNA reacts with formaldehyde (Fig. 1) as does the native virus. This reaction is given by RNA (Fraenkel-Conrat, 1954; Staehelin, 1958) and by heat denatured DNA, but not by native DNA

(Hoard, 1957). It is an indication that the amino groups of the purine and pyrimidine rings are accessible and are not involved in a tightly hydrogen bonded structure.

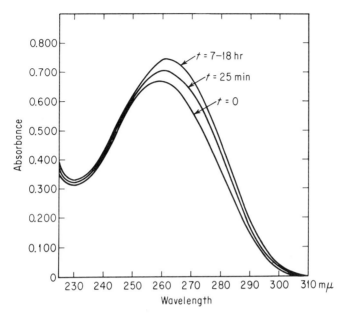

Fig. 1. Effect of formaldehyde (1.8%) upon the ultraviolet absorption of ϕX DNA in 0.2 M-NaCl at 37°C. Concentration of DNA = 25.5 μg/ml.

Upon thermal denaturation of native DNA there is a disruption of the hydrogen bonded structure with a concomitant increase of ultraviolet absorption. With native DNA this transition takes place within a narrow temperature zone in the region of 80° to 90°C (Thomas, 1954; Lawley, 1956; Shack, 1958). Over the temperature range of 20° to 70°C there is very little influence of temperature upon the absorption of native DNA.

In contrast, the ultraviolet absorption of ϕX DNA is a marked function of temperature over a very wide range (Fig. 2). A temperature dependence of ultraviolet absorption of this nature is also observed with thermally denatured DNA (Shack, 1958), although the variation observed does not appear to be as great over the temperature region 20° to 50°C (Fig. 2). This variation of absorption with temperature is presumably the result, in part, of rupture of random intramolecular hydrogen bonds and, in part, a consequence of thermal expansion of the molecule.

Similarly, the ultraviolet absorption of ϕX DNA is strongly dependent upon ionic strength at values of ionic strength in which the absorption of native DNA is unaffected (Thomas, 1954; Lawley, 1956; Shack, 1958) (Fig. 3). Again the increase of absorption at lower ionic strength is presumably the result of decreased intramolecular hydrogen bonding and molecular expansion (*vide infra*) brought about by an increase of net charge upon the DNA.

It may be noted that $E(P)$, the absorbance per mole of phosphorus (Chargaff & Zamenhof, 1948), is 8700 for ϕX DNA in 0.2 M-NaCl at 37°C.

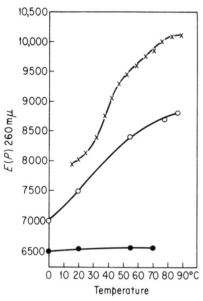

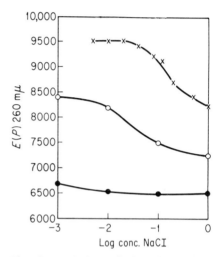

Fig. 2. Variation of the ultraviolet absorption of ϕX DNA at 260 mμ with temperature. $E(P)$ = absorbance of a solution containing one mole of phosphorus per liter.

x ——— x DNA from ϕX in 0.2 M-NaCl + 10^{-3} M-phosphate buffer, pH 7.5.
• ——— • Native thymus DNA in 0.1 M-NaCl (from Shack, 1958).
o ——— o Heat denatured thymus DNA in 0.1 M-NaCl (from Shack, 1958).

Fig. 3. Variation of the ultraviolet adsorption at 260 mμ of ϕX DNA' with salt concentration.

x ——— x DNA from ϕX, at 37°C.
• ——— • Native thymus DNA, at 22°C (from Shack, 1958).
o ——— o Heat denatured thymus DNA, at 22°C (from Shack, 1958).

This is considerably higher than has been observed with native or denatured DNA under comparable conditions. In accord with this observation, there is only an 11% increase in the ultraviolet absorption of ϕX DNA upon degradation with pancreatic DNase in 0.2 M-sodium chloride at 37°C, as compared to the 30 to 35% increase observed with native thymus DNA (Kunitz, 1950).

Stevens & Duggan (1957) showed that thermally denatured thymus DNA is precipitated by Pb++ ion under conditions such that native DNA remained soluble. Similarly, ϕX DNA is completely precipitated from a solution in 0.1 M sodium chloride containing 165 μg per ml. by addition of Pb++ ions to 0.017 M.

Light Scattering Observations

The particle weight of ϕX DNA has been measured by light scattering[10] (Figs. 4 and 5). Several preparations have been used under various

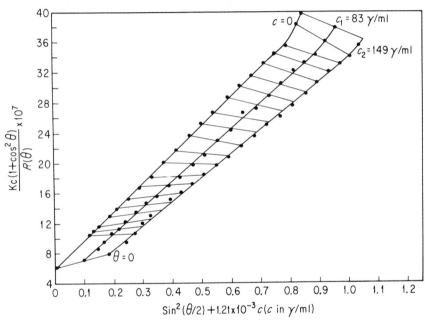

Fig. 4. Light scattering of ϕX DNA in 0.02 M-NaCl + 10^{-3} M-phosphate buffer, pH 7.5 at 37°C.

ionic conditions and the weights obtained have always been within the range of 1.6 to 1.8×10^6. This is in good agreement with the weight of DNA per ϕX particle calculated from the particle weight, 6.2×10^6, and the DNA content, 25.5%.[11] Hence there is one molecule of DNA per ϕX particle.

[10] In this calculation, the refractive increment of the DNA has been assumed to be 0.201 cm³/g at 4358 Å (Northrop, Nutter & Sinsheimer, 1953), although this value may not be quite correct for a DNA of this type.

[11] The DNA content of ϕX was calculated from colorimetric analysis by the diphenylamine and p-nitrophenylhydrazine methods. In ordinary DNA these methods are believed to measure purine deoxyribosides (Dische, 1955). If this is still true with ϕX DNA, the total DNA content of ϕX will be slightly greater than 25.5%, because the purine deoxyribosides comprise less than 50% of the total DNA.

In 0.02 M-NaCl at 37°C the ϕX DNA has a radius of gyration of 1140 Å. Upon addition of salt to 0.2 M, this decreases to 440 Å (Fig. 6), while in 0.02 M-NaCl plus 4×10^{-3} M-Mg++ the radius of gyration is 325 Å.[12] ϕX DNA is thus a highly flexible molecule. With native DNA, almost no change of radius of gyration is observed with change of ionic strength (Ehrlich & Doty, 1958). With alkali denatured DNA, a considerable variation is observed, nearly equal to that of ϕX DNA.

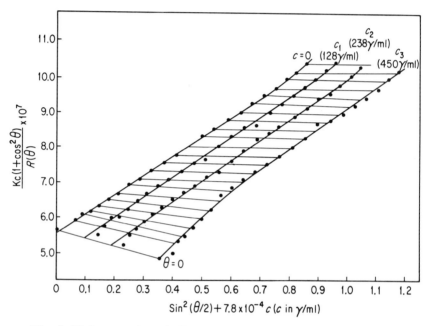

Fig. 5. Light scattering of ϕX DNA in 0.2 M-NaCl + 10^{-3} M-phosphate buffer, pH 7.5 at 37°C.

In 0.2 M-NaCl, the scattering envelope agrees well with that of a random coil (Doty & Steiner, 1950). For a random coil the radius of gyration should vary as $M^{0.5}$ (Tompa, 1956). For ϕX DNA in 0.2 M-sodium chloride, the ratio of $\sqrt{M}/\rho_g$ (M is the molecular weight in molecular weight units, ρ_g is the radius of gyration in Å) is 3.0. This may be compared with the ratio of 1.1 observed for native and sonicated thymus DNA (Reichmann, Rice, Thomas & Doty, 1954; Doty, McGill & Rice, 1958) and with a ratio of 2.5 to 2.6 observed with heat, acid, or alkali denatured thymus DNA in 0.2 M-sodium chloride (Rice & Doty, 1957; Thomas & Doty, 1956; Ehrlich & Doty, 1958). ϕX DNA is evidently more flexible than either native DNA or denatured DNA of thymus.

---

[12] At the same time, the ultraviolet absorption decreases by 14% upon addition of Mg++, and the sedimentation velocity increases (*vide infra*).

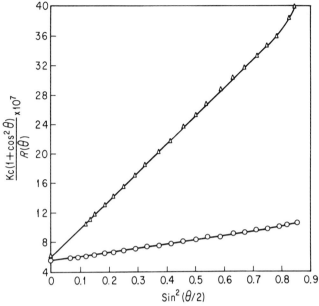

Fig. 6. Comparison of the scattering envelopes (extrapolated to zero concentration) of X DNA in 0.02 M and 0.2 M-NaCl:

$$\triangle - \triangle \quad \text{in 0.02 M-NaCl.}$$
$$o - o \quad \text{in 0.2 M-NaCl.}$$

KINETICS OF DEGRADATION BY PANCREATIC DEOXYRIBONUCLEASE

As shown by Charlesby (1954) (also Tobolsky, 1957) the decline of the weight average molecular weight of a monodisperse single chain polymer upon random degration of the inter-monomeric links will be described by

$$\frac{M(p)}{M(O)} = \frac{2}{\gamma^2} [e^{-\gamma} + \gamma - 1]$$

where $M(p)$ is the weight average molecular weight when the probability of rupture of any link is p, $M(O)$ is the initial molecular weight and γ is proportional to p.

For a double chain structure, with cross linkage between the chains, the same equation applies except that γ is proportional to p^2, as shown by Thomas (1956).

Thomas and also Schumaker, Richards & Schachman (1956) have shown that the rate of splitting of bonds by pancreatic DNase is initially uniform with time ($p = kt$). Therefore, measurements were made of the decline with time (and thus with p) of the weight average molecular weight of ϕX DNA under attack by DNase. The form of the curve thus obtained (Fig. 7) agrees well with that expected for a single-stranded molecule and is clearly distinct from that expected for a two-stranded molecule with linked strands, such as native DNA.[13]

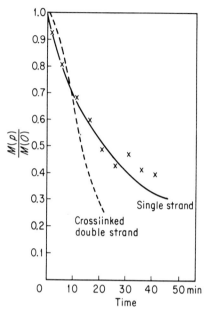

Fig. 7. Decline of weight-average molecular weight, as measured by light scattering, of ϕX DNA acted upon by pancreatic deoxyribonuclease. At $t = 0$, DNase in a final concentration of 3.7×10^{-7} μg/ml. was added to a solution containing 60 μg/ml. of ϕX DNA in a 0.2 M-NaCl + 0.001 M-phosphate buffer, pH 7.5 + 0.02 M-magnesium acetate. The temperature was maintained at 34°C.

——— Function expected for a single-stranded molecule.

– – – Function expected for a cross-linked double-stranded molecule.

xxx Experimental observation.

The theoretical functions were fitted to intersect a smooth curve representing the experimental data at one point, at $\dfrac{M(p)}{M(O)} = 0.74$.

ULTRACENTRIFUGE STUDIES

When banded by the cesium chloride density gradient equilibrium method of Meselson, Stahl & Vinograd (1957), ϕX DNA appears at a density of 1.72. This is distinctly higher than the density of native DNA (1.70) (Plate I (a)) and is very closely the density at which heat denatured salmon sperm DNA is observed to band (Meselson & Stahl, 1958).

In velocity centrifugation in 0.2 M-NaCl, ϕX DNA sediments as a single, rather sharp boundary, of $S = 23.8$ (Plate I (b)). At lower ionic strength, the sedimentation rate decreases, and below 0.08 M-NaCl the boundary splits in two indicating the presence of two centrifugal components (Plate I (c)).

A similar splitting of the boundary can be observed in 0.2 M-sodium chloride after treatment with formaldehyde (Plate I(d)). The sedimentation constants of the two components are 15.8 and 13.9 (measured in the presence of formaldehyde). The relative proportions of the two components observed either in 0.04 M-sodium chloride or after formaldehyde treatment are the same for a given ϕX DNA preparation, although variations are observed in different prepa-

[13] On some occasions, with considerably lower concentrations of DNase a slight curvature (concave downwards) has been observed in the initial stages of the digestion. This curvature, which was evident as an increase in slope to a value greater than the always finite initial slope, was not reproducible and has never been observed at the enzyme concentration employed in Fig. 7.

rations. The boundaries obtained after formaldehyde treatment are very sharp. A densitometer tracing is shown in Fig. 8.

The splitting of the boundary observed in dilute salt is completely reversible; upon addition of salt or Mg++ a single boundary is again observed.

DISCUSSION

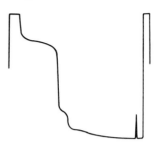

Fig. 8. Densitometer tracing of frame 11 of Plate I(d) indicating the relative proportion of the two centrifugal components.

The chemical reactivity of ϕX DNA, its ultraviolet absorption properties, its density, and its flexibility as demonstrated by light scattering, all serve to distinguish the DNA of ϕX174 from conventional DNA. In several ways, such as the dependence of ultraviolet absorption upon temperature and ionic strength, and the dependence of the radius of gyration upon ionic strength, the properties of ϕX DNA appear to be an exaggeration of the properties of a denatured DNA, as contrasted to those of native DNA. The nucleotide composition rules out the possibility of a complementary structure, native or denatured. The simplest explanation of the properties observed is that the DNA of ϕX174 is a single-stranded structure. Such an explanation is also at least consistent with the high efficiency of inactivation of the ϕX virus by the decay of incorporated [32]P.

In order to test the possibility that some of the properties of ϕX DNA were artifacts produced by the method of extraction and purification, samples of native thymus and of native *E. coli* DNA were taken through the entire extraction and purification procedures. It was shown that these procedures have no effect upon the density of these DNA samples in the density gradient equilibrium method, or upon the increase in ultraviolet absorption observed when they were degraded with deoxyribonuclease. In addition the reactivity of ϕX DNA with formaldehyde before extraction from the virus may be cited.

The presence of two centrifugal components in the ϕX DNA preparation is not understood. They appear when the molecule is caused to take an extended form, either by destruction of intramolecular hydrogen bonds by formaldehyde or by lowering of the ionic strength. At one time it was thought that these might represent complementary strands of a DNA which had been separated biologically before incorporation into separate virus particles. However, it has been observed that the proportions of the two components varied from 62/38 to 79/21 in different preparations. Despite these variations, the preparations had identical nucleotide composition. This observation would appear to rule out the hypothesis of complementary chains.

The nucleotide composition of this DNA fulfils neither the adenine, thymine and cytosine, guanine equalities of ordinary DNA, nor the guanine plus uracil (thymine) equals adenine plus cytosine relation proposed for RNA by Elson & Chargaff (1954). In this respect, as in molecular size, this DNA is similar to the ribonucleic acid of the small plant viruses. It is, however, a DNA and differs notably from the RNA of TMV, for instance, with respect to stability and to several physical properties.

DNA fractions with compositions deviating from complementarity have been reported on other occasions (Lucy & Butler, 1954; Bendich, Pahl & Beiser, 1956). It might be very worth while to examine such fractions for the possible presence of single-stranded DNA components, by comparison of their properties with any of the distinctive properties of ϕX DNA. The existence of a single-stranded DNA would seem to imply the existence of a distinct mode of DNA replication (Watson & Crick, 1953b; Meselson & Stahl, 1958). It would be surprising if this were limited to a special class of bacterial viruses.

It is a pleasure to acknowledge the capable technical assistance of Miss Sharon Palmer.

REFERENCES

Allen, R. J. L. 1940. Biochem. J. 34: 858.

Beaven, G. H., Holiday, E. R., and Johnson, E. A. 1955. Chap. 14 in The Nucleic acids, Vol. I. Ed. by E. Chargaff, and J. N. Davidson. New York, Academic Press.

Bendich, A., Pahl, H. B., and Beiser, S. M. 1956. Cold Spring Harbor Symp. Quant. Biol. 21: 31.

Chargaff, E. 1955. Chap. 10 in The nucleic acids, Vol. I. Ed. by E. Chargaff, and J. N. Davidson. New York, Academic Press.

Chargaff, E., and Zamenhof, S. 1948. J. Biol. Chem. 173: 327.

Charlesby, A. 1954. Proc. Roy. Soc. A. 224: 120.

Dische, Z. 1955. Chap. 9 in The nucleic acids, Vol. I. Ed. by E. Chargaff, and J. N. Davidson. New York, Academic Press.

Doty, P., McGill, B. B., and Rice, S. A. 1958. Proc. Nat. Acad. Sci. 44: 432.

Doty, P., and Steiner, R. F. 1950. J. Chem. Phys. 18: 1211.

Ehrlich, P., and Doty, P. 1958. J. Am. Chem. Soc. 80: 4251.

Elson, D., and Chargaff, E. 1954. Nature. 173: 1037.

Fraenkel-Conrat, H. 1954. Biochim. Biophys. Acta. 15: 307.

Gierer, A., and Schramm, G. 1956. Zeitschr. Naturforschg. 11b: 138.

Hershey, A. D., Dixon, J., and Chase, M. 1953. J. Gen. Physiol. 36: 777.

Hoard, D. E. 1957. Ph.D. Thesis. University of California, Berkeley.

Kirby, K. S. 1957. Biochem. J.: 495.

Koerner, J. F., and Sinsheimer, R. L. 1957. J. Biol. Chem.: 1049.

Kunitz, M. 1950. J. Gen. Physiol. 33: 349.

Lawley, P. D. 1956. Biochim. Biophys. Acta. 21: 481.

Lucy, J. A., and Butler, J. V. 1954. Nature. 174: 32.

Marshak, A., and Vogel, H. J. 1951. J. Biol. Chem. 189: 597.

Meselson, M., and Stahl, F. W. 1958. Proc. Nat. Acad. Sci. 44: 671.

Meselson, M., Stahl, F. W., and Vinograd, J. 1957. Proc. Nat. Acad. Sci. 43: 581.

Northrup, T. G., Nutter, R. L., and Sinsheimer, R. L. 1953. J. Am. Chem. Soc. 75: 5134.

Nutter, R. L., and Sinsheimer, R. L. 1959. Virology. In press.

Porter, R. R. 1955. Pages 98-112 in Methods in enzymology, Vol. I. Ed. by S. P. Colowick, and N. O. Kaplan. New York, Academic Press.

Reichmann, M. E., Rice, S. A., Thomas, C. A., and Doty, P. 1954. J. Am. Chem. Soc. 76: 3047.

Rice, S. A., and Doty, P. 1957. J. Am. Chem. Soc. 79: 3937.

Schumaker, V. N., Richards, E. G., and Schachman, H. K. 1956. J. Am. Chem. Soc. 78: 4230.

Shack, J. 1958. J. Biol. Chem. 233: 677.

Shugar, D., and Fox, J. J. 1952. Biochim. Biophys. Acta. 9: 199.

Sinsheimer, R. L. 1954. J. Biol. Chem. 208: 445.

Sinsheimer, R. L. 1959. J. Mol. Biol. 1: 37.

Sinsheimer, R. L., and Koerner, J. F. 1951. Science. 114: 42.

Staehelin, M. 1958. Biochim. Biophys. Acta. 29: 410.

Stevens, V. L., and Duggan, E. L. 1957. J. Am. Chem. Soc. 79: 5703.

Tessman, I. 1958. Personal communication.

Thomas, C. A., Jr. 1956. J. Am. Chem. Soc. 78: 1861.

Thomas, C. A., Jr., and Doty, P. 1956. J. Am. Chem. Soc. 78: 1854.

Thomas, R. 1954. Biochim. Biophys. Acta. 14: 231.

Tobolosky, A. 1957. J. Polym. Sci. 26: 247.

Tompa, H. 1956. Polymer solutions. London, Butterworths Scientific Publications.

Watson, J. D., and Crick, F. H. C. 1953a. Nature. 171: 737.

Watson, J. D., and Crick, F. H. C. 1953b. Nature. 171: 964.

Wyatt, G. R. 1951. Biochem. J. 48: 584.

Wyatt, G. R. 1952. J. Gen. Physiol. 36: 201.

1959

A Negative Staining Method for High Resolution Electron Microscopy of Viruses[1]

by S. Brenner and R. W. Horne

Medical Research Council Unit for Molecular Biology and
Electron Microscopy Group, Cavendish Laboratory,
Cambridge (Great Britain)

*Knowledge of the architecture of viruses, particularly at the
molecular level, was advanced considerably with the development of a staining technique for contrast enhancement of virus
particles viewed under the electron microscope. The technique
termed "negative staining" involves the use of phosphotungstate which enters the contours of the specimen thereby allowing high resolution of the internal structure. Whereas previous
techniques obscured the internal components of viruses, negative staining has revealed the orderly substructure of some
viruses with their surface molecules arranged on triangular
faces. The technique has become a powerful tool for understanding and correlating the assembly of molecular functional
units in relation to virus structure.*

SUMMARY

A simple technique has been de-
veloped for the study of the external form and structure of virus particles.
High contrast with good preservation is obtained by mixing virus preparations with 1% phosphotungstic acid adjusted to pH 7.5 and spraying

[1] Reprinted by permission of the author and publisher from Biochemica at Bio-
physica Acta. **34**: 103-110 (1959).

directly onto electron microscope supporting films made from evaporated carbon. The application of the technique to tobacco mosaic virus and turnip yellow mosaic virus is described. Structural details suggested by X-ray diffraction methods have been resolved.

INTRODUCTION

Electron microscopical observation of virus particles offers the possibility of giving direct information about their external form and structure. Instruments with extremely high resolving power are available but there are major limitations in the techniques of specimen preparation.[2] The introduction of the critical-point method [3] and freeze-drying[4] improved the preservation of three-dimensional morphology but the problem of attaining sufficient contrast, without obscuring structural detail, has not been completely solved. Metal shadowing gives information about the size and shape of viruses but it does not reveal internal structure and often obscures surface regularities. It also enhances the roughness of the substrate film which may make detailed observation of small viruses difficult. The study of virus particles in ultra-thin sections of pellets or infected cells raises problems of fixation artefacts and there is often ambiguity in interpreting the contrast produced by the stains used.

In this paper, we wish to describe a technique which extends the range of electron microscopical study of virus structure. It consists very simply in "embedding" the virus particles in an electron dense material, in this case, potassium phosphotungstate, which introduces contrast by negative staining. The potentialities of this technique have been previously recognised by Hall [5] and by Huxley.[6] When bushy stunt virus particles were treated with phosphotungstic acid and the stain incompletely removed by washing, Hall found that better definition of the particles was often obtained by outlining them by the stain. Huxley showed that it was possible to reveal the central hole in tobacco mosaic virus by what amounted to the same procedure. We have been able to define exact conditions for the routine use of this technique. Under these conditions, the phosphotungstate has never been observed to stain directly either the protein or the nucleic acid of virus particles which remain relatively electron transparent. If there are any cavities within the virus which are accessible to the phosphotungstate, these will be revealed and the technique is thus capable of disclosing internal structure. We have used it most successfully in a recent study of bacteriophage struc-

[2] Williams, R. C. Advances virus research. 2: 184 (1954).

[3] Anderson, T. F. Trans. N.Y. Acad. Sci. II (13): 130 (1951).

[4] Williams, R. C. Exp. Cell. Research. 4: 188 (1953).

[5] Hall, C. E. J. Biophys. Biochem. Cytol. I: 1 (1955).

[6] Huxley, H. E. First European Conference on Electron Microscopy, Stockholm: 260 (1956).

ture where it could be shown that in addition to the high contrast available there was excellent preservation of external form.[7] The application
of the technique to tobacco mosaic virus and turnip yellow mosaic virus
will be described in this paper. These viruses were chosen as representative of a rod-shaped and small spherical virus respectively and also because their structure has been intensively studied by electron microscopy,
X-ray diffraction and other physico-chemical methods.

MATERIALS AND METHODS

Before describing the technique for negative staining, it is of importance
to discuss the methods used for preparing the substrates necessary for
specimen supports. Nitrocellulose and formvar films were found unsuitable due to thermal drift in the electron microscope. It was further noted
that this type of substrate frequently ruptured immediately after spraying
these particular virus preparations.

Evaporated carbon, stripped from mica surfaces was found to be sufficiently stable and rigid to support the droplet patterns.[8,9] Freshly cleaved
mica, cut to the size of microscope slides, was placed in an experimental
evaporator using well trapped mercury pumps.[10] Carbon was then evaporated onto the cleaved mica surface from a distance of approximately
20 cm. The estimated thickness of the films appeared to be of the order
of 150-200 Å. By slowly immersing the coated mica into water, a sheet of
carbon can be floated onto the surface. Electron microscope grids are
placed below the carbon film and raised slowly, resulting in the entire
grid area being covered with the carbon substrate.

Carbon substrates prepared in evaporator plants, using oil pumps,
frequently caused the spray droplet patterns to form dense spherical
areas with little evidence of the spreading effect produced on carbon films
from Hg units. The possibility of "backstreaming" oil vapour onto the
carbon surface may result in different surface conditions being unsuitable
for spraying techniques.

PHOSPHOTUNGSTIC ACID PREPARATIONS

A 2% solution of phosphotungstic acid was made up and adjusted to
pH 7.4 using normal KOH. To 1.0 ml of virus suspension in water or
ammonium acetate is added 1.0 ml of PTA, and the solution poured into
a commercial atomiser spray. The type used in these experiments was a
Vaponefrin glass unit with a normal hand bulb. The solutions are then
sprayed directly onto the carbon-coated grids. It was found necessary to

[7] Brenner, S., Streisinger, G., Horne, R. W., Champe, S. P., Barnett, L., and Benzer,
S. J. Mol. Biol. In press (1959).

[8] Bradley, D. E. Brit. J. Appl. Phys. 5: 65 (1954).

[9] Hall, C. E., and Litt, M. J. Biophys. Biochem. Cytol. 4: 1 (1958).

[10] Cosslett, V. E., and Horne, R. W. Vacuum. 5: 109 (1955).

adjust the concentration of each virus preparation. Droplet patterns containing low concentrations of virus tend to remain as dense opaque spheres, whereas ideal concentrations produced relatively large thin areas with particles clearly visible.

Specimens were examined in the Siemens Elmiskop electron microscope and photographed at instrumental magnifications of 40,000 to 80,000 ×. All the electron micrographs were taken using the double condenser lens system producing an illuminating beam of approximately 10-20 μ in diameter. Single condenser lens illumination or broad beam conditions frequently resulted in heating the droplet pattern causing serious distortion and decomposition effects in the PTA. Microdiffraction patterns taken from droplet patterns containing PTA suggested that the dense areas were amorphous.

From measurements made during investigations of the components of bacteriophage, structures approaching 15 Å or less could be resolved.[6] The limitations in terms of resolving power are difficult to estimate as much of the structure below 15 Å is confused by phase-contrast effects and contamination.

RESULTS AND DISCUSSION

Tobacco Mosaic Virus

Fig. 1 is a low power micrograph of TMV prepared by the phosphotungstate method. The rod-shaped viruses are clearly outlined by the electron dense background and, even at this magnification, the axial hole running down the centre of the rod can be readily seen. A high power micrograph is shown in Fig. 2. The rods are generally 150 Å in diameter and the mean diameter of the axial hole is 35-40 Å. The size of this hole agrees well with that found by Franklin and Holmes[11] using X-ray diffraction. Although the inter-particle distance in dry orientated TMV is found to be 152 Å by X-ray diffraction it has been shown that the diameter of the particle is greater than this and could be as much as 180 Å. The radial density distribution shows a strong maximum at about 78 Å and Franklin and Klug[12] reached the conclusion that while the *mean* diameter of the particle is 154 Å, the particle is deeply furrowed by a helical groove which follows the helical arrangement of the protein subunits. In dry orientated preparations the particles interlock to give the interparticle distance of 152 Å.

We have been unable to reveal the helix with the phosphotungstate method. It would appear that the protein surrounding the helical grooves is occluded by the phosphotungstate, which explains why the observed particle diameter is only 150 Å. Further evidence for this is provided by

[11] Franklin, R., and Holmes, K. C. Acta Cryst. **11:** 213 (1958).
[12] Franklin, R., and Klug, A. Biochim. Biophys. Acta. **19:** 403 (1956).

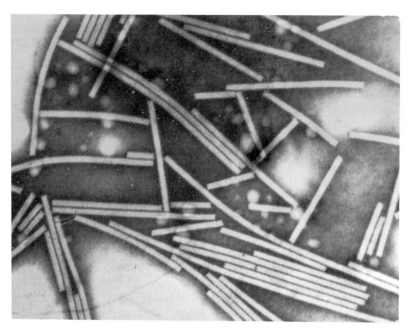

Fig. 1. Low magnification of droplet pattern area showing tobacco mosaic virus rods "embedded" in phosphotungstic acid. No staining of the protein is evident. × 59,000.

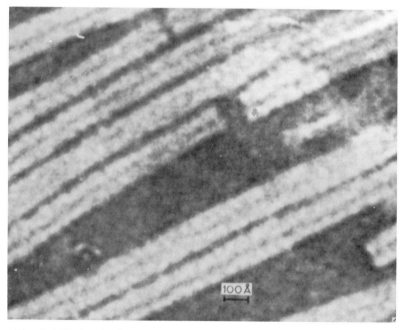

Fig. 2. TMV rods showing penetration of PTA along central region of virus rods. × 645,000.

the finding that parallel particles are never seen to interlock and the closest distance measured between centres of adjacent particles is 170-180 Å. In this case therefore the interparticle distance is a reflection of the *maximum* diameter of the particles, while the observed diameter reveals that part of the protein which is impermeable to the phosphotungstate.

A comparison of the radial density distribution of the intact protein and of repolymerized protein lacking RNA, showed a density maximum at radius 40 Å in the virus to be replaced by a density minimum in the nucleic acid-free protein.[11] This suggested that the RNA followed a helical path through the length of the particle at a radius of 40 Å (see also Hart[13]). We have attempted to display the cavity occupied by the RNA in the following way. Nucleic acid-free protein was prepared from TMV using the acetic acid procedure of Fraenkel-Conrat.[14] At pH 7 such solutions were clear and when observed in the electron microscope showed no visible structures. After dialysis against 1% ammonium acetate adjusted to pH 5 with acetic acid the solution became opalescent, and a micrograph of a PTA preparation is shown in Fig. 3. Rods of varying length can be recognised but their structure appears to be more disorganised than the intact particles. All rods show the central hole of 40 Å diameter again confirming the X-ray diffraction results. There is, however, no indication of any increased density at a radius of 40 Å. In addition to particles lying on their sides, the micrograph also shows particles lying on their ends. These discs show a central hole which is much wider than 40 Å. Measurements show the average diameter to be 70-80 Å. It is possible that, in this case, the increase in diameter of the hole is due to PTA filling up the helical tunnel occupied by RNA and that we are unable to resolve the 20 Å of protein between the central hole and the helical tunnel. In particles in this orientation the density of the PTA would be summed over a number of turns of the helix and hence sufficient contrast might be available which would not be the case in particles lying on their sides.

TURNIP YELLOW MOSAIC VIRUS

When a suspension of crystals of this virus in half saturated ammonium sulphate is rapidly diluted fifty times with 1% ammonium acetate and prepared by the phosphotungstate method, regularly packed virus particles can be observed in the electron microscope (Fig. 4). This arrangement is due to fragments of crystals and is not produced by rafting of individual particles as can be readily shown by preparing dialysed solutions of the virus at the same concentration. In these crystal layers the particles are hexagonally close packed and each particle appears to be polygonal in shape. The diameter of the virus is 210 Å, and the inter-

[13] Hart, R. Biochim. Biophys. Acta. 28: 457 (1958).
[14] Fraenkel-Conrat, H. Virology. 4: 1 (1957).

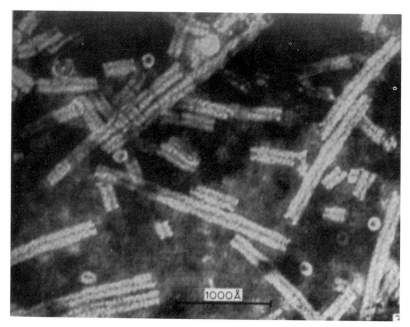

Fig. 3. Reaggregated nucleic acid-free protein. A number of particles can be seen as hollow discs with central hole diameters of 70-80 Å. $\times$ 252,000.

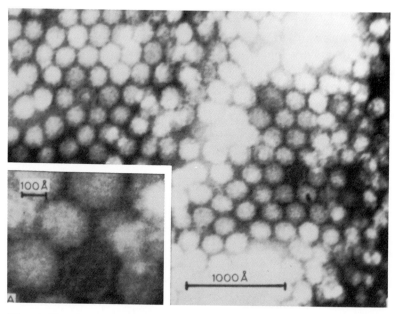

Fig. 4. Turnip yellow mosaic virus crystal layer showing internal structure with particles in typical hexagonal close packing. $\times$ 256,000.

Fig. 4a. Enlargement showing empty protein shell packed in the structure. $\times$ 645,000.

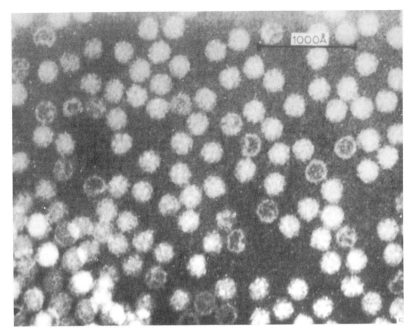

Fig. 5. Isolated TYMV particles from preparations dialysed against distilled water. The structural detail appears as a granularity. Empty particles may also be seen. × 245,000.

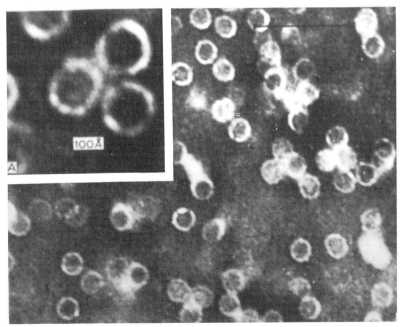

Fig. 6. Empty protein shells in top component of TYMV showing little evidence of granularity. × 254,000.

Fig. 6a. Enlargement of a group of these "ghosts." × 645,000.

particle distances 240 Å, which is to be compared with the diameter of 280 Å estimated by X-ray diffraction of crystals.[15] It should be mentioned that, in such preparations, the ammonium sulphate does not interfere with observation since it crystallizes on drying and areas free of crystals are frequently found.

Isolated particles may be seen in preparations made from crystals dialysed against distilled water as shown in Figs. 4 and 5. The polygonality of the particles is not as marked as in the intact crystals, but many particles show structural detail. This appears as a granularity and is reminiscent of the structure found by Steere[16] in frozen-replica preparations. In both the crystal and isolated particle preparations "ghost" particles can often be seen (Figs. 4 and 5). These are clearly particles without nucleic acid and are therefore the empty protein shells characteristic of the so-called top component.[17] Figs. 6 and 6a are electron micrographs of a purified preparation of top component, which shows most of the particles to be empty. The thickness of the protein membrane in such particles is 20-25 Å; this should be compared with the value of 35 Å estimated by X-ray diffraction. Such empty particles never show the granular appearance of the complete virus and it is possible that this reflects some organisation of the RNA in the particle.

ACKNOWLEDGEMENTS

We wish to thank Dr. Helga Doty for supplying suspensions of purified TMV, and Dr. Roy Markham, F.R.S. for the TYMV and top component preparations.

The Siemens microscope was purchased through a generous grant from the Nuffield Foundation. One of us (R. W. Horne) wishes to thank the Agricultural Research Council for financial aid.

[15] Klug, A., Finch, J. T., and Franklin, R. Biochim. Biophys. Acta. 25: 242 (1957).
[16] Steere, R. L. J. Biophys. Biochem. Cytol. 3: 45 (1957).
[17] Markham, R. Discussions Faraday Soc. 11: 221 (1951).

1961

The Dependence
of Cell-Free Protein Synthesis
in E. Coli Upon Naturally Occurring
or Synthetic Polyribonucleotides[1]

by Marshall W. Nirenberg and
J. Heinrich Matthaei

National Institutes of Health, Bethesda, Maryland

Virus research has made prominent contributions to recent advances in molecular biology. Because viruses have as their genetic material either DNA or RNA and are amenable to quantitative titration, they have become invaluable aids for following and characterizing the pathways of molecular reactions. Currently, viruses have an integral part in studies for understanding the mechanisms involved in protein formation based on the genetic information transmitted by DNA in an orderly sequence to intermediate forms of RNA (messenger, ribosomal, soluble or transfer). They are, in addition, active participants in studies to determine the behavior of viral RNA acting both as its own genetic determinant and as a messenger to guide the assembly of amino acids into proteins. Progress on these aspects of molecular biology is proceeding at such a phenomenal rate that often it is difficult to establish precedence for important discoveries.

Recently, a vital link in the comprehension of protein synthesis was recognized based primarily on work with bacteriophages. These studies confirmed the formation of an unstable form of RNA made on a DNA template which acts as a messenger for transmitting the genetic code to nonspecific ribosomes

[1] Supported by a NATO Postdoctoral Research Fellowship. Reprinted by permission of the author and publisher from The Proceedings of the National Academy of Sciences 47: 1588-1602 (1961).

(ribonucleoprotein particles) where the protein molecules are synthesized.[2]

The work of Nirenberg and Matthaei, presented here, established conclusively the messenger concept by their demonstration of a 20-fold increase in protein formation after the addition of macromolecular RNA from either E. coli *or tobacco mosaic virus (TMV) in a cell-free system of* E. coli *extracts. Another significant aspect of their study resides in the finding that polyuridylic acid (single-stranded like TMV-RNA) directs the synthesis of polyphenylalanine. This suggested that polyuridylic acid acts as a messenger-RNA molecule which itself is single-stranded. A new approach, therefore, was available for investigating the biological coding problem.*

Nirenberg and Matthaei's disclosure that TMV-RNA stimulates the incorporation of amino acids into protein molecules by cell-free extracts of E. coli, *suggested that the plant viral RNA acts as its own template or messenger. This finding, demonstrated under* in vitro *conditions, proffered a system highly suited for probing the role of RNA in virus synthesis. From subsequent studies in other laboratories with RNA- animal, bacterial, and plant viruses, evidence that viral RNA synthesis does not proceed through an intermediate form of DNA substantiated the thesis that the messenger function of RNA resides in viral RNA.[3]*

Directly related to these significant findings are the demonstrations with RNA derived from plant, bacterial, and animal viruses on the formation of specific viral capsid protein in vitro.[4] *These provocative results presage important contributions of virus research in elucidating biological mechanisms and functions at the molecular level.*

A stable cell-free system has been obtained from E. *coli* which incorporates C[14]-valine into protein at a rapid rate. It was shown that this apparent protein synthesis was energy-dependent, was stimulated by a mixture of L-amino acids, and was

[2] Brenner *et al.* Nature. **190**: 576 (1961); Gros *et al.* Nature. **190**: 581 (1961); Hall and Spiegelman. Proc. Natl. Acad. Sci. **47**: 137 (1961); Tissières and Hopkins. Proc. Natl. Acad. Sci. **47**: 2015 (1961).

[3] Simon, Virology. **13**: 105 (1961); Cooper and Zinder. Virology. **18**: 405 (1962); Ofengand and Haselkorn. Biochem. Biophys. Res. Communs. **6**: 469 (1962).

[4] Tsugita *et al.* Proc. Nat. Acad. Sci. **48**: 846 (1962); Nathans *et al.* Proc. Nat. Acad. Sci. **48**: 1424 (1962); Warner *et al.* Virology. **19**: 393 (1963).

markedly inhibited by RNAase, puromycin, and chloramphenicol (1). The present communication describes a novel characteristic of the system, that is, a requirement for template RNA, needed for amino acid incorporation even in the presence of soluble RNA and ribosomes. It will also be shown that the amino acid incorporation stimulated by the addition of template RNA has many properties expected of *de novo* protein synthesis. Naturally occurring RNA as well as a synthetic polynucleotide were active in this system. The synthetic polynucleotide appears to contain the code for the synthesis of a "protein" containing only one amino acid. Part of these data have been presented in preliminary reports (2,3).

METHODS AND MATERIALS

The preparation of enzyme extracts was modified in certain respects from the procedure previously presented (1). *E. coli* W3100 cells harvested in early log phase where washed and were disrupted by grinding with alumina (twice the weight of washed cells) at 5° for 5 min as described previously (1). The alumina was extracted with an equivalent weight of buffer containing 0.01 M Tris(hydroxymethyl)aminomethane, pH 7.8, 0.01 M magnesium acetate, 0.06 M KCl, 0.006 M mercaptoethanol (standard buffer). Alumina and intact cells were removed by centrifugation at 20,000 × g for 20 min. The supernatant fluid was decanted, and 3 μg DNAase per ml (Worthington Biochemical Co.) were added, rapidly reducing the viscosity of the suspension, which was then centrifuged again at 20,000 × g for 20 min. The supernatant fluid was aspirated and was centrifuged at 30,000 × g for 30 min to clear the extract of remaining debris. The liquid layer was aspirated (S-30) and was centrifuged at 105,000 × g for 2 hr to sediment the ribosomes. The supernatant solution (S-100) was aspirated, and the solution just above the pellet was decanted and discarded. The ribosomes were washed by resuspension in the standard buffer and centrifugation again at 105,000 × g for 2 hr. Supernatant fluid was discarded and the ribosomes were suspended in standard buffer (W-Rib). Fractions S-30, S-100, and W-Rib were dialyzed against 60 volumes of standard buffer overnight at 5° and were divided into aliquots for storage at −15°.

In some cases, fresh S-30 was incubated for 40 min at 35°. The reaction mixture components in μmoles per ml were as follows: 80 Tris, pH 7.8; 8 magnesium acetate; 50 KCl; 9 mercaptoethanol; 0.075 each of 20 amino acids (1); 2.5 ATP, K salt; 2.5 PEP, K salt; 15 μg PEP kinase (Boehringen & Sons, Mannheim, Germany). After incubation, the reaction mixture was dialyzed at 5° for 10 hr against 60 volumes of standard buffer, changed once during the course of dialysis. The incubated S-30 fraction was stored in aliquots at −15° until needed (Incubated-S-30).

RNA fractions were prepared by phenol extraction using freshly distilled phenol. Ribosomal RNA was prepared from fresh, washed ribosomes obtained by the method given above. In later RNA preparations, a 0.2% solution of sodium dodecyl sulfate recrystallized by the method of Crestfield *et al.* (4) was added to the suspension of ribosomes before phenol treatment. The suspension was shaken at room temperature for 5 min. Higher yields of RNA appeared to be obtained when the sodium dodecyl sulfate step was used; however, good RNA preparations were also obtained when this step was omitted. An equal volume of H_2O-saturated phenol was added to ribosomes suspended in standard buffer after treatment with sodium dodecyl sulfate, and the suspension was shaken vigorously at room temperature for 8-10 min. The aqueous phase was aspirated from the phenol phase after centrifugation at 1,450 × g for 15 min. The aqueous layer was extracted two more times in the same manner, using $\frac{1}{2}$ volume of H_2O-saturated phenol in each case. The final aqueous phase was chilled to 5° and NaCl was added to a final concentration of 0.1%. Two volumes of ethyl alcohol at −20° were added with stirring to precipitate the RNA. The suspension was centrifuged at 20,000 × g for 15 min and the supernatant solution was decanted and discarded. The RNA pellet was dissolved in minimal concentrations of standard buffer (minus mercaptoethanol) by gentle homogenization in a glass Potter-Elvehjem homogenizer (usually the volume of buffer used was about $\frac{1}{3}$ the volume of the original ribosome suspension). The opalescent solution of RNA was dialyzed for 18 hr against 100 volumes of standard buffer (minus mercaptoethanol) at 5°. The dialyzing buffer was changed once. After dialysis, the RNA solution was centrifuged at 20,000 × g for 15 min and the pellet was discarded. The RNA solution, which contained less than 1% protein, was divided into aliquots and was stored at −15° until needed.

Soluble RNA was prepared from 105,000 × g supernatant solution by the phenol extraction method described above. Soluble RNA was also stored at −15°. Alkali-degraded RNA was prepared by incubating RNA samples with 0.3 M KOH at 35° for 18 hr. The solutions then were neutralized and dialyzed against standard buffer (minus mercaptoethanol). RNAase-digested samples of RNA were prepared by incubating RNA with 2 μg per ml of crystalline RNAase (Worthington Biochemical Company) at 35° for 60 min. RNAase was destroyed by four phenol extractions performed as given above. After the last phenol extraction, the samples were dialyzed against standard buffer minus mercaptoethanol. RNA samples were treated with trypsin by incubation with 20 μg per ml of twice recrystallized trypsin (Worthington Biochemical Company) at 35° for 60 min. The solution was treated four times with phenol and was dialyzed in the same manner.

The radioactive amino acids used, their source, and their respective specific activities are as follows: U-C14-glycine, U-C14-L-isoleucine, U-C14-L-tyrosine, U-C14-L-leucine, U-C14-L-proline, L-histidine-2(ring)-C14, U-C14-L-phenylalanine, U-C14-L-threonine, L-methionine (methyl-C14),

U-C^{14}-L-arginine, and U-C^{14}-L-lysine obtained from Nuclear-Chicago Corporation, 5.8, 6.2, 5.95, 6.25, 10.5, 3.96, 10.3, 3.9, 6.5, 5.8, 8.3 mC/mM, respectively; C^{14}-L-aspartic acid, C^{14}-Lglutamic acid, C^{14}-L-alanine, obtained from Volk, 1.04, 1.18, 0.75 mC/mM, respectively; D-L-tryptophan-3 C^{14}, obtained from New England Nuclear Corporation, 2.5 mC/mM; S^{35}-L-cystine obtained from the Abbott Laboratories, 2.4 mC/mM; U-C^{14}-L-serine obtained from the Nuclear-Chicago Corporation, 0.2 mC/mM. Other materials and methods used in this study are described in the accompanying paper. All assays were performed in duplicate.

RESULTS—STIMULATION BY RIBOSOMAL RNA

In the previous paper (1), it was shown that DNAase markedly decreased amino acid incorporation in this system after 20 min. For the purpose of this investigation, 30,000 × g supernatant fluid fractions previously incubated with DNAase and other components of the reaction mixtures (Incubated-S-30 fractions) were used for many of the experiments.

Figure 1 shows that incorporation of C^{14}-L-valine into protein by Incubated-S-30 fraction was stimulated by the addition of purified E. coli

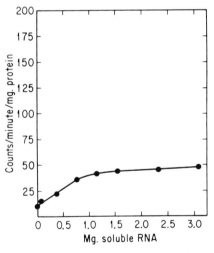

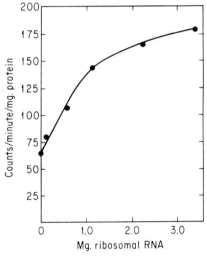

Fig. 1. Stimulation of amino acid incorporation into protein by E. coli soluble RNA. Composition of reaction mixtures is specified in Table 1. Samples were incubated at 35° for 20 min. Reaction mixtures contained 4.4 mg. of Incubated-S-30 protein.

Fig. 2. Stimulation of amino acid incorporation into protein by E. coli ribosomal RNA in the presence of soluble RNA. Composition of reaction mixtures is specified in Table 1. Samples were incubated at 35° for 20 min. Reaction mixtures contained 4.4 mg of Incubated-S-30 protein and 1.0 mg E. coli soluble RNA.

soluble RNA. Maximal stimulation was obtained with approximately 1 mg soluble RNA. In some experiments, increasing the concentration 5-fold did not further stimulate the system. Soluble RNA was added to all reaction mixtures unless otherwise specified.

Figure 2 demonstrates that *E. coli* ribosomal RNA preparations markedly stimulated incorporation of C^{14}-valine into protein even though maximally stimulating concentrations of soluble RNA were present in the reaction mixtures. A linear relationship between the concentration of ribosomal RNA and C^{14}-valine incorporation into protein was obtained when low concentrations of ribosomal RNA were used. Increasing the soluble RNA concentration up to 3-fold did not replace the effect observed when ribosomal RNA was added.

The effect of ribosomal RNA in stimulating incorporation of C^{14}-valine into protein is presented in more detail in Figure 3. In the absence of ribosomal RNA, incorporation of C^{14}-valine into protein by the incubated-S-30 fraction was quite low when compared with S-30 (not incubated before storage at $-15°$) and stopped almost completely after

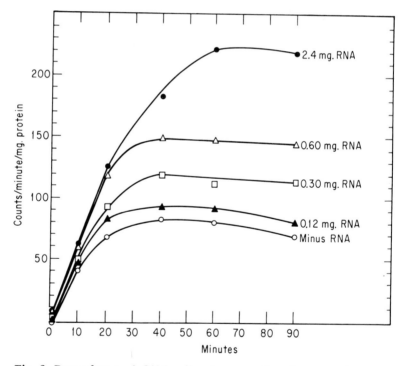

Fig. 3. Dependence of C^{14}-L-valine incorporation into protein upon ribosomal RNA. The composition of the reaction mixtures and the incubation conditions are presented in Table 1. Reaction mixtures contained 0.98 mg of *E. Coli* soluble RNA and 4.4 mg of Incubated-S-30-protein.

20. Siminovitch, L., and Graham, A. F. 1956. Canad. J. Microbiol. **2:** 585.

21. Davern, C. I., and Meselson, M. 1960. J. Mol. Biol. **2:** 153.

22. Siekevitz, P. 1952. J. Biol. Chem. **195:** 549.

23. Britten, R. J., and Roberts, R. B. 1960. Science. **131:** 32.

24. Martin, R., and Ames, B. 1961. J. Biol. Chem. **236:** 1372.

25. Bamford, C. H., Elliott, A., and Hanby, W. E. 1956. Page 322 in Synthetic polypeptides. New York, Academic Press.

1962

The Quest for
Human Cancer Viruses[1]

A New Approach to an Old Problem Reveals Cancer
Induction in Hamsters by Human Adenovirus

by John J. Trentin, Yoshiro Yabe, Grant Taylor

The final paper in the collection is concerned with viral tumors. Interest in this subject has been continual since the early history of virology. In the past decade, a substantial volume of information has been accumulated on the intimate properties of oncogenic (tumor inducing) viruses, and many new tumors of animals have been discovered in which viruses have been established as the causal agents.[2,3,4,5] The recent progress in this area of virology may be attributed to the use of newborn animals for tumor cultivation, improvements in tissue culture methodology for the propagation of the viral entities, and the extensive use of the electron microscope to visualize the viruses and to study the detailed structure of normal and malignant cells.

Although much has been learned, the problem that confronted early workers still exists today—to prove conclusively

---

[1] Reprinted by permission of the author and publisher from Science. 137: 835-841 (1962).

The authors are affiliated with the division of experimental biology of Baylor University College of Medicine and with the section of experimental pediatrics. University of Texas M. D. Anderson Hospital and Tumor Institute, Houston. Dr. Yabe is on leave from Okayama University Medical School, Japan.

[2] Gross. Cancer. 3: 1073 (1950).

[3] Stewart. Anat. Record. 117: 532 (1953).

[4] Friend. Ann. N.Y. Acad. Sci. 68: 522 (1957).

[5] Moloney. Natl. Cancer Inst. Monograph No. 4. 7: (1960).

tissue transplants from other
hamsters are actually more
virus of the mouse than are
advantages of inbred mice in
excluded as test animals in
(and nontumor) viruses whic
past experience with interfer
human cancer viruses by othe

One of the first groups of
was the adeno group, because
viruses, including polyoma v
viruses in a large percentage
nucleus, and their nucleic
particles occur in crystalline
Bunting in benign human ski
in tissue culture cells infected

MATERI

An isolated building was d
three separately air-conditioned
a sterile room, and a wash roo
was used exclusively for a han
their mothers were transferred
needed for inoculation. The o
for a concomitant study involv
human cancer tissue or extract
lated with human cancer tissue
the two experimental rooms to
was established originally with
free colony of the National In
cedures were instituted from t
of animals and to human visi
virus laboratory is referred to h

FL amnion cells and HeLa
(11) were used. The FL amnion
10 percent calf serum. The lung
medium consisting of either m
medium with 10 percent calf s
Eagle's minimum essential med

Human adenovirus types 2, 3
from the American Type Cult
fluids thus obtained were directl
the maintenance medium descri
the same time titrated in tissue

that at least one type of human cancer has a viral origin. A number of reports have been published on the transmission of various human oncogenic agents to laboratory animals, but in view of the many pitfalls and difficulties associated with this problem, these findings are difficult to interpret and demand critical evaluation. The demonstration by Trentin and his associates that a human virus, adenovirus type 12, possesses oncogenic properties on intrapulmonary injection of newborn hamsters is a significant and exciting discovery. Tumor induction by adenovirus has been confirmed and demonstrated also with adenovirus type 18.[6] That the property of oncogenesis exhibited by human adenoviruses is not unique and may be common to other groups of human viruses, may be revealed by further investigations utilizing this promising approach. These findings add another truss which may eventually complete the span between conjective and experimental proof on the viral origin of some human cancers.

Many forms of cancer in many species of animals are now known to be caused by viruses (1). While all attempts to isolate causative viruses from human cancer have thus far been unsuccessful, it would appear to be biologically unusual if at least some forms of human cancer were not also caused by viruses. By far the most fruitful technique for the demonstration of tumor viruses in animals has been the inoculation of extracts of tumors, or of nontumorous tissues from tumor-bearing animals, into newborn animals of the same species. This technique is obviously denied to the searcher for human cancer viruses. Attempts to induce cancer in the young of other species by inoculation of human tumor extracts have thus far been negative or inconclusive.

The technique perhaps most widely used at present is the attempted propagation of human cancer viruses in vitro by inoculation of tissue cultures with human cancer materials. Yet this tissue culture technique has not resulted in the discovery of a single animal tumor virus, and only secondarily has it been possible to grow easily some exceptional animal tumor viruses in tissue culture. Because of the severe limitations imposed on the virologist concerned with human cancer, we must continue to use the tissue culture screening approach. But the need for new approaches is obvious. One such new approach is described in this article.

It was demonstrated by Duran-Reynals (2) that known animal tumor viruses can, under certain conditions of host susceptibility, produce acute

[6] Huebner *et al.* Proc. Nat. Acad. Sci. **48**: 2051 (1962).

noncancerous diseas
manifestation of the
therefore appeared
their acute disease
resistance or in a ho
festation known as
human viruses of a
cancer viruses.

Another large gr
—the human "orpha
from humans but wh
search of disease." C
these viruses are at p
initiated a program
effect in newborn an
the test animal of ch
tumor induction by t
relatively poor defen

TABLE 1. *Tumor*

Virus type	Virus titer* (MTCID$_{100}$/ 0.1 ml)
2	10^2
3	10^2
7	10^2
7a	10^2
9	10^2
10	10^2
11	10^2
12	10^2‡ 10^2§
14	10^3

* All titers represent 1:1
Culture Collection.

† "Injected hamsters" si
viving longer than 3 weeks.
under observation at the tin

‡ First shipment of type
Type Culture Collection.

§ Second shipment of typ
ican Type Culture Collectio

TABLE 2. *Tumor induction by cell-free filtrate type 12 adenovirus tissue culture fluid injected intrapulmonarily (dose, 0.05 ml)*

Tissue culture passage*	Virus titer (MTCID$_{100}$/ 0.1 ml)	Tumorous hamsters/ injected hamsters†	Tumor deaths (days)	Dead without tumors		Alive without tumors	
				No.	Days	No.	Days
1st	10^2	7/8	33-91			1	376
3rd	10^3	26/27‡	35-157	1	156		
8th	10^3	6/6	29-45				
Control culture§	None	0/7		2	321, 327	5	374-376

* The second shipment of type 12 adenovirus from American Type Culture Collection was used for tissue culture passage.

† "Injected hamsters" signifies hamsters injected at birth and surviving over 3 weeks.

‡ Four hamsters of this group developed large tumors in the liver in addition to tumors in the thorax.

§ Noninoculated HeLa cell tissue culture fluid centrifuged at 1500 revolutions per minute for 10 minutes to remove cells.

preceding paragraph. Later, however, type 12 virus was propagated in HeLa cells in the tissue culture room of the hamster laboratory and used for further experiments.

Polyoma virus (13) was recultured in, and stored in, a building separate from the hamster-laboratory. No tissue culture work with polyoma virus was done during the period of the experiment under discussion.

The polyoma virus hemagglutination inhibition test was carried out according to the procedure of Rowe *et al.* (14) on sera collected by exsanguination.

At first Earle's balanced salt solution, medium 199, or Eagle's basal medium with 5 percent horse serum was used as the maintenance medium for the tenfold serial dilutions of each adenovirus tissue culture fluid. Each dilution (0.1 ml) was inoculated into two tubes containing a monolayer of either FL amnion or human embryonic lung cells newly replenished with 1 milliliter of maintenance medium. Inoculated tubes were incubated at 36°C for 5 days, and the final reading was made on the 5th day of incubation. Later, however, HeLa cells and Eagle's basal medium with 10 percent horse serum were consistently used for the titration of type 12 virus, and the procedure was modified as follows. Maintenance medium was used for tenfold serial dilutions of virus tissue culture fluid; to 0.1 milliliter of each dilution, 1 milliliter of freshly prepared 0.1 percent HeLa cell suspension in maintenance medium was added; the tubes were incubated at 36°C for 5 days, and the final reading was made on the 5th day. The highest dilution which produced clear cytopathic effect (CPE) in both tubes was taken as the minimum 100 *that at least one type of human cancer has a viral origin. A number of reports have been published on the transmission of various human oncogenic agents to laboratory animals, but in view of the many pitfalls and difficulties associated with this problem, these findings are difficult to interpret and demand critical evaluation. The demonstration by Trentin and his associates that a human virus, adenovirus type 12, possesses oncogenic properties on intrapulmonary injection of newborn hamsters is a significant and exciting discovery. Tumor induction by adenovirus has been confirmed and demonstrated also with adenovirus type 18.[6] That the property of oncogenesis exhibited by human adenoviruses is not unique and may be common to other groups of human viruses, may be revealed by further investigations utilizing this promising approach. These findings add another truss which may eventually complete the span between conjective and experimental proof on the viral origin of some human cancers.*

Many forms of cancer in many species of animals are now known to be caused by viruses (1). While all attempts to isolate causative viruses from human cancer have thus far been unsuccessful, it would appear to be biologically unusual if at least some forms of human cancer were not also caused by viruses. By far the most fruitful technique for the demonstration of tumor viruses in animals has been the inoculation of extracts of tumors, or of nontumorous tissues from tumor-bearing animals, into newborn animals of the same species. This technique is obviously denied to the searcher for human cancer viruses. Attempts to induce cancer in the young of other species by inoculation of human tumor extracts have thus far been negative or inconclusive.

The technique perhaps most widely used at present is the attempted propagation of human cancer viruses in vitro by inoculation of tissue cultures with human cancer materials. Yet this tissue culture technique has not resulted in the discovery of a single animal tumor virus, and only secondarily has it been possible to grow easily some exceptional animal tumor viruses in tissue culture. Because of the severe limitations imposed on the virologist concerned with human cancer, we must continue to use the tissue culture screening approach. But the need for new approaches is obvious. One such new approach is described in this article.

It was demonstrated by Duran-Reynals (2) that known animal tumor viruses can, under certain conditions of host susceptibility, produce acute

---

[6] Huebner *et al.* Proc. Nat. Acad. Sci. **48**: 2051 (1962).

noncancerous diseases. The production of tumors appeared to be a late manifestation of the slow growth of virus in a relatively resistant host. It therefore appeared possible that some human viruses already known for their acute disease manifestations might, under other conditions of host resistance or in a host surviving the acute disease, produce the late manifestation known as cancer. Some of the already known (or unknown) human viruses of acute diseases of childhood might therefore also be cancer viruses.

Another large group of already isolated viruses should also be suspect —the human "orphan" viruses. These are viruses that have been isolated from humans but whose disease manifestations are unknown—"viruses in search of disease." Cancer may well be the disease that some or many of these viruses are at present "orphan" to! With these concepts in mind, we initiated a program of testing known human viruses for cancer-inducing effect in newborn animals. The newborn Syrian hamster was selected as the test animal of choice because of its known relative susceptibility to tumor induction by tumor viruses of other species (3), and because of its relatively poor defense against the growth of normal-tissue and tumor-

TABLE 1. *Tumors resulting from injection of human adenoviruses into newborn hamsters*

Virus type	Virus titer* ($MTCID_{100}$/ 0.1 ml)	Dose (ml)	Route of injection	Tumorous hamsters/ injected hamsters[†]	Tumor deaths (days)
2	10^2	0.1	Intraperitoneal	0/6	
		0.01	Intracranial	0/2	
3	10^2	0.1	Intraperitoneal	0/2	
		0.01	Intracranial	0/3	
7	10^2	0.05	Intrapulmonary	0/6	
7a	10^2	0.05	Intrapulmonary	0/8	
9	10^2	0.05	Intrapulmonary	0/2	
10	10^2	0.05	Intrapulmonary	0/5	
11	10^2	0.05	Intrapulmonary	0/4	
12	10^2[‡]	0.05	Intrapulmonary	8/10	33-90
	10^2[§]	0.05	Intrapulmonary	1/1	82
14	10^3	0.05	Intrapulmonary	0/5	

* All titers represent 1:10 dilution of the culture fluids sent from the American Type Culture Collection.

† "Injected hamsters" signifies hamsters injected within 24 hours after birth and surviving longer than 3 weeks. Most nontumorous hamsters are 8 to 11 months old and still under observation at the time of writing.

‡ First shipment of type 12 adenovirus tissue culture fluid received from the American Type Culture Collection.

§ Second shipment of type 12 adenovirus tissue culture fluid, received from the American Type Culture Collection about 5 months after the first shipment.

tissue transplants from other species, including the human (4). Newborn hamsters are actually more susceptible to tumor induction by polyoma virus of the mouse than are newborn mice (5). In spite of the many great advantages of inbred mice in other areas of cancer research, mice were excluded as test animals in this study because of the numerous tumor (and nontumor) viruses which they are known to harbor, and because of past experience with interference by such viruses in attempts to isolate human cancer viruses by other methods (6).

One of the first groups of human viruses chosen for extensive testing was the adeno group, because of similarities to some known animal tumor viruses, including polyoma virus, and because of the latency of adeno-viruses in a large percentage of children. The adeno viruses grow in the nucleus, and their nucleic acid is deoxyribonucleic acid. The virus particles occur in crystalline arrays comparable to those reported by Bunting in benign human skin papillomas (7), and by Banfield et al. (8) in tissue culture cells infected with polyoma virus.

MATERIALS AND METHODS

An isolated building was designed and constructed for the study, with three separately air-conditioned hamster rooms, a tissue culture laboratory, a sterile room, and a wash room and sterilizing facility. One of the rooms was used exclusively for a hamster breeding colony. Newborn litters and their mothers were transferred to one of the other two hamster rooms as needed for inoculation. The other experimental hamster room was used for a concomitant study involving inoculation of newborn hamsters with human cancer tissue or extracts, or with fluids from tissue cultures inoculated with human cancer tissue. No animals were transferred back from the two experimental rooms to the breeding room. The breeding colony was established originally with Syrian hamsters from the polyoma-virus-free colony of the National Institutes of Health (9). Strict isolation procedures were instituted from the outset with respect to all other species of animals and to human visitors. This combined hamster colony and virus laboratory is referred to hereafter as the hamster laboratory.

FL amnion cells and HeLa cells (10) and lung cells of human embryos (11) were used. The FL amnion cells were cultured in medium 199 with 10 percent calf serum. The lung cells of human embryos were cultured in medium consisting of either medium 199 or Eagle's minimum essential medium with 10 percent calf serum. The HeLa cells were cultured in Eagle's minimum essential medium with 10 percent calf serum (12).

Human adenovirus types 2, 3, 7, 7a, 9, 10, 11, 12, and 14 were obtained from the American Type Culture Collection. The virus tissue culture fluids thus obtained were directly diluted to a concentration of 1:10 with the maintenance medium described later, injected into animals, and at the same time titrated in tissue culture tubes of the cells described in the

TABLE 2. *Tumor induction by cell-free filtrate type 12 adenovirus
tissue culture fluid injected intrapulmonarily (dose, 0.05 ml)*

Tissue culture passage*	Virus titer (MTCID$_{100}$/ 0.1 ml)	Tumorous hamsters/ injected hamsters†	Tumor deaths (days)	Dead without tumors		Alive without tumors	
				No.	Days	No.	Days
1st	10^2	7/8	33-91			1	376
3rd	10^3	26/27‡	35-157	1	156		
8th	10^3	6/6	29-45				
Control culture§	None	0/7		2	321, 327	5	374-376

* The second shipment of type 12 adenovirus from American Type Culture Collection was used for tissue culture passage.

† "Injected hamsters" signifies hamsters injected at birth and surviving over 3 weeks.

‡ Four hamsters of this group developed large tumors in the liver in addition to tumors in the thorax.

§ Noninoculated HeLa cell tissue culture fluid centrifuged at 1500 revolutions per minute for 10 minutes to remove cells.

preceding paragraph. Later, however, type 12 virus was propagated in HeLa cells in the tissue culture room of the hamster laboratory and used for further experiments.

Polyoma virus (13) was recultured in, and stored in, a building separate from the hamster-laboratory. No tissue culture work with polyoma virus was done during the period of the experiment under discussion.

The polyoma virus hemagglutination inhibition test was carried out according to the procedure of Rowe *et al.* (14) on sera collected by exsanguination.

At first Earle's balanced salt solution, medium 199, or Eagle's basal medium with 5 percent horse serum was used as the maintenance medium for the tenfold serial dilutions of each adenovirus tissue culture fluid. Each dilution (0.1 ml) was inoculated into two tubes containing a monolayer of either FL amnion or human embryonic lung cells newly replenished with 1 milliliter of maintenance medium. Inoculated tubes were incubated at 36°C for 5 days, and the final reading was made on the 5th day of incubation. Later, however, HeLa cells and Eagle's basal medium with 10 percent horse serum were consistently used for the titration of type 12 virus, and the procedure was modified as follows. Maintenance medium was used for tenfold serial dilutions of virus tissue culture fluid; to 0.1 milliliter of each dilution, 1 milliliter of freshly prepared 0.1 percent HeLa cell suspension in maintenance medium was added; the tubes were incubated at 36°C for 5 days, and the final reading was made on the 5th day. The highest dilution which produced clear cytopathic effect (CPE) in both tubes was taken as the minimum 100 percent tissue culture infectious dose ($MTCID_{100}$). No very significant difference was observed between the $MTCID_{100}$ obtained by the two procedures, but the latter procedure was simpler and the effect was a little sharper. The 50 percent tissue culture infectious dose ($TCID_{50}$) was determined in a similar manner, with four tubes used for each dilution.

HeLa cells were infected with type 12 adenovirus. Tissue culture fluid was harvested 2 days after complete cytopathic effect was observed. It was centrifuged at 1500 to 2000 revolutions per minute for 10 minutes and filtered through Selas 02 filter candles. To test the completeness of filtration, 0.5 milliliter of fresh *Serratia marcescens* broth culture was mixed in the tissue culture fluid before filtration. About 0.5 milliliter of each of the fluids, before and after filtration, was inoculated into broth and tested for the growth of *Serratia marcescens*.

Newborn hamsters less than 24 hours old were moved with their mothers from the breeder room to the experimental room and inoculated with viruses intraperitoneally, intracerebrally, or intrapulmonarily. For intrapulmonary inoculation the virus was injected through the chest wall with a 30-gauge needle. The young were usually observed every day for the first week and thereafter at least three times a week; they were weaned at 3 to 4 weeks of age.

Healthy-looking whitish portions of tumor were taken aseptically and minced with scissors, and about 27 cubic millimeters of tumor tissue was transplanted subcutaneously or intraperitoneally, by trocar, into otherwise untreated (unconditioned) hamsters of different ages.

Human serum (stored at temperature of $-70°C$) was inactivated by heating at $56°C$ for 30 minutes and diluted in twofold series to a concentration of 1:64 with Eagle's basal medium containing 10 percent horse serum. To 0.1 milliliter of each serum dilution, 0.1 milliliter of virus fluid (10^2 $TCID_{50}/0.1$ ml) was added, and the mixture was kept at room temperature for 30 minutes. To each mixture, 1 milliliter of freshly prepared 0.1 percent HeLa cell suspension in Eagle's basal medium with 10 percent horse serum was added, and the resulting mixtures were incubated at $36°$ to $36.5°C$. On the 5th day of incubation a reading was made, and the highest serum dilution which completely inhibited the cytopathic effect of adenovirus type 12 was taken as the neutralizing antibody titer.

Four human sera with type 12 adenovirus CPE-neutralizing antibody titers of 1:16 or higher (as a result of exposure in nature) and four negative human sera (with titers lower than 1:2) were otherwise randomly selected from among 700 sera tested at random from among 1870 patients admitted to the M. D. Anderson Hospital and Tumor Institute for all causes over a period of approximately 6 months. These eight sera were inactivated by heating at $56°C$ for 30 minutes, mixed with an equal volume of virus fluid ($10^{3.3}$ $TCID_{50}/0.1$ ml), and kept at room temperature for 30 minutes; then 0.05 milliliter of this mixture was injected into newborn hamsters less than 24 hours old.

Rabbit anti-simian-virus-40 serum was obtained from the National Institutes of Health. The neutralizing antibody titer of this serum, as determined by B. E. Eddy, was 1:1500 when tested against 100 $TCID_{50}$ of SV-40 and read in 10 days (13). Control rabbit serum was obtained from normal rabbits in our laboratory. One volume of undiluted serum was mixed with 3 volumes of type 12 adenovirus fluid ($10^{3.3}$ $TCID_{50}$/0.1 ml) and kept at 4°C overnight. Of this mixture, 0.05 milliliter was inoculated intraperitoneally into newborn hamsters and 0.1 milliliter was inoculated into 1 ml of HeLa cell tissue culture.

One-tenth milliliter of the particular dilution of simian virus 40 (SV-40) fluid (13) which showed cytopathic effect of 3+ to 4+ (vacuolation) on the 7th day of inoculation in green monkey kidney cell (15) was mixed with 0.1 milliliter each of a 1:4 dilution of rabbit anti-SV-40 serum and a 1:4 dilution of control rabbit serum or undiluted patient's serum. The mixture was kept at room temperature for 30 minutes, inoculated into 1 milliliter of green monkey kidney cell culture, and observed for 2 weeks. Eagle's basal medium with 2 percent horse serum was used as the maintenance medium for green monkey kidney cells.

RESULTS

Of the first nine types of human adenovirus injected into newborn hamsters, none except type 12 has shown tumorigenic effects to date. Of ten hamsters injected intrapulmonarily with type 12 virus and surviving longer than 3 weeks, eight developed tumors in 33 to 90 days (Table 1). Tumors developed in the mediastinum, on the internal chest wall, or on the diaphragm. Most adhered to the surrounding organs or tissues, and bloody pleural fluid was present. In gross appearance the tumors were whitish with red hemorrhagic areas. In some hamsters metastases to the mediastinal lymph nodes were observed. No extrathoracic tumors were observed in these first eight tumorous hamsters.

A second shipment of human adenovirus, type 12, obtained from the American Type Culture Collection about 5 months after the first shipment induced a similar tumor in a hamster intrapulmonarily injected within 24 hours after birth.

To determine whether the tumors arising in hamsters injected with type 12 adenovirus might possibly be the result of transplantation of malignant tissue culture cells, cell-free filtrates of this second shipment of type 12 adenovirus tissue culture fluid on HeLa cells were prepared, by the method described earlier. There was a very high incidence of intrathoracic tumors, similar to those observed earlier, 1 to 3 months after injection of cell-free filtrates of tissue cultures infected with type 12 adenovirus but not after the injection of filtrates of control tissue culture

TABLE 3. *Trocar transplantation of tumors induced by human type 12 adenovirus*

Site of primary (induced) tumor	Transplant generation	Age of host (days)	Site of transplant	"Takes"/No. transplanted	Days to death from tumor growth
		Tumor A12, No. 15			
Thorax	T_1	<1	Intraperitoneal	1/1*	20
Thorax	T_1	<1	Subcutaneous	1/1*	34
Thorax	T_1	23-25	Intraperitoneal	4/4	26-50
Thorax	T_1	23-25	Subcutaneous	3/3	26-36
		Tumor A12, No. 14†			
Thorax	T_1	28-31	Intraperitoneal	3/4	35-62
Thorax	T_1	28-31	Subcutaneous	2/3	28‡-80
		Tumor A12, No. 6			
Thorax	T_1	25	Intraperitoneal	2/3	20, 24
Thorax	T_1	25	Subcutaneous	2/3	24, 30
Thorax	T_1	51-53	Intraperitoneal	2/2	28, 31
Thorax	T_1	51-53	Subcutaneous	1/2	63
		Tumor A12, No. 5			
Thorax	T_1	84	Intraperitoneal	2/2	117, 139
Thorax	T_1	84	Subcutaneous	0/1	
		Tumor A12, No. 20			
Thorax	T_1	24-25	Intraperitoneal	1/2	51
Thorax	T_1	24-25	Subcutaneous	1/2	36
Liver	T_1	20-21	Intraperitoneal	2/3	35, 87
Liver	T_1	20-21	Subcutaneous	1/3	45
		Tumor A12a			
Thorax	T_1	54, 55	Intraperitoneal	2/2	15, 27
Thorax	T_2	31	Intraperitoneal	3/3	16-20
Thorax	T_3	23	Intraperitoneal	3/3	25-27
Thorax	T_4	30	Intraperitoneal	3/3	19-21
Thorax	T_5	27-28	Intraperitoneal	3/3	22-42
Thorax	T_6	30	Intraperitoneal	2/3§	72§
Thorax	T_6	30	Subcutaneous	2/3§	72§, 73§
Thorax	T_7	29	Intraperitoneal	2/3§	
Thorax	T_7	29	Subcutaneous	2/3§	
		Tumor A12b			
Thorax	T_1	26-27	Intraperitoneal	4/4	17-30
Thorax	T_1	182	Intraperitoneal	2/3	58, 91
Thorax	T_2	28	Intraperitoneal	3/3	16-27
		Tumor A12c			
Thorax	T_1	26	Intraperitoneal	3/3	13-14
Thorax	T_2	37	Intraperitoneal	2/2	22, 22
Thorax	T_3	32-34	Intraperitoneal	3/3	20-26

* Animal transplanted with tumor within 24 hours after birth, which survived longer than 7 days.

† This tumor was taken from a hamster which was found dead.

‡ This hamster showed a take, but actually died of submandibular abscess.

§ Smaller inoculum used to prolong host survival.

(Table 2). These tumors developed in or on the mediastinum, the internal chest wall, the diaphragm, the lung, and the heart. In many hamsters multiple intrathoracic tumors were found. In four of 26 tumorous hamsters which had been injected with the virus fluid of the 3rd passage, one to three large tumors were found in the liver in addition to the tumors in the thorax (Fig. 1). Active propagation of the virus in HeLa cells is indicated by increased tumor-inducing ability and shorter period of latency after eight tissue-culture passages.

TABLE 4. *Evidence against involvement of simian virus 40 in the tumor-inducing activity of type 12 adenovirus tissue culture fluids*

Approx. titer ($TCID_{50}$/0.1 ml)	Treatment	Cercopithecus kidney cells		HeLa cells		Observation period before cell deterioration (days)	Tumor induction in newborn hamsters by 54 days (No. with tumors/No. injected)
		Vacuolation	Adeno-type CPE	Vacuolation	Adeno-type CPE		
		Simian virus 40					
10^9	None	+	−	−	−		
10^9	Heat (60°C, 30 min)	+	−	−	−		
10^8	Rabbit anti-SV-40 serum	−	−	−	−	14	
10^7	Rabbit anti-SV-40 serum	−	−	−	−	14	
		Human adenovirus type 12					
10^1	None	−	+	−	+		
10^{-3}	None	−	−	−	−	14	
Subculture at 14 days	None	−	−	−	−	9	
10^1	Heat (60°, 30 min)	−	−	−	−	14	
10^{3*}	Heat (60°, 30 min)	−	−	−	−	14	
$10^{3.3}$	Rabbit anti-SV-40 serum	−	+	−	+		3/4†
10^2	Rabbit anti-SV-40 serum	−	+	−	+		
$10^{3.3}$	Normal rabbit serum	−	+	−	+		4/5†
10^2	Normal rabbit serum	−	+	−	+		
		None					
	Control tissue culture	−	−	−	−		

* The same dilution before heat inactivation gave 6/6 tumors in 45 days (see Table 2).
† One animal was still alive and tumor-free at 54 days of age.

Histological sections of several of the tumors at the site of injection and in the liver were seen by four pathologists, who agreed that the tumors were undifferentiated sarcomas (Figs. 2 and 3). While the liver tumors may be metastatic, the following isolated observation indicates the possibility that some of them may be primary. Of three hamsters injected intravenously at birth with type 12 adenovirus, one is still alive, one died at 60 days with a subcutaneous tumor at the site of injection, and one died at 40 days with a large liver tumor but no other detectable tumors.

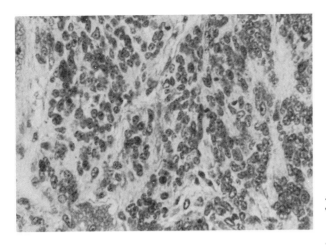

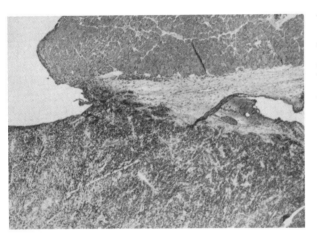

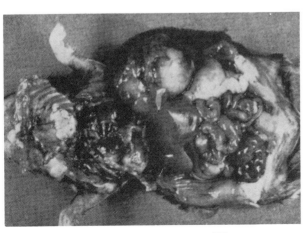

Figs. 1-3. Fig. 1 (left). Tumors filling the right thoracic cavity and in the liver of a hamster injected intrapulmonarily on the right side, at birth, with 0.05 milliliter of type 12 adenovirus (10^3 MTCID$_{100}$/0.1 ml) (about $\times$ 1/2). Fig. 2 (middle). Intrathoracic sarcoma adherent to the diaphragm at the site of intrapulmonary injection, 45 days previously, of type 12 adenovirus into a newborn hamster (about $\times$ 17). Fig. 3 (right). Higher magnification of a portion of the sarcoma shown in Fig. 2 (about $\times$ 175).

All of eight tumors induced in the thorax by type 12 adenovirus and one of the liver tumors, when transplanted intraperitoneally or subcutaneously into unconditioned hamsters from 1 to 182 days old, grew and killed a high percentage of the host animals in 13 to 139 days (Table 3).

Thus far, 220 and 950 untreated hamsters in the breeder room have been observed over periods of 12 and 6 months, respectively. Of these, one developed a spontaneous tumor involving the intestine and mesenteric lymph nodes in the duodenal region at 14 months of age. The rest are nontumorous.

The following facts indicate that the tumors observed are not attributable to contamination of animals or cultures by polyoma virus.

(1) Sera of 30 untreated hamsters and of 14 hamsters that developed tumors after injection of type 12 adenovirus were tested for polyoma (hemagglutination inhibiting) antibodies at dilutions of 1 to 10 and higher. All were negative.

(2) The tumor-inducing activity of the type 12 cultures was readily propagable in HeLa cells, whereas polyoma virus is not.

(3) The tumors induced by type 12 adenovirus do not resemble those induced in the hamster by polyoma virus, which produces primarily kidney sarcomas, of which we saw none. The type 12 adenovirus tumor is, by contrast, typically at the site of injection.

Hamsters have been shown to develop sarcomas at the site of injection, in the newborn animal, of cell extracts of frozen and ground primary cultures of rhesus monkey kidney (16). The oncogenic agent involved has more recently been shown to be simian virus 40 (SV-40) (17). The occurrence of sarcomas at the site of injection in the experiments under discussion therefore suggests involvement of simian virus 40. However, the tumor-inducing capacity of the type 12 adenovirus cultures is readily propagable in HeLa cells, whereas simian virus 40 is not. In our experiments tumors began to appear by 29 days (the 8th HeLa passage filtrate), and almost all injected animals had tumors by 90 days, whereas tumors induced by simian virus 40 usually do not appear until after $3\frac{1}{2}$ months (17). Nevertheless, experiments were performed as follows with *Cercopithecus* monkey kidney cells, simian virus 40, and rabbit anti-SV-40 serum. These experiments were performed in a building separate from the hamster isolation building and tissue culture laboratory, since only human viruses and human tissue culture cell types are permitted in the latter.

In retrospect it appears indeed fortunate that these tests for simian virus 40 were performed. Whereas the catalogue of the American Type Culture Collection states in the passage history of prototype 12 adenovirus that only human tissue culture cell types (KB and HeLa) are involved, an announcement made on 13 April 1962 amended the passage history to include monkey kidney cells, as follows: "Isolated in and passed for an unknown number of passages in human embryonic kidney cells. It then was passed one or more times in monkey kidney cells. After receipt in Huebner's laboratory, it was passed twice in KB cells after 12 passages in KB or HeLa cells." From the results of our experiments, however, it appears improbable that SV-40 contamination could have been responsible for the tumors induced (Table 4).

Simian virus 40 produced typical vacuolation in *Cercopithecus* kidney cell cultures, not in HeLa cells. Tumor-inducing type 12 adenovirus cultures produced typical adenovirus-type cytopathic effect (rounding up and clumping of cells) on both HeLa and *Cercopithecus* cells, but no vacuolation.

Simian virus 40 grows poorly if at all on HeLa cells. In order to test the possibility that slight contamination with simian virus 40 was being obscured by the adenovirus-type cytopathic effect, type 12 adenovirus cultures were heated to 60°C for 30 minutes. This treatment is known to inactivate adenovirus but not simian virus 40. This treatment did inactivate the adenovirus-type cytopathic effect of the type 12 adenovirus cultures and did not inactivate the vacuolating effect of the simian virus 40 cultures, yet it did not "unmask" a vacuolating effect in the type 12 cultures. Likewise, dilution of type 12 adenovirus to the point where it no longer destroyed the tissue culture cells by adenovirus-type cytopathic effect (dilution of 1:10,000) failed to reveal vacuolation even after subculture.

Rabbit anti-SV-40 serum inactivated the vacuolating effect of the SV-40 cultures but did not inactivate the adenovirus-type cytopathic effect of the type 12 cultures. In vivo testing of the type 12 cultures treated with anti-SV-40 serum has progressed for 54 days at the time of writing. Simian-virus-40 antiserum did not inactivate the tumor-inducing ability of our type 12 adenovirus cultures or prolong the period of latency; the first tumor arose in 31 days (Table 4).

Granted that the tumor-inducing activity is not attributable to polyoma virus or to contamination with simian virus 40, is it indeed due to the type 12 adenovirus rather than to yet a third, unrecognized, contaminant virus? Electron micrographs of HeLa cells infected with type 12 adenovirus reveal abundant virus particles of a single type concordant in location, size, arrangement, and morphology with the adenoviruses (Fig. 4). They occur as crystalline arrays in the nucleus, have a nucleoid surrounded by an outer limiting membrane, and have an average particle size of about 56 millimicrons. This finding, together with the other tissue culture characteristics mentioned and the adenovirus-type cytopathic effect, leaves little doubt that the predominant if not the only virus is an adenovirus. The data of Table 5 indicate a strong positive association between the adenovirus-type cytopathic effect and the tumor-inducing activity.

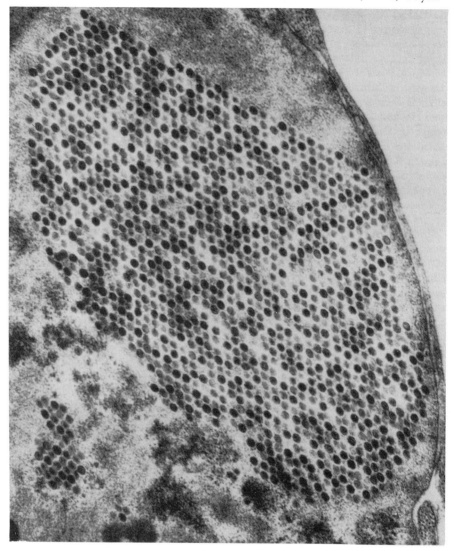

Fig. 4. Electron micrograph of an intranuclear crystalline array of virus particles in HeLa cell tissue culture infected with type 12 adenovirus (about × 39,000).

Sera of 700 randomly selected patients from the M. D. Anderson Hospital were tested for neutralizing antibodies against the adenovirus-type cytopathic effect of our type 12 cultures. Approximately 26 percent showed neutralization at a dilution of 1:4 or higher. Approximately 6 percent showed neutralization at a dilution of 1:8 or higher. (Another 20 percent showed neutralization only at a dilution of 1:2.)

TABLE 5. *Neutralization of both cytopathic effect and tumor-inducing activity of human type 12 adenovirus by human antisera (convalescent)*

Human serum donor (No.)	Anti-SV-40 titer (vacuolation on *Cercopithecus* kidney)	Anti-type-12 adenovirus titer (CPE on HeLa)	Ratio of serum to adenovirus type 12 ($10^{3.3}$ $TCID_{50}$/ 0.1 ml)	No. of tumors/ No. hamsters injected	Age at death of hamster with tumor (days)	Age of hamster alive and tumor-free (days)
None*			1:1	6/6	29-45	
38478	<1:1	<1:2	1:1	7/7	35-79	
40003	<1:1	<1:2	1:1	1/1	42	
40186	<1:1	<1:2	1:1	4/4	32-155	
40146	Not tested	<1:2	1:1	5/7	45-83	170
40378	<1:1	1:32	1:1	0/8		167-175†
39835	<1:1	1:32	1:1	0/4		167
39528	<1:1	1:16	1:1	0/3		166-172
40523	<1:1	1:16	1:1	0/3		171

* Tissue culture medium was used instead of human serum.

† Two were dead, tumor-free, at 41 and 80 days.

Four such positive "convalescent" antisera, each with a titer of 1:16 or higher, and four negative human sera were randomly selected. Aliquots of type 12 adenovirus cultures were incubated with each of these eight human sera and with tissue culture medium as a control. It may be seen that the four negative sera (those that did not neutralize the adenovirus-type cytopathic effect) did not neutralize the tumor-inducing effect, whereas the four positive sera (those that neutralize the adenovirus-type cytopathic effect) completely neutralized the tumor-inducing effect. None of the four positive sera contained SV-40 antibodies. These data provide strong indication that the tumor-inducing activity is indeed attributable to the type 12 adenovirus rather than to an unrecognized passenger virus.

DISCUSSION

That human type 12 adenovirus is highly tumorigenic for the hamster is indicated by the following results.

(1) Each of two separate shipments of type 12 adenovirus received 5 months apart from the American Type Culture Collection produced fast-growing malignant tumors at the site of intrapulmonary injection into newborn hamsters.

(2) Tumor-inducing activity was retained or increased after at least eight tissue culture passages in HeLa cells and cell-free filtration.

(3) The incidence of the tumors was high, and the periods of latency were short.

(4) The tumors grew progressively in, and killed, a high percentage of the unconditioned young adult hamsters into which they were transplanted.

(5) No such tumors occurred in hamsters injected with control tissue culture fluid or with the other viruses tested, or in control breeder hamsters.

(6) The possibility that polyoma virus or simian virus 40 (the only other viruses at present known to cause tumors when injected into newborn hamsters) might be responsible for the tumors observed was specifically excluded by a variety of tests.

(7) The possible involvement of still other, as yet unknown, contaminant viruses was excluded by a positive association of the tumor-inducing ability with the adenovirus content. Of human sera tested, all those, and only those, which neutralized the adenovirus-type cytopathic effect also neutralized the tumor-inducing effect. This latter result indicates that tumor induction is the result of the type 12 adenovirus, and that newly isolated strains of the same virus should therefore also have tumor-inducing effect.

Whereas most of the tumors arose at the site of intrathoracic injection, four hamsters also developed from one to three large tumors of the same histological type in the liver. The question of whether these are metastatic or primary is under investigation.

All animal tumor viruses that are now known to produce tumors in a heterologous species, and that have been adequately tested in the species of origin, also produce tumors in the species of origin. Simian virus 40, which has recently been found to have a tumorigenic effect in hamsters, has not yet been adequately tested in newborn monkeys. It is yet to be determined what tumors, if any, may be produced by type 12 adenovirus in humans. While tumor induction studies in subhuman primates and in human cells in vitro (malignant transformation) may be helpful, the direct approach via tumor induction studies in the species of origin has obvious drawbacks in the case of human tumor viruses.

If human type 12 adenovirus were injected into newborn infants one might confidently expect, from what is known of animal tumor viruses, that it would induce tumors. Yet such a result would by no means prove that in nature this virus is responsible for even a single "spontaneous" human tumor. Polyoma virus of the mouse produces a high incidence of tumors when injected into newborn mice or newborn hamsters. Polyoma virus is enzootic in most laboratory and wild mouse populations (18). Yet all of the evidence at present indicates that polyoma virus is responsible for very few, if any, "spontaneous" tumors in wild or laboratory mice. On the other hand there is strong evidence that certain other animal tumor viruses, such as the mouse mammary tumor milk agent, the mouse leukemia virus (or viruses), and the avian leukosis viruses are responsible for a high incidence of "spontaneous" breast cancer and leukemia in several strains of mice and of diverse "spontaneous" leukemias, lymphomas, and sarcomas in chickens. Whether type 12 adenovirus will be found to resemble polyoma virus or these other animal tumor viruses in this regard remains to be determined. The more feasible line of investigation in the human population would appear to be careful and extensive studies of the epidemiology of this and other adenoviruses, with special reference to cancer. Such studies would include (i) attempts to isolate this and other adenoviruses from the cancer tissue, body fluids, and excreta of cancer patients, and (ii) study of the occurrence of antibodies against this and other adenoviruses in the human population, with special reference to cancer and to individuals in young age groups.

Type 12 adenovirus was originally isolated by Kibrick et al. from the stool of a case of suspected nonparalytic poliomyelitis (19). It was classified as a new antigenic type of adenovirus by Rowe et al. (20), designated type 12, and placed in the American Type Culture Collection as a prototype, though its clinical and pathological significance has been obscure.

A large proportion of adenovirus infections occur in early childhood. Infection with types 1, 2, and 5 is prevalent chiefly in infancy and early childhood (21). Adenovirus respiratory disease epidemics in the general population have most often yielded types 3 and 7; epidemics among military recruits have generally yielded types 4 and 7. Adenovirus vaccines have been effective for the control of acute respiratory illness caused by the adenoviruses (22), and protective antibodies produced by adenovirus infections persist for many years (21). This offers real hope of prophylactic vaccination against other illnesses with which adenoviruses may be associated in the human population, including perhaps cancer.

Ginsberg has pointed out (22) that the properties of the adenoviruses should render them ideal as potential latent agents. They are very stable with respect to changes in temperature or pH; the principal site of propagation is in the nucleus; they do not dissociate readily from the cells that they infect; and they apparently do not kill the cells in which they multiply, although they can damage them markedly. These properties could explain their ability to persist in human tissues for long periods. Ginsberg goes on to state, "It is not unreasonable to believe that adenoviruses, like the herpes simplex virus, could then, by a still-unknown mechanism, be provoked to cause another disease episode, albeit the proof of such etiology by our present techniques may not be possible. If the hypothesis presented were true, this might explain the major role of adenoviruses as etiological agents in man."

The results presented here focus attention on the human adenoviruses as potential tumorigenic viruses etiologically related to cancer in man. The possibility that other human orphan viruses, or viruses of acute diseases, may have a delayed tumorigenic manifestation in man should be seriously considered and investigated. The described method of testing such already isolated and classified viruses for tumorigenic activity in newborn laboratory animals may prove to be an important tool in the armamentarium of the cancer researcher.

SUMMARY

A new approach to the important but difficult task of revealing possible human tumor viruses has been presented in this article. By systematic testing of already known human viruses for oncogenic properties, it was found that in hamsters injected intrapulmonarily with tissue culture fluid of human type 12 adenovirus within 24 hours after birth there was a very high incidence of malignant tumors at the site of injection in from 1 to 3 months. The tumor inducing activity was not lost by filtration through Selas 02 filters or by tissue culture passages in HeLa cells. Tumors thus induced grew in, and killed, a high percentage of the unconditioned young adult hamsters into which they were transplanted. No such tumors occurred in hamsters injected with control tissue culture fluid or with culture fluids of the other viruses tested, or in control breeder hamsters. The possibility that contamination with polyoma virus and simian virus 40 might be responsible for the tumors induced was specifically excluded by a variety of tests. The possible involvement of still other, as yet unknown, contaminant viruses was excluded by a positive association of the tumor-inducing ability with the adenovirus content. Of eight human sera tested, only those four which neutralized the adenovirus-type cytopathic effect also neutralized the tumor-inducing effect. Of 700 human sera tested, 26 percent contained CPE-neutralizing antibodies for type 12 adenovirus at titers of 1:4 and higher (23).

REFERENCES AND NOTES

1. 1960. Natl. Cancer Inst. Monograph. No. 4.
2. Duran-Reynals, F. 1959. Chap. 7 in The physiopathology of cancer. New York, Hoebner.
3. Eddy, B. E., Stewart, S. E., Young, R. D., and Mider, G. B. 1958. J. Nat. Cancer Inst. **20**: 747.
4. Foley, G. E., and Handler, A. H. 1957. Proc. Soc. Exp. Biol. Med. **94**: 611.
5. Stewart, S. E. 1961. Gann. **51** Suppl.: 291.
6. Neriishi, S., Yabe, Y., Oda, N., Ida, N., Gonzales F., Sutow, W., Kirschbaum, A., Taylor, H. G., and Trentin, J. J. 1961. J. Natl. Cancer Inst. **26**: 611.
7. Bunting, H. 1953. Proc. Soc. Exp. Biol. Med. **84**: 327.
8. Banfield, W. G., Dawe, C. J., and Brindley, D. C. 1959. J. Natl. Cancer Inst. **23**: 1959.
9. The hamsters were obtained through the cooperation of Dr. Charles McPherson.
10. The FL amnion cells and HeLa cells were obtained from Microbiological Associates, Inc.

11. This material was kindly supplied by Drs. Koprowski and Hayflick of Wistar Institute.

12. These materials were obtained from Microbiological Associates, Inc.

13. The polyoma virus, the simian virus 40 (strain A 426), and the rabbit anti-SV-40 serum were kindly supplied by Dr. B. E. Eddy of the National Institutes of Health.

14. Rowe, W. P., Hartley, J. W., Law, L. W., and Huebner, R. J. 1959. J. Exp. Med. **109**: 449.

15. Some of the *Cercopithecus aethiops* kidney cell culture was supplied by Dr. B. E. Eddy of the National Institutes of Health and some was obtained from Microbiological Associates, Inc.

16. Eddy, B. E., Borman, G. S., Berkeley, W. H., and Young, R. D. 1961. Proc. Soc. Exp. Biol. Med. **107**: 191.

17. Girardi, A. J., Sweet, B. H., Slotnick, V. B., and Hilleman, M. R. 1962. *Ibid.* **109**: 649; Eddy, B. E., Borman, G. S., Grubbs, G. E., and Young, R. D. 1962. Virology. **17**: 65.

18. Rowe, W. P. 1961. Bacteriol. Rev. **25**: 18.

19. Kibrick, S., Meléndez, L., and Enders, J. F. 1957. Ann. N.Y. Acad. Sci. **67**: 311.

20. Rowe, W. P., Hartley, J. W., and Huebner, R. J. 1958. Proc. Soc. Exp. Biol. Med. **97**: 465.

21. Huebner, R. J., Bell, J. A., Rowe, W. P. 1957. N.Y. Acad. Sci. Spec. Publs. **5**: 393.

22. Hilleman, M. R. 1957. *Ibid.* **5**: 403.

23. This investigation has been supported by research grants from the National Cancer Institute (grant C-2461), the American Cancer Society (grants E-27 and E-56), and the El Paso Better Health Foundation and by a grant from Mr. Earl Hollandsworth through the Greater Longview (Texas) United Fund. We are grateful to Drs. B. E. Eddy, W. P. Rowe, and R. J. Huebner for consultation, to Drs. W. G. Banfield, M. Stanton, J. Furth, and A. P. Stout for examination of histological sections of the induced tumors, to Mrs. Ayako Yabe, Miss Yuki Sato, Mrs. Amelia Dunquez, and Miss Bernadette Borchers for technical assistance, and to Dean Stanley W. Olson, Dr. Michael E. DeBakey, Mrs. Ara Verner, and Miss Eleanor Macdonald for administrative assistance.